Visit the Freeman and Herron Web Companion at

www.prenhall.com/freeman

CUSTOM EDITION FOR THE UNIVERSITY OF ILLINOIS, CHICAGO

EVOLUTIONARY ANALYSIS

Taken from:

Evolutionary Analysis
Second Edition

Scott Freeman
University of Washington

Jon C. Herron
University of Washington

Taken from:

Evolutionary Analysis, Second Edition
by Scott Freeman and Jon C. Herron
Copyright © 2001, 1998 by Scott Freeman and Jon C. Herron
Published by Prentice-Hall, Inc.
A Pearson Education Company
Upper Saddle River, New Jersey 07458

This special edition published in cooperation with Pearson Custom Publishing.

Printed in the United States of America

10 9 8 7 6 5 4 3 2 1

Please visit our web site at *www.pearsoncustom.com*

ISBN 0–536–72418–0

BA 996546

PEARSON CUSTOM PUBLISHING
75 Arlington Street, Suite 300, Boston, MA 02116
A Pearson Education Company

CONTENTS

CHAPTER 3

Darwinian Natural Selection

The blue leg bands on this male medium ground finch mark it for study. Researchers have observed natural selection in action by studying this species on the Galápagos islands. (Peter R. Grant, Princeton University)

IN THE INTRODUCTION TO *ON THE ORIGIN OF SPECIES,* DARWIN (1859, p. 3) wrote that "a naturalist, reflecting on the mutual affinities of organic beings, on their embryological relations, their geographical distribution, geological succession, and other such facts, might come to the conclusion that each species had not been independently created, but had descended ... from other species. Nevertheless, such a conclusion, even if well founded, would be unsatisfactory, until it could be shown *how* the innumerable species inhabiting this world have been modified ..." (emphasis added).

With this statement, Darwin pinpointed the relationship between the pattern and process components of a scientific theory. The early evolutionists had discovered an important phenomenon. A growing body of facts indicated that both fossilized and living organisms had descended from a common ancestor. The evidence that Darwin amassed to support this hypothesis was indirect, but persuasive enough that scientific controversy over the pattern component of the theory of evolution had virtually ended by the mid-1870s. Thanks to Darwin and his intellectual forebears, evolution became a well-established fact.

But what process could produce the pattern called evolution? Understanding the mechanism that produces a pattern in nature is the heart and soul of a scientific explanation. Chapter 2 focused on the evidence for the pattern called descent with modification; this chapter introduces a process, called natural selection, that produces the pattern.

3.1 Natural Selection: Darwin's Four Postulates

Natural selection is the logical outcome of four postulates, which Darwin laid out in his introduction to *On the Origin of Species by Means of Natural Selection*. He considered the rest of the book "one long argument" in their support (Darwin 1859, p. 459). The postulates are as follows:

1. Individuals within species are variable.
2. Some of these variations are passed on to offspring.
3. In every generation, more offspring are produced than can survive.
4. The survival and reproduction of individuals are not random: The individuals who survive and go on to reproduce, or who reproduce the most, are those with the most favorable variations. They are naturally selected.

Natural selection is a process that produces descent with modification, or evolution.

As a result of this process, the characteristics of populations change from one generation to the next. The logic is clear: If there is variation among the individuals in a population that can be passed on to offspring, and if there is differential success among those individuals in surviving and/or reproducing, then some traits will be passed on more frequently than others. As a result, the characteristics of the population will change slightly with each succeeding generation. This is Darwinian evolution: gradual change in populations over time. Changes in populations result from natural selection on individuals.

To drive this point home, recall the HIV virions described in Chapter 1. Individual virions within the same host varied in their ability to synthesize DNA in the presence of AZT, because of differences in the amino acid sequences of the reverse transcriptase active site. Virions with forms of reverse transcriptase that were less likely to bind AZT reproduced more than virions with forms that bound AZT readily. In the next generation, then, a higher percentage of virions had the modified form of reverse transcriptase than in the generation before. This is evolution by natural selection.

Darwin referred to the individuals who win this competition (it is rarely an actual head-to-head contest), and whose offspring make up a greater percentage of the population in the next generation, as more fit. In doing so he gave the everyday English words "fit" and "fitness" a new meaning. **Darwinian fitness** is the ability of an individual to survive and reproduce in its environment.

An adaptation is a characteristic that increases the fitness of an individual compared to individuals without the trait.

An important aspect of fitness is its relative nature. Fitness refers to how well an individual survives and how many offspring it produces compared to other individuals of its species. Biologists use the word **adaptation** to refer to a trait or characteristic of an organism, like a modified form of reverse transcriptase, that increases its fitness relative to individuals without the trait.

The same theory had, incidentally, been developed independently by a colleague of Darwin's named Alfred Russel Wallace. Though trained in England, Wallace had been making his living in Malaysia by selling natural history specimens to private collectors. While recuperating from a bout with malaria in 1858, he wrote a manuscript explaining natural selection and sent it to Darwin. Darwin, who had written his first draft on the subject in 1842 but never published it, immediately realized that he and Wallace had formulated the same theory independently. Brief papers by Darwin and by Wallace were read together before the Linnean Society of London, and Darwin then rushed *On the Origin of Species* into publication (17 years after he had written the first draft). Today, Darwin's name is more prominently associated with the Theory of Evolution by Natural Selection for two reasons: He had clearly thought of it first, and his book provided a full exposition of the idea, along with massive documentation.

One of the most attractive aspects of the Darwin-Wallace theory is that each of the four postulates—and their logical consequence—can be verified independently. That is, the theory is testable. There are neither hidden assumptions nor anything that has to be accepted uncritically. In the next section, we examine each of the four assertions by reviewing an ongoing study of finches in the Galápagos Islands off the coast of Ecuador. Can the Theory of Evolution by Natural Selection be tested rigorously, by direct observation?

The Theory of Evolution by Natural Selection is testable.

3.2 The Evolution of Beak Shape in Galápagos Finches

Peter Grant and Rosemary Grant and their colleagues have been studying several species of Galápagos finches continuously and on various islands in the Galápagos archipelago since 1973 (see Boag and Grant 1981; Grant 1981a, 1991, 1999; Grant and Grant 1989). The 14 finch species found on the islands are similar in size and coloration. They range from four to six inches in length and from brown to black in color. Two traits do show remarkable variation among species, however: the size and shape of their beaks.

The beak is the primary tool used by birds in feeding, and the enormous range of beak morphologies among the Galápagos finches reflects the diversity of foods they eat (Figure 3.1). The warbler finch (*Certhidea olivacea*) feeds on insects, spiders, and nectar; woodpecker and mangrove finches (*C. pallida* and *C. heliobates*) use twigs or cactus spines as tools to pry insect larvae or termites from dead wood; several ground finches in the genus *Geospiza* pluck ticks from iguanas and tortoises in addition to eating seeds; the vegetarian finch (*Platyspiza crassirostris*) eats leaves and fruit.

To test the Theory of Evolution by Natural Selection, we focus on data Grant and Grant and colleagues have gathered on the medium ground finch, *Geospiza fortis,* on Isla Daphne Major.

Because it is the most important trait used in acquiring food, the size and shape of a bird's beak has important consequences for its fitness.

Daphne Major's size and location make it a superb natural laboratory. The island is tiny. It is just under 40 hectares (about 80 football fields) in extent, with a maximum elevation of 120 meters. Like all of the islands in the Galápagos, it is the top of a volcano. The climate is seasonal even though the location is equatorial (Figure 3.2). A warmer, wetter season from January through May alternates with a cooler, drier season from June through December. The vegetation consists of dry forest and scrub, with several species of cactus present.

The *Geospiza fortis* on Daphne Major make an ideal study population because few finches migrate onto or off of the island, and the population is small enough to be studied exhaustively. In an average year, there are about 1200 individual finches on the island. By 1977, Grant and Grant's team had captured and marked over half of them; since 1980, virtually 100% of the population has been marked.

The medium ground finch is primarily a seed eater. The birds crack seeds by grasping them at the base of the bill and then applying force. Grant and Grant and their colleagues have shown that both within and across finch species, beak size is

(a)

(b)

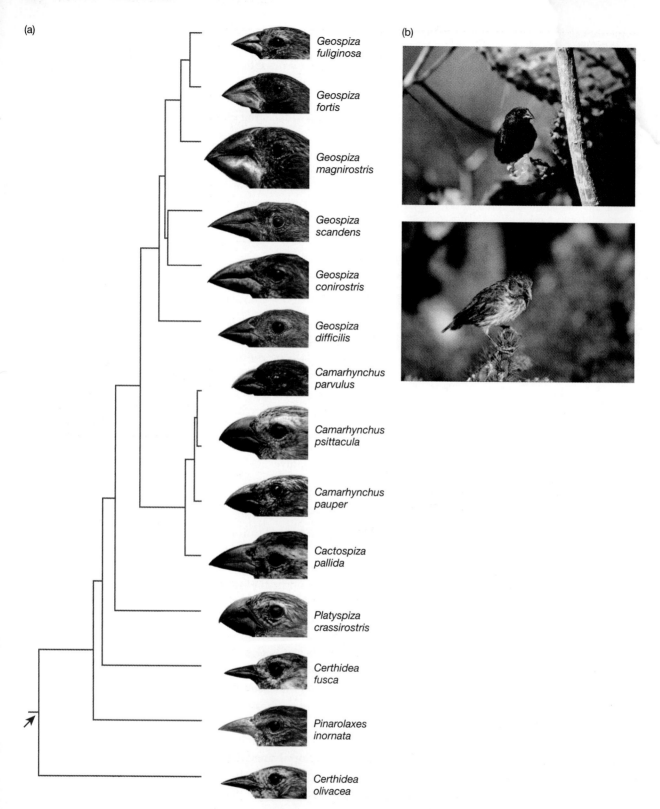

Figure 3.1 **The Galápagos finches, and the medium ground finch** *Geospiza fortis* (a) This phylogeny was estimated from similarities and differences in DNA sequences by Kenneth Petren and colleagues (1999), and shows the evolutionary relationships among 14 species of Darwin's finches. The photos show the extensive variation in beak size and shape among species. From Petren et al. (1999). (b) A male (top) and female (bottom) medium ground finch. (Photos: Peter R. Grant, Princeton University)

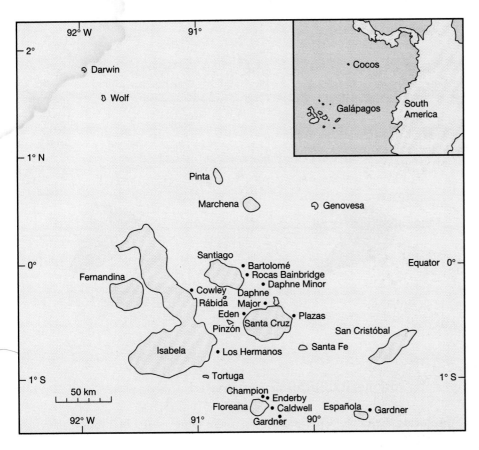

Figure 3.2 **The Galápagos islands** Fourteen species of finch inhabit the Galápagos, and one finch resides on Cocos. On this map, Isla Daphne Major is a tiny speck between Santa Cruz and Santiago.

correlated with the size of seeds harvested. In general, birds with bigger beaks eat larger seeds, and birds with smaller beaks eat smaller seeds. This is because birds with different beak sizes are able to handle different sizes of seeds more efficiently (Bowman 1961; Grant et al. 1976; Abbott et al. 1977; Grant 1981b).

Testing Postulate 1: Are Populations Variable?

The researchers mark every finch they catch by placing colored aluminum bands around each of its legs. This allows them to identify individual birds in the field. The scientists also weigh each finch and measure its wing length, tail length, beak width, beak depth, and beak length. All of the traits they have investigated are variable. For example, when Grant and Grant plotted measurements of beak depth in the Isla Daphne Major population of *G. fortis,* the data indicated that beak depth varies (Figure 3.3). All of the finch characteristics they have measured clearly conform to Darwin's first postulate. As we will see in Chapter 4, variation among the individuals within populations is virtually universal.

Testing Postulate 2: Is Some of the Variation Among Individuals Heritable?

Within a population, individual finches could vary in beak depth because the environments they have experienced are different or because their genotypes are different, or both. There are several ways that environmental variation could cause the variation in beak depth recorded in Figure 3.3. Variation in the amount of food that individual birds happened to have received as chicks can lead to variation in beak

Some Geospiza fortis have beaks that are only half as deep as other individuals.

Figure 3.3 Beak depth in medium ground finches This histogram shows the distribution of beak depth in medium ground finches on Daphne Major in 1976, at the start of the Grant study. A few birds have shallow beaks, less than 8 mm deep. Most birds have medium beaks, 8 to 11 mm deep. A few birds have deep beaks, more than 11 mm deep. (*N* stands for sample size; the blue arrow along the *x* axis indicates the mean, or average.)

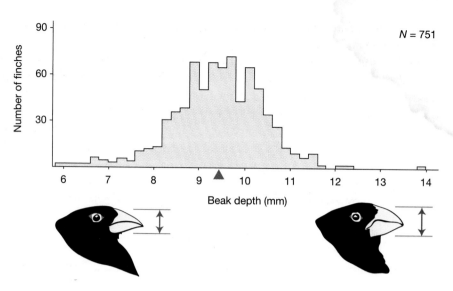

When variation in the characteristics of organisms is plotted, it is common to observe a bell-shaped curve like the one formed by this histogram. The extent, cause, and nature of variation in traits is a focus of Chapter 4 and Chapter 7.

BOX 3.1   Issues that complicate how heritabilities are estimated

Heritabilities are estimated by measuring the similarity of traits among closely related individuals. But relatives share their environment as well as their genes, and any correlation that is due to their shared environment inflates the estimate of heritability. For example, it is well known that birds tend to grow larger when they have abundant food as young. But the most food-rich breeding territories are often won and defended by the largest adults in the population. Young from these territories will tend to become the largest adults in the next generation. As a result, a researcher might measure a strong relationship between parent and offspring beak and body size and claim a high heritability for these traits when in reality there is none. In this case, the real relationship is between the environments that parents and their young each experienced as chicks.

In many species, this problem can be circumvented by performing what are called cross-fostering, common garden, or reciprocal-transplant experiments. In birds, these experiments involve taking eggs out of their original nest and placing them in the nests of randomly assigned foster parents. Measurements in the young, taken when they are fully grown, are then compared with the data from their biological parents. This experimental treatment removes any bias in the analysis created by the fact that parents and offspring share environments. Unfortunately, even cross-fostering experiments cannot remove environmental effects that are due to differences in the nutrient stores of eggs or seeds. We simply have to assume that these maternal effects are too small to seriously bias the result.

Cross-fostering experiments in a wide variety of bird species have confirmed large heritabilities in most or all of the morphological characters analyzed. It was not possible for Boag and Grant (1978) to perform this critical experiment on the Galápagos finches, however. Because the Galápagos are a national park, experiments that manipulate individuals beyond catching and marking are forbidden. To get around this limitation, Peter Grant (1991) compared individuals that were raised in food-poor versus food-rich territories to see if they bred in a similar environment once they reached adulthood. The data showed no correlation between the quality of the territory a bird was raised in and the quality of the territory where it, in turn, raised its young. This result bolsters the claim that the large heritabilities estimated in finch traits, like beak dimensions, are real, and not an artifact of parents and offspring sharing a similar environment.

depth among adults. Injuries or abrasion against hard seeds or rocks can also affect beak size and shape.

To determine whether at least part of the variability among finch beaks is genetically based, and thus capable of being passed from parents to offspring, a colleague of Peter Grant and Rosemary Grant's named Peter Boag estimated a quantity known as **heritability**.

Heritability is the proportion of the variation observed in a population that is due to variation in the effects of genes. Because it is a proportion, heritability varies between 0 and 1. We will develop the theory behind how heritability is estimated much more fully in Chapter 7. For now, we simply point out that it is usually estimated by measuring the similarity between pairs of relatives. This is a valid approach, because similarities between relatives are caused, at least in part, by the alleles they share (for more detail, see Box 3.1). Data are usually collected from siblings, or from parents and offspring.

Boag compared the beak depth of *G. fortis* young after they had attained adult size to the average bill depth of their mother and father, and found a strong correspondence between relatives. As the data plotted in Figure 3.4 show, parents with deep beaks tend to have offspring with deep beaks, and parents with shallow beaks tend to have chicks with shallow beaks. This is evidence that a large proportion of the observed variation in beak depth is genetic, and can be transmitted to offspring (Boag and Grant 1978; Boag 1983). The result is consistent with hundreds of similar studies. In most traits of most organisms, a significant amount of the variation that exists within populations is due to variation in the genetic makeup of individuals.

In finches, the beak depth of parents and offspring are similar. This observation suggests that some alleles tend to produce shallow beaks, while other alleles tend to produce deeper beaks.

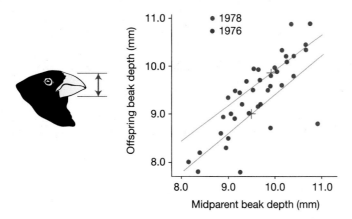

Figure 3.4 Heritability of beak depth in *Geospiza fortis* This graph shows the relationship between the beak depth of parents and their offspring. Midparent value is the average of the maternal and paternal measurements. Using this measurement is important because male *G. fortis* are bigger than females.

The lines in the graph are the result of a statistical procedure called regression analysis. In the type of regression used here, the line is placed in a way that minimizes the sum of the squared vertical distances between each point in the plot and the line. This is called the best-fit line. If the slope of the line is flat, or 0, then there is no relationship between the two variables plotted—meaning that all variation among individuals is caused by differences in the environments they have experienced. If the slope is 1, then all of the variation among individuals is caused by variation in their genotypes.

The red line and circles are from 1978 data, and the blue line and circles are from 1976 data. The results from the two years are consistent. Both show a strong relationship between the beak depth of parents and their offspring. We can infer that the association is a product of their shared genes. From Boag (1983).

Testing Postulate 3: Is There an Excess of Offspring, So That Only Some Individuals Live to Reproduce?

A drought on Daphne Major produced a dramatic selection event.

Because they routinely censused the ground finch population over several years, the researchers were able to observe a dramatic event. In 1977, there was a severe drought at the study site. Instead of the normal 130 mm of rainfall during the wet season, only 24 mm fell. Over the course of 20 months, 84% of the Darwin's medium ground finch population on Daphne Major disappeared (Figure 3.5a). The team inferred that most died of starvation: There was a strong correspondence between population size and seed availability (Figure 3.5b); 38 emaciated birds were actually found dead, and none of the missing birds reappeared the following year. It is clear that only a fraction of the population survived to reproduce. This sort of mortality is not unusual. For example, Rosemary Grant has shown that 89% of *Geospiza conirostris* individuals die before they breed (Grant 1985). Trevor Price and co-workers (1984) determined that an additional 19% and 25% of the *G. fortis* on Daphne Major died during subsequent drought events in 1980 and 1982, respectively.

In fact, in every natural population studied, more offspring are produced each generation than survive to breed. If a population is not increasing in size, then

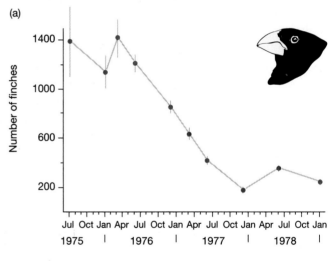

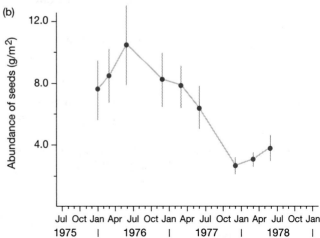

Figure 3.5 Decline of ground finch population and available seeds, during the 1977 drought (a) This graph shows the number of ground finches found on Daphne Major before, during, and after the drought. The vertical lines through each data point represent a quantity called the standard error, which indicates the amount of variation in census estimates. The lines in this graph are simply drawn from point to point to make the trend easier to see.

(b) This graph shows the abundance of seeds on Daphne Major before, during, and after the drought. Reprinted with permission from Boag and Grant (1981). Copyright © 1981, American Association for the Advancement of Science.

each parent will, in the course of its lifetime, leave an average of one offspring that survives to breed. But the reproductive capacity (or biotic potential) of organisms is astonishing (Table 3.1).

Similarly, data show that, in most populations, some individuals are more successful at mating and producing offspring than others. Variation in reproductive success represents an opportunity for selection, as does variation in survival.

Testing Postulate 4: Are Survival and Reproduction Nonrandom?

Darwin's fourth claim was that the individuals who survive and go on to reproduce, or who reproduce the most, are those with certain, favorable variations. Did a nonrandom, or selected, subset of the ground finch population survive the 1977 drought? By measuring the same traits they had measured in 1976 on a large and random sample of surviving birds early in 1978, the Grant team found that a distinct subset of the population had survived best: those with the deepest beaks (Figure 3.6). Because the average survivor had a deeper beak than the average nonsurvivor, the average bill size in the population changed.

In what way were deep beaks favorable? Can we link ecological cause with evolutionary effect? The answer is yes: Not only the number, but also the types of seeds available during the 1977 drought changed dramatically (Figure 3.7). Specifically, the large, hard fruits of an annual plant called *Tribulus cistoides* became a key food item. These seeds are largely ignored in normal years, but during the drought the supply of small, soft seeds quickly became exhausted. Only large birds with deep, narrow beaks can crack and eat *Tribulus* fruits successfully. In addition, large birds defend food sources more successfully during conflicts. Because large size and deep beaks are positively correlated, the two traits responded to selection together.

The 1977–1978 selection event, as dramatic as it was, was not an isolated occurrence. In 1980 and 1982 there were similar droughts, and selection again favored individuals with large body size and deep beaks (Price et al. 1984). Then, in 1983, an

Natural selection occurs because (1) only a fraction of offspring survive long enough to breed, and (2) of the individuals that do breed, some are much more successful than others.

During the drought, finches with larger, deeper beaks had an advantage.

Table 3.1   Reproductive potential

This table gives the number of offspring that a single individual (or pair of individuals, for sexual species) can produce under optimal conditions, assuming that all progeny survive to breed, over various time intervals. Darwin picked the elephant for his calculations because it was the slowest breeder then known among animals.

Organism	Reproductive potential	Citation
Aphis fabae (an aphid)	524 billion in one year	Gould 1977
Elephant	19 million in 750 years	Darwin 1859
Housefly	191×10^{18} in 5 months	Keeton 1972
Mycophila speyeri (a fly that feeds on mushrooms)	20,000/square foot in 35 days	Gould 1977
Staphylococcus aureus (a bacterium)	Cells would cover the Earth 7 feet deep in 48 hours	Audesirk and Audesirk 1993
Starfish	10^{79} in 16 years*	Dodson 1960

*10^{79} is the estimated number of electrons in the visible universe.

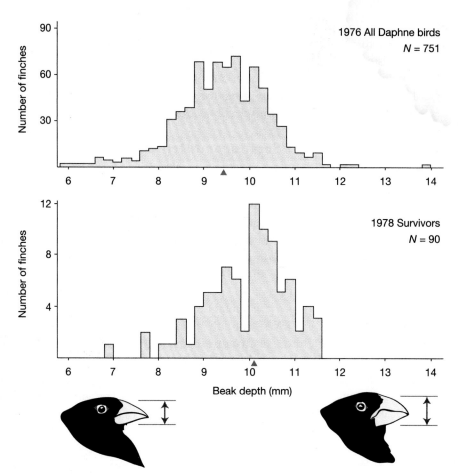

Figure 3.6 **Beak depth before and after natural selection** These histograms show the distribution of beak depth in medium ground finches on Daphne Major, before and after the drought of 1977 (Grant 1986). Copyright © 1986, Princeton University Press. Reprinted by permission of Princeton University Press.

influx of warm surface water off the South American coast, called an El Niño event, created a wet season with 1359 mm of rain on Daphne Major. This dramatic environmental change (almost 57 times as much rain as in 1977) led to a superabundance of small, soft seeds and, subsequently, to strong selection for smaller body size (Gibbs and Grant 1987). After wet years, small birds with shallow beaks survive better and reproduce more because they harvest small seeds much more efficiently than large birds with deep beaks. Larger birds were favored in drought conditions, but smaller birds were favored in wet years. Natural selection—as we pointed out in our analysis of HIV evolution in Chapter 1—is dynamic.

Did Evolution Occur?

Selection occurs within generations; evolution occurs between generations.

The changes observed in finch beaks are examples of natural selection in action. But we said earlier that evolution was a *response* to selection—a change in the characteristics of a population from one generation to the next. Selection produces a distinct change in trait distributions within a generation; evolution is a change in trait distributions between generations. Did evolution occur in the Galápagos finches? The answer is yes: As the data in Table 3.2 show, the offspring of birds surviving the 1977 drought were significantly larger, on average, than the population that existed before the drought.

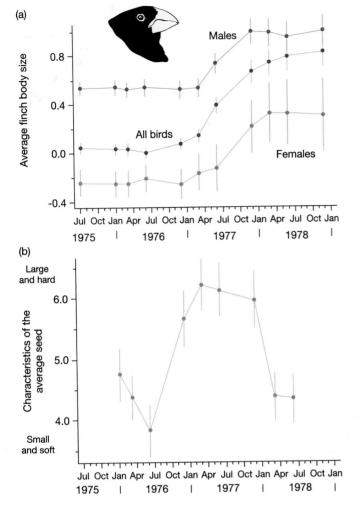

Figure 3.7 **Changes in the overall body size of ground finches and in seed characteristics** (a) These plots show the overall body size of finches caught before, during, and after the drought on Daphne Major. (The axis has no units because body size was calculated as a composite measure called a principal component score.) The "All birds" line represents the average of males and females. As in Figure 3.5, the data points represent population means, the vertical lines represent standard errors, and the horizontal lines are drawn between data points simply to make the trends easier to see. (b) This graph shows changes in the hardness of seeds available on Daphne Major before, during, and after the drought. The hardness index plotted on the *y*-axis is a special measure created by Boag and Grant (1981). Reprinted with permission. Copyright © 1981, American Association for the Advancement of Science.

3.3 The Nature of Natural Selection

Although the Theory of Evolution by Natural Selection can be stated concisely, tested rigorously in natural populations, and validated, it can be difficult to understand thoroughly. One reason is that it is essentially a statistical process: a change in the trait distributions of populations. Statistical thinking does not come naturally to most people, and there are a number of widely shared ideas about natural selection that are incorrect. In this section our goal is to cover some key points about how selection does and does not operate.

Natural Selection Acts on Individuals, but Its Consequences Occur in Populations

When HIV strains were selected by exposure to AZT, or finch populations were selected by changes in seed availability, none of the selected individuals (virions or finches) changed in any way. They simply lived through the selection event while others died, or reproduced more than competing virions or birds. What changed after the selection process were the characteristics of the populations of virions and finches, not the affected individuals themselves. Specifically, a higher frequency of

Table 3.2 Evolutionary response to selection

These data summarize changes in the population means of body and beak traits in *Geospiza fortis,* before and after the 1976–1977 drought. "SE" is an abbreviation for standard error, which quantifies the amount of variation around the average, or mean, value. The delta (Δ) column shows the differences between generations.

Trait	Before Selection 1976		Next Generation 1978		
	Mean	SE	Mean	SE	Δ
Weight (g)	16.06	0.06	17.13	0.13	+1.07
Wing length (mm)	67.88	0.10	68.87	0.20	+0.99
Tarsus length (mm)	19.08	0.03	19.29	0.07	+0.21
Bill length (mm)	10.63	0.03	10.95	0.06	+0.32
Bill depth (mm)	9.21	0.03	9.70	0.06	+0.49
Bill width (mm)	8.58	0.02	8.83	0.05	+0.25
Sample size	634		135		

Source: Grant and Grant 1995

Natural selection does not change the characteristics of individuals. It changes the characteristics of populations.

HIV virions in the population were able to replicate in the presence of AZT, and a higher proportion of finches had deep beaks.

To state this point another way, the effort of cracking *Tribulus* seeds did not make finch beaks become deeper and their bodies larger, and the effort of transcribing RNA in the presence of AZT did not change the amino acid composition of the reverse transcriptase active site. Instead, the average beak depth and body size in the finch population increased because more smaller finches died than larger ones, and the average active site sequence in reverse transcriptase changed because certain mutants did a better job of making new virions.

Natural Selection Acts on Phenotypes, but Evolution Consists of Changes in Allele Frequencies

Finches with large bodies and deep beaks would have been favored during the drought even if all of the variation in the population had been environmental in origin (that is, if heritabilities had been zero). But no evolution would have occurred. The frequencies of the phenotypes observed before and after selection would have changed, but in the next generation the phenotype distribution might have gone back to what it was before selection occurred.

Because evolution is the response to selection, it occurs only when the selected traits have a genetic basis. The variation in finch phenotypes that selection acted on had a genetic basis. As a result, the phenotype distribution changed in the next generation.

Natural Selection Is Backward Looking, Not Forward Looking

Each generation is a product of selection by the environmental conditions that prevailed in the generation before. The offspring of the HIV virions and finches that underwent natural selection are better adapted to environments dominated by

AZT and drought conditions, respectively, than their parents' generation was. If the environment changed again during the lifetime of these offspring, however, they would not necessarily be adapted to the new conditions.

There is a common misconception that organisms can be adapted to future conditions, or that selection can look ahead in the sense of anticipating environmental changes during future generations. This is impossible. Evolution is always a generation behind any changes in the environment.

Natural selection adapts populations to conditions that prevailed in the past, not conditions that might occur in the future.

Natural Selection Can Produce New Traits, Even Though It Acts on Existing Traits

Natural selection can select only from the variations that already exist in a population. Selection cannot, for example, instantly create a new and optimal beak for cracking *Tribulus* fruits. It only selects from the range of beaks already present in the population.

Over time, however, natural selection *can* produce new traits. This seems paradoxical, given that the process acts only on existing traits. The evolution of new traits is possible because, in each generation, mutations produce new variants, and thus a new suite of existing traits, for selection to act upon. To understand why this is important, consider the results of an artificial selection experiment conducted at the University of Illinois (Leng 1962). A research team started with 163 ears of corn, tested the oil content in the kernels of each, and found that the amount of oil ranged from 4–6%. They selected the 24 ears with the highest oil content to be the parents of the next generation, raised the offspring, tested their kernels for oil content, and again selected the individuals with the highest oil content to be the parents of the next generation. By continuing this selection regime for 60 years, the researchers succeeded in producing corn plants whose kernels had an oil content of about 16% (Figure 3.8). There is no overlap between the distribution of oil content in the ancestral and descendant populations. Evolution produced a new trait value.

Natural selection can also lead to novel characteristics. This is possible because selection is able to "repurpose" existing behaviors, structures, or genes for new functions. The giant panda's thumb is a good example (Gould 1980). Pandas use this

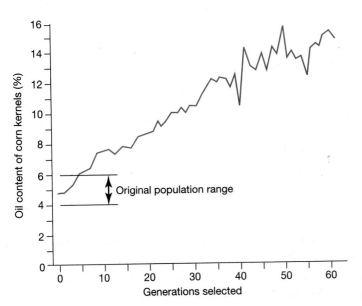

Figure 3.8   Continued selection can result in dramatic changes in traits   See text for explanation. Modified from Leng (1962). Reprinted by permission of Blackwell Wissenschafts-Verlag GmbH.

structure like a sixth finger when eating their favorite food, bamboo. As Figure 3.9 shows, they pass the stalks through the slot between the thumb and their other five digits to strip off the leaves and expose the shoots, which they eat. But this sixth digit is not a true thumb at all. Anatomically, the bone that forms the "thumb" is a highly modified radial sesamoid, which in closely related species is a component of the wrist. Knowing how natural selection works in contemporary populations, we surmise that when panda populations first began exploiting bamboo, there was variation among individuals in the length of the radial sesamoid bone. As a result of strong and continued selection over many generations, the average length of the bone increased in the populations until it reached its present proportions.

A trait that is used in a novel way and is eventually elaborated by selection into a completely new structure, like the radial sesamoid of the ancestral panda, is known as a **preadaptation**. An important point about preadaptations is that they represent a happenstance. A preadaptation improves an individual's fitness by accident—not because natural selection is conscious or forward looking.

Natural Selection Is Not "Perfect"

The previous paragraphs stressed that natural selection continually improves adaptation. Although this is true, it is equally important to realize that evolution does not result in "perfect" traits.

To drive this point home, consider that when Boag and Grant analyzed their data on the survival of finches after the 1977 drought, they noticed that individuals with relatively narrow beaks also survived better. This makes sense, because finches push down and to either side when cracking *Tribulus* fruits, and narrower beaks concentrate these twisting forces more effectively. But beak width is positively correlated with beak depth and large body size. As a result, birds with deep beaks, which are good for applying downward force, tend also to have wider beaks, which are less effective at applying the twisting force. Presumably, this correlation

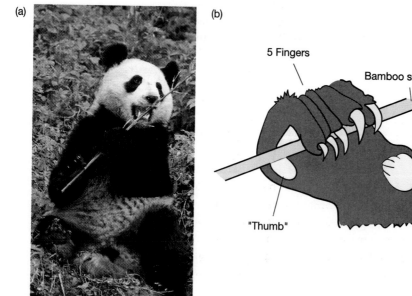
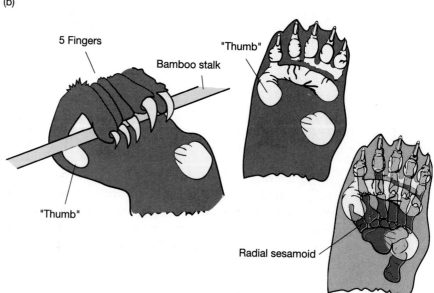

Figure 3.9 The panda's thumb (a) Giant pandas strip the leaves from bamboo by passing the stalk through their hands. (Bill Kamin/ Visuals Unlimited) (b) This drawing shows how the panda's "thumb" forms a slot for bamboo stalks to pass through. After Endo et al. 1999.

exists because the same genes affect beak depth and width and overall body size, making all three traits smaller, or larger, together. The upshot is that selection for larger size and deeper beaks resulted in wider beaks, even when narrower beaks should have been favored.

This is an important point. Because of the genetic correlations among characters, natural selection did not optimize all of the traits involved. Natural selection results in adaptation, not perfection.

Natural Selection Is Nonrandom, but It Is Not Progressive

Evolution by natural selection is sometimes characterized as a random or chance process, but nothing could be further from the truth. Evolution by natural selection is nonrandom because it increases adaptation to the environment.

As the HIV, finch, and panda examples demonstrate, however, the process of nonrandom selection is completely free of any entity's conscious intent. Darwin actually came to regret coining the phrase "naturally selected," because people thought the word selection implied a conscious act or choice by some entity. Nothing of the sort happens.

Also, although evolution has tended to increase the complexity, degree of organization, and specialization of organisms over time, it is not progressive in the sense of leading toward some predetermined goal. Evolution makes organisms "better" only in the sense of increasing their adaptation to their environment. There is no inexorable trend toward more advanced forms of life. For example, contemporary tapeworms have no digestive system, and have actually evolved to be simpler than their ancestors. Snakes evolved from ancestors that had limbs. The earliest birds in the fossil record had teeth.

Unfortunately, a progressivist view of evolution dies hard. Even Darwin had to remind himself to "never use the words higher or lower" when discussing evolutionary relationships. It is true that some organisms are the descendants of ancient lineages and some are the descendants of more recent lineages, but all organisms in the fossil record and those living today were adapted to their environments. They are all able to survive and reproduce. None is "higher" or "lower" than any other.

There is no such thing as a higher or lower plant or animal.

Fitness Is Not Circular

The Theory of Evolution by Natural Selection is often criticized—by nonbiologists—as tautological, or circular in its reasoning. That is, after reviewing Darwin's four postulates, one could claim, "Of course individuals with favorable variations are the ones that survive and reproduce, because the theory defines favorable as the ability to survive and reproduce."

The key to resolving the issue is to realize that the word "favorable," although a convenient shorthand, is misleading. The only requirement for natural selection is for certain variants to do better than others, as opposed to random ones. As long as a nonrandom subset of the population survives better and leaves more offspring, natural selection will result. In the examples we have been analyzing, research not only determined that nonrandom groups survived a selection event, but also uncovered why those groups were favored.

It should also make sense by now that Darwinian fitness is not an abstract quantity. Fitness can be measured in nature. This is done by counting the offspring that individuals produce during their lifetime, or by observing the ability of individuals to survive a selection event, and comparing each individual's performance to that of other individuals in the population. These are independent, measurable, and objective criteria for assessing fitness.

Natural Selection Acts on Individuals, Not Groups

One of the most pervasive misconceptions about natural selection, especially selection on animal behavior, is that individual organisms will perform actions for the good of the species. Self-sacrificing, or altruistic, acts do occur in nature. Prairie dogs give alarm calls when predators approach, which draws attention to themselves. Lion mothers sometimes nurse cubs that are not their own. But selection cannot favor traits unless they increase the bearer's fitness relative to competing individuals. If an allele existed that produced a truly altruistic behavior—that is, a behavior that reduced the bearer's fitness and increased the fitness of others—it would be strongly selected against. As we will see in Chapter 10, every altruistic behavior that has been studied in detail has been found to increase the altruist's fitness either because the beneficiaries of the behavior are close genetic relatives (as in prairie dogs) or because the beneficiaries reciprocate (as in nursing lions).

Individuals do not do things for the good of the species. They behave in a way that maximizes their individual fitness.

The idea that animals will do things for the good of the species is so ingrained, however, that we will make the same point a second way. Consider lions again. Lions live in social groups called prides. Coalitions of males fight to take over prides. If a new group of males defeats the existing pride males in combat, the newcomers quickly kill all of the pride's nursing cubs. These cubs are unrelated to them. Killing the cubs increases the new males' fitness, because pride females become fertile again sooner and will conceive offspring by the new males (Packer and Pusey 1983, 1984). Infanticide is widespread in animals. Clearly, behavior like this does not exist for the good of the species. Rather, infanticide exists because, under certain conditions, it enhances the fitness of the individuals who perform the behavior relative to individuals who do not.

3.4 The Evolution of Darwinism

Because evolution by natural selection is a general organizing feature of living systems, Darwin's theory ranks as one of the great ideas in intellectual history. Its impact on biology is analogous to that of Newton's laws on physics, Copernicus's Sun-Centered Theory of the Universe on astronomy, and the Theory of Plate Tectonics on geology. In the words of evolutionary geneticist Theodosius Dobzhansky (1973), "Nothing in biology makes sense except in the light of evolution."

For all its power, though, the Theory of Evolution by Natural Selection was not universally accepted by biologists until some 70 years after it was initially proposed. There were three serious problems with the theory, as originally formulated by Darwin, that had to be resolved.

1. Because Darwin knew nothing about mutation, he had no idea how variability was generated in populations. As a result, he could not answer critics who maintained that the amount of variability in populations was strictly limited, and that natural selection would grind to a halt when variability ran out. It was not until the early 1900s, when geneticists such as Thomas Hunt Morgan began experimenting with fruit flies, that biologists began to appreciate the continuous and universal nature of mutation. Morgan and colleagues showed that mutations occur in every generation and in every trait.

2. Because Darwin knew nothing about genetics, he had no idea how variations are passed on to offspring. It was not until Mendel's experiments with peas were rediscovered and verified, 35 years after their original publication, that biologists understood how parental traits are passed on to offspring. Mendel's laws of segregation and independent assortment confirmed the mechanism behind postulate 2, which states that some of the variation observed in populations is heritable.

Until then, many biologists proposed that genes acted like pigments in paint. Advocates of this hypothesis, called **blending inheritance**, argued that favorable mutations would simply merge into existing traits and be lost. In 1867, a Scottish engineer named Fleeming Jenkin published a mathematical treatment of blending inheritance, along with a famous thought experiment concerning the offspring of light-skinned and dark-skinned people. For example, if a dark-skinned sailor became stranded on an equatorial island inhabited by light-skinned people, Jenkins' model predicted that no matter how advantageous dark skin might be (in reducing skin cancer, for example), the population would never become dark-skinned because traits like skin color blended. If the dark-skinned sailor had children by a light-skinned woman, their children would be brown-skinned. If they, in turn, had children with light-skinned people, their children would be light-brown-skinned, and so on. Conversely, if a light-skinned sailor became stranded on a northern island inhabited by dark-skinned people, blending inheritance argued that, no matter how advantageous light skin might be (in facilitating the synthesis of vitamin D from UV light, for example), the population would never become light. Under blending inheritance new variants are swamped, and new mutations diluted, until they cease to have a measurable effect. For natural selection to work, favorable new variations have to be passed on to offspring intact, and remain discrete.

We understand now, of course, that phenotypes blend in some traits, like skin color, but genotypes never do. Jenkins's hypothetical population would, in fact, become increasingly darker or lighter skinned if selection were strong and mutation continually added darker- or lighter-skinned variants to the population via changes in the genes involved in the production of melanin (Figure 3.10).

Darwin himself struggled with the problem of inheritance, and eventually adopted an entirely incorrect view based on the work of Jean-Baptiste Lamarck. Lamarck was a great French biologist of the early 19th century who proposed that species evolve through the inheritance of changes wrought in individuals. Lamarck's idea was a breakthrough for two reasons: It recognized that species have changed through time, and proposed a mechanism for producing change. His theory was wrong, however, because offspring do not inherit phenotypic changes acquired by their parents. If people build up muscles lifting weights, their offspring are not more powerful; if giraffes stretch their necks reaching for leaves in treetops, it has no consequence for the neck length of their offspring.

3. Lord Kelvin, the foremost physicist of the 19th century, published an important series of papers in the early 1860s calculating the age of the Earth at a maximum of 15–20 million years. Kelvin's analyses were based on measurements of the Sun's heat and the current temperature of the Earth. Because fire was the only known source of heat at the time, Kelvin assumed that the Sun was combusting like an enormous lump of coal. This had to mean that the Sun was gradually burning down, releasing progressively less heat with each passing millennium. Likewise, both geologists and physicists had come to believe that

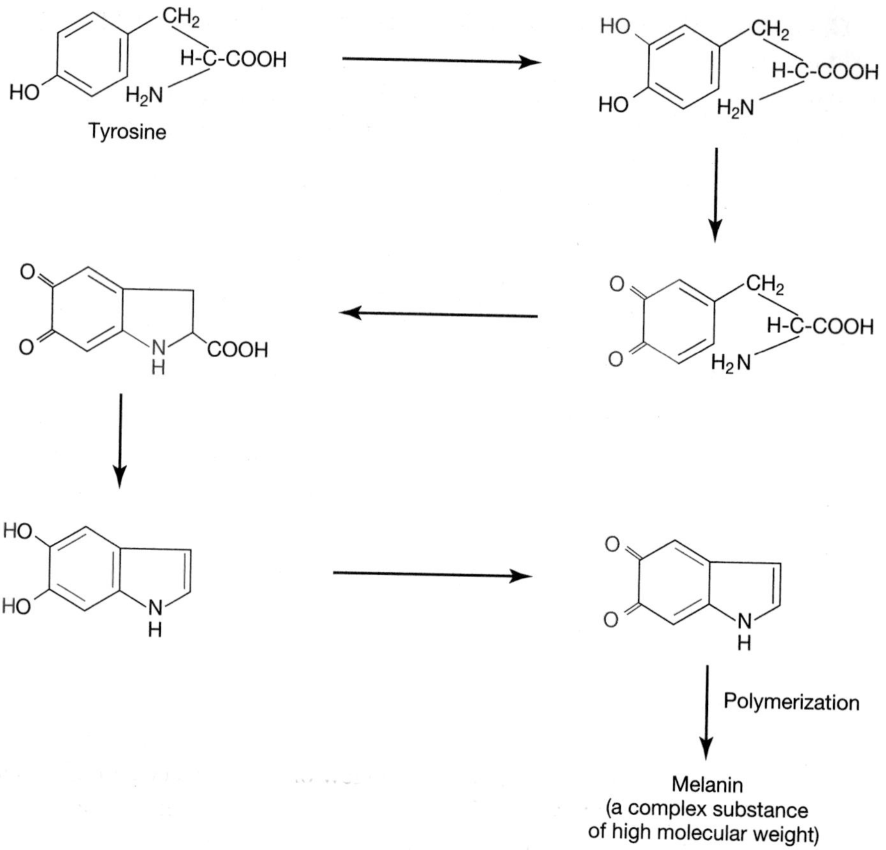

Figure 3.10 Why blending inheritance does not occur This diagram shows the biochemical pathway for melanin, the dark pigment in human skin. The pathway involves a series of steps starting with phenylalanine or tyrosine, which are common dietary amino acids. The enzymes responsible for catalyzing each reaction shown are coded for by several different genes. Because different alleles of these genes have different levels of activity, and because the pathway to melanin involves numerous steps, skin color is a product of the activities of many genes and alleles. In this way, the actions of genes blend to form a phenotype. Because each allele is distinct, however, each enzyme's effect on the biochemical pathway is passed on to offspring intact. This is why there is no such thing as blending inheritance.

the surface of the Earth was gradually cooling. This was based on the assumption that the Earth was changing from a molten state to a solid one by radiating heat to the atmosphere. This assumption seemed to be supported by measurements of progressively higher temperatures deeper down in mineshafts. These data allowed Kelvin to calculate the rate of radiant cooling.

The bottom line from Kelvin's calculations was that the transition from a hot to cold Sun and hot to cold Earth created a narrow window of time when life on Earth was possible. The window was clearly too narrow to allow the gradual changes of Darwinism to accumulate, and strongly supported a role for instantaneous and special creation in explaining adaptation and diversity.

The discovery of radioactive isotopes early in the 20th century changed all that. Kelvin's calculations were unassailable, but his assumptions were dead wrong. Geologists and physicists confirmed that the Earth's heat is a by-product of radioactive decay and not radiant cooling, and that the Sun's energy is from nuclear fusion, not combustion.

The Modern Synthesis

The Modern Synthesis resolved decades of controversy over the validity of evolution by natural selection.

Understanding variability, inheritance, and time was so difficult that the first 70 years of evolutionary biology were characterized by turmoil (see Provine 1971; Mayr 1980, 1991). But between 1932 and 1953 a series of landmark books was published that successfully integrated genetics with Darwin's four postulates and led to a reformulation of the Theory of Evolution. This restatement, known as the Modern Synthesis or the Evolutionary Synthesis, was a consensus grounded in two propositions:

- Gradual evolution results from small genetic changes that are acted upon by natural selection.
- The origin of species and higher taxa, or macroevolution, can be explained in terms of natural selection acting on individuals, or microevolution.

With the synthesis, Darwin's original four postulates—and their outcome—could be restated along the following lines:

1. As a result of mutation creating new alleles, and segregation and independent assortment shuffling alleles into new combinations, individuals within populations are variable for nearly all traits.
2. Individuals pass their alleles on to their offspring intact.
3. In most generations, more offspring are produced than can survive.
4. The individuals that survive and go on to reproduce, or who reproduce the most, are those with the alleles and allelic combinations that best adapt them to their environment.

The outcome is that alleles associated with higher fitness increase in frequency from one generation to the next.

This View of Life

Darwin ended the introduction to the first edition of *On the Origin of Species* with a statement that still represents the consensus view of evolutionary biologists (Darwin 1859, p. 6): "Natural Selection has been the main but not exclusive means of modification." We now think of modification in terms of changes in the frequencies of the alleles responsible for traits like beak depth and AZT resistance. We are more keenly aware of other processes that cause evolutionary change in addition to natural selection. (Chapters 4–6 explore these processes in detail.) But the Darwinian view of life, as a competition between individuals with varying abilities to survive and reproduce, has proven correct in almost every detail.

As Darwin wrote in his concluding sentence (1859, p. 490): "There is grandeur in this view of life, with its several powers, having been originally breathed into a few forms or into one; and that, whilst this planet has gone cycling on according to the fixed law of gravity, from so simple a beginning endless forms most beautiful and most wonderful have been, and are being, evolved."

3.5 The Debate over "Scientific Creationism"

Scientific controversy over the fact of evolution ended in the late 1800s, when the evidence reviewed in Chapter 2 simply overwhelmed the critics. Whether natural selection was the primary process responsible for both adaptation and diversity was still being challenged until the 1930s, when the works of the Modern Synthesis provided a mechanistic basis for Darwin's four postulates and unified micro- and macroevolution. Evolution by natural selection is now considered the great unifying idea in biology. Although scientific discourse about the validity of evolution by natural selection ended well over a half-century ago, a political and philosophical controversy in the United States and Europe still continues (Holden 1995; Kaiser 1995). What is this debate, and why is it occurring?

Creationists want the Theory of Special Creation to be taught in public schools, even though it was dismissed as a viable alternative to the Theory of Evolution by Natural Selection over a century ago.

History of the Controversy

The Scopes Monkey Trial of 1925 is perhaps the most celebrated event in a religious debate that has raged since Darwin first published (see Gould 1983, essay 20). John Scopes was a biology teacher who assigned reading about Darwinism in violation of the State of Tennessee's Butler Act, which prohibited the teaching of evolution in public schools. William Jennings Bryan, a famous politician and a fundamentalist orator, was the lawyer for the prosecution; Clarence Darrow, the most renowned defense attorney of his generation, represented Scopes. Although Scopes was convicted and fined $100, the trial was widely perceived as a great triumph for evolution because Bryan had suggested, on the witness stand, that the six days of creation described in Genesis 1:1–2:4 may each have lasted far longer than 24 hours. This was considered a grave inconsistency and a blow to the integrity of the creationist viewpoint. But far from ending the debate over teaching evolution in U.S. schools, the Scopes trial was merely a way station.

The Butler Act, in fact, stayed on the books until 1967; it was not until 1968, in *Epperson v. Arkansas,* that the U.S. Supreme Court struck down laws that prohibit the teaching of evolution. The court's ruling was made on the basis of the U.S. Constitution's separation of church and state. In response, fundamentalist religious groups in the United States reformulated their arguments as "creation science" and demanded equal time for what they insisted was an alternative theory for the origin of species. By the late 1970s, 26 state legislatures were debating equal-time legislation (Scott 1994). Arkansas and Louisiana passed such laws only to have them struck down in state courts. The Louisiana law was then appealed all the way to the U.S. Supreme Court, which decided in 1987 (*Edwards v. Aquillard*) that because creationism is essentially a religious idea, teaching it in the public schools was a violation of the first amendment. Two justices, however, formally wrote that it would still be acceptable for teachers to present alternative theories to evolution (Scott 1994).

One response from opponents of evolution has been to drop the words creation and creator from their literature and call either for equal time for teaching that no evolution has occurred, or for teaching a proposal called Intelligent Design Theory, which infers the presence of a creator from the perfection of adaptation in contemporary organisms (Scott 1994; Schmidt 1996). The complexity and perfection of organisms is actually a time-honored objection to evolution by natural selection. Darwin was aware of it; in his *Origin* he devoted a section of the chapter titled "Difficulties on Theory" to "Organs of extreme perfection." How can natural selection, by sorting random changes in the genome, produce elaborate and integrated traits like the vertebrate eye?

Perfection and Complexity in Nature

The English cleric William Paley, writing in 1802, promoted the Theory of Special Creation with a now-classic argument. If a person found a watch and discovered that it was an especially complex and accurate instrument, they would naturally infer that it had been made by a highly skilled watchmaker. Paley then drew a parallel between the watch and the perfection of the vertebrate eye, and asked his readers to infer the existence of a purposeful and perfect Creator. He contended that organisms are so well-engineered that they have to be the work of a conscious designer. This logic, still used by creationists today, is called the Argument from Design (Dawkins 1986).

Because we perceive perfection and complexity in the natural world, evolution by natural selection seems to defy credulity. There are actually two concerns here. The first is how random changes can lead to order. Mutations are chance events, so the generation of variation in a population is random. But the selection of those variants, or mutants, is nonrandom: It is directed in the sense of increasing fitness. And adaptations—structures or behaviors that increase fitness—are what we perceive as highly ordered, complex, or even perfect in the natural world. But there is nothing conscious or intelligent about the process. The biologist Richard Dawkins captured this point by referring to natural selection as a "blind watchmaker."

A second, and closely related, concern is, How can complex, highly integrated structures, like the vertebrate eye, evolve through the Darwinian process of gradual accumulation of small changes? Each evolutionary step would have to increase the fitness of individuals in the population. A creationist named Michael Behe (1996), for example, claims that biological systems such as biochemical pathways are "irreducibly complex," and that it is not possible for them to result from natural selection. Darwinism, in contrast, predicts that complex structures have evolved through a series of intermediate stages, or graded forms. Is this true? For example, when we consider a structure like the eye, do we find a diversity of forms, some of which are more complex than others?

The answer to these questions is yes. In some unicellular species there are actually subcellular organelles with functions analogous to the eye. The eyespots of a group of protozoans called euglenoids, for example, contain light-absorbing molecules that are shaded on one side by a patch of pigment. When these molecules absorb light, they undergo structural changes. Because light can reach them from one side only, a change in the light-absorbing molecule contains useful information about where light is coming from. Some dinoflagellates even have a subcellular, lenslike organelle that can concentrate light on a pigment cup. It is unlikely that these single-celled protists can form an image, however, because they are not capable of neural processing. Rather, their eye probably functions in transmitting information about the cell's depth in the water column, helping the cell orient itself and swim toward light.

More complex eyes have a basic unit called the photoreceptor. This is a cell that contains a pigment capable of absorbing light. The simplest type of multicellular eye, consisting of a few photoreceptor cells in a cup or cuplike arrangement, is shown in Figures 3.11a and 3.11b. This type of eye is found in a wide diversity of taxa, including flatworms, polychaetes (segmented worms in the phylum Annelida), some crustaceans (the shrimps, crabs, and allies), and some vertebrates. These organs are used in orientation and day-length monitoring (Willson 1984; Brusca and Brusca 1990). Slightly more complex eyes, like those illustrated in Figure 3.11c, have optic cups with a narrow aperture acting as a lens, and may be capable of forming images in at least some species. These are found in a few nemerteans (ribbon worms) and annelids (segmented worms), copepod crustaceans, and abalone and nautiloids (members of the phylum Mollusca). The most complex eyes (Figure 3.11d) fall into two functional categories based on whether the photoreceptor cells are arrayed on a retina that is concave, like the eyes of vertebrates and octopuses, or convex, like the compound eyes of insects and other arthropods (Goldsmith 1990). These eyes have lenses, and in most cases are capable of forming images.

It is important to recognize, however, that the simpler eyes we have just reviewed do not represent intermediate forms on the way to more advanced structures. The

The Argument from Design contends that adaptations must result from the actions of a conscious entity.

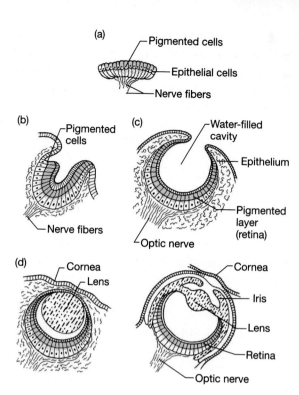

Figure 3.11 **Variation in mollusc eyes** (a) A pigment spot; (b) a simple pigment cup; (c) the simple optic cup found in abalone; (d) the complex lensed eyes of a marine snail called *Littorina* and the octopus. Pigmented cells are shown in color.

eyespots, pigment cups, and optic cups found in living organisms are contemporary adaptations to the problem of sensing light. They are not ancestral forms. It is, however, sensible to argue that the types of eyes discussed here form an evolutionary pathway (Gould 1983, essay 1). That is, it is conceivable that eyes like these formed intermediate stages in the evolution of the complex eyes found in vertebrates, octopuses, and insects. This is exactly what Darwin argued in his section on "organs of extreme perfection." (To learn more about the evolution of the eye, see Salvini–Plawen and Mayr 1977; Nilsson and Pelger 1994; Quiring et al. 1994; Dawkins 1994.)

Other Objections

We have found four additional arguments that creationists use regularly, and have added responses from an evolutionary perspective (see Gish 1978; Kitcher 1982; Futuyma 1983; Gould 1983 essays 19, 20, 21; Dawkins 1986; Swinney 1994):

1. Evolution by natural selection is unscientific because it is not falsifiable and because it makes no testable predictions. Each of Darwin's four postulates is independently testable, so the theory meets the classical criterion that ideas must be falsifiable to be considered scientific. Also, the claim that evolutionary biologists do not make predictions is not true. Paleontologists routinely (and correctly) predict which strata will bear fossils of certain types (a spectacular example was that fossil marsupial mammals would be found in Antarctica); Peter Grant and Rosemary Grant have used statistical techniques based on evolutionary theory to correctly predict the amount and direction of change in finch characteristics during selection events in the late 1980s and early 1990s (Grant and Grant 1993, 1995). Scientific creationism, on the other hand, amounts to an oxymoron; in the words of one of its leading advocates, Dr. Duane Gish (1978, p. 42): "We cannot discover by scientific investigations anything about the creative processes used by God."

2. Because the Earth was created as little as 6000–8000 years ago, there has not been enough time for Darwinian evolution to produce the adaptation and diversity observed in living organisms. Creation scientists present short-Earth theories and argue that most geological landforms and strata resulted from the flood during the time of Noah. (For example, see Gish 1978 and Swinney 1994.) Most simply disbelieve the assumptions behind radiometric dating and deny the validity of the data. The assumption of uniformitarianism in the evolution of life and landforms is also rejected by creation scientists. Again, we quote Gish (1978, p. 42): "We do not know how God created, what processes He used, *for God used processes which are not now operating anywhere in the natural universe*" (emphasis original).

The assumptions of radiometric dating have been tested, however, and demonstrated to be correct. Radiometric dating has demonstrated that rock strata differ in age, and that the Earth is about 4.6 billion years old.

3. Because organisms progress from simpler to more complex forms, evolution violates the Second Law of Thermodynamics. Although the Second Law has been stated in a variety of ways since its formulation in the late 19th century, the most general version is: "Natural processes tend to move toward a state of greater disorder" (Giancoli 1995). The Second Law is focused on the concept of entropy. This is a quantity that measures the state of disorder in a system. The Second Law, restated in terms of entropy, is "The entropy of an isolated system never decreases. It can only stay the same or increase" (Giancoli 1995).

The key to understanding the Second Law's relevance to evolution is the word "isolated." The Second Law is true only for closed systems. Organisms, however, live in an open system: the Earth, where photosynthetic life-forms capture the radiant energy of the sun and convert it to chemical energy that they and other organisms can use. Because energy is constantly being added to living systems, the Second Law does not apply to their evolution.

4. No one has ever seen a new species formed, so evolution is unproven. And because evolutionists say that speciation is too slow to be directly observed, evolution is unprovable and thus based on faith. Although speciation is a slow process, it is ongoing and can be studied. In Chapter 12 we explore one of the best-studied examples: the divergence of apple maggot flies into separate host races. The two forms of these flies lay their eggs in different fruits, which serve as a food source for their maggots. As a result of different patterns of natural selection on traits like food preferences and timing of breeding, marked genetic differences between the two populations are beginning to emerge. Research on these organisms is documenting key events early in the process of one species splitting into two.

Because there are tens of millions of insect species, and because most insects are specialist plant eaters, what is happening in apple maggot flies is of general interest: They may now be undergoing an event that has occurred many times in the course of evolution. Chapter 12 introduces other experimental and observational studies of "speciation in action" as well.

What Motivates the Controversy?

For decades, evolution by natural selection has been considered one of the best documented and most successful theories in the biological sciences. Many scientists see no conflict between evolution and religious faith (Easterbrook 1997; Scott

1998), and many Christians agree. In 1996, for example, Pope John Paul II acknowledged that Darwinian evolution was a firmly established scientific result, and stated that accepting Darwinism was compatible with traditional Christian understandings of God.

If the fact of evolution and the validity of natural selection are utterly uncontroversial, and if belief in evolution is compatible with belief in God, then why does the creationist debate continue?

During a discussion about whether material on evolution should be included in high school textbooks, a member of the Alabama State School Board named David Byers said, "It's foolish and naive to believe that what children are taught about who they are, how they got here, doesn't have anything to do with what they conclude about why they are here and what their obligations are, if, in fact, they have any obligations, and how they should live" (National Public Radio 1995). This statement suggests that, for some creationists, the controversy is not about the validity of the scientific evidence or its compatibility with religion. Instead, the concern is about what evolution means for human morality and behavior.

Creationists and evolutionists share the desire that children should grow up to become morally responsible adults. Creationists fight evolution because they believe it is morally dangerous. Evolutionary biologists, on the other hand, believe that children should learn what science says about how living things came to be, and let them sort out the moral implications, if any, on their own.

Summary

Before Darwin began to work on the origin of species, many scientists had become convinced that species change through time. The unique contribution made by Darwin and Wallace was to realize that the process of natural selection provided a mechanism for this pattern, which Darwin termed descent with modification.

Evolution by natural selection is the logical outcome of four facts: (1) Individuals vary in most or all traits; (2) some of this variation is genetically based and can be passed on to offspring; (3) more offspring are born than can survive to breed, and of those that do breed, some are more successful than others; and (4) the individuals that reproduce the most are a nonrandom, or more fit, subset of the general population. This selection process causes changes in the genetic makeup of populations over time, or evolution.

Questions

1. In everyday English, the word adaptation means "an adjustment to environmental conditions." How is the evolutionary definition of adaptation different from the everyday English sense?

2. Think about how the finch bill data demonstrate Darwin's postulates.
   - What would Figure 3.3 have looked like if bill depth was not variable?
   - What would the data in Table 3.2 look like if bill depth was variable, but the variation was not heritable?

   - In Figure 3.4, why is the line drawn from 1978 data, after the drought, higher on the y-axis than the line drawn from 1976 data, before the drought?

3. According to the text, it is legitimate to claim that most finches died from starvation during the 1977 drought because "there was a strong correspondence between population size and seed availability." Do you accept this hypothesis? If so, why don't the data in Figure 3.5 show a perfect correspondence between when seed availability started declining and when population size started declining?

4. Suppose that you are starting a long-term study of a population of annual, flowering plants isolated on a small island. Reading some recent papers has convinced you that global warming is real and will lead to significant, long-term changes in the amount of rain the island receives. Outline the observations and experiments you would need to do in order to document whether natural selection occurs in your study population over the course of your research. What traits would you measure, and why?

5. At the end of an article on how mutations in variable number tandem repeat (VNTR) sequences of DNA are associated with disease, Krontiris (1995, p. 1683) writes: "the VNTR mutational process may actually be positively selected; by culling those of us in middle age and beyond, evolution brings our species into fighting trim." This researcher proposes that natural selection on humans favors individuals who die relatively early in life. His logic is that the trait of dying from VNTR mutations is beneficial and should spread, because the population as a whole becomes younger and healthier as a result. Can this hypothesis be true, given that selection acts on individuals? Explain.

6. Many working scientists are relatively uninterested in the history of their fields. Did the historical development of Darwinism, reviewed in Section 3.4, help you understand the theory better? Why or why not? Do you think it is important for practicing scientists to spend time studying history?

7. Recently, the Alabama School Board, after reviewing high school biology texts, voted to require that this disclaimer be posted on the inside front cover of the approved book (National Public Radio 1995):

> This textbook discussed evolution, a controversial theory some scientists present as a scientific explanation for the origin of living things, such as plants, animals, and humans. No one was present when life first appeared on Earth; therefore, any statement about life's origins should be considered as theory, not fact.

Do you accept the last sentence in this statement? Does the insert's point of view pertain to other scientific theories, such as the Cell Theory, the Atomic Theory, the Theory of Plate Tectonics, and the Germ Theory of Disease?

8. A 1991 Gallup poll of U.S. adults found that 47% of the respondents believed that God created man within the last 10,000 years (Root-Bernstein, 1995). Given the evidence for evolution by natural selection, comment on why so few people in the United States accept it.

Exploring the Literature

9. During the past 50 years, hundreds of viruses, bacteria, fungi, and insects have evolved resistance to drugs, herbicides, fungicides, or pesticides. These are outstanding examples of evolution in action. In several of these cases, we know the molecular mechanisms of the evolutionary changes involved. To explore this topic further, look up the following papers. Think about how the evidence from these studies compares with the evidence for evolution in Darwin's finches and HIV.

Anthony, R. G., T. R. Waldin, J. A. Ray, S. W. J. Bright, and P. J. Hussey. 1998. Herbicide resistance caused by spontaneous mutation of the cytoskeletal protein tubulin. *Nature* 393: 260–263.

Cohen, M. L. 1992. Epidemiology of drug resistance: Implications for a post-antimicrobial era. *Science* 257: 1050–1055.

Davies, J. 1994. Inactivation of antibiotics and the dissemination of resistance genes. *Science* 264: 375–382.

Van Rie, J., W. H. McGaughey, D. E. Johnson, B. D. Barnett, and H. Van Melleart. 1990. Mechanism of insect resistance to the microbial insecticide *Bacillus thuringiensis*. *Science* 247: 72–74.

10. It seems unlikely that selection of traits "for the good of the group" can occur. However, some evolutionary biologists contend that under certain conditions, group selection of altruistic behaviors may in fact be possible. Look up the following papers to learn more about this topic:

Avilés, L., and P. Tufino. 1998. Colony size and individual fitness in the social spider *Anelosimus eximius*. *American Naturalist* 152: 403–418.

Morell, V. 1996. Genes vs. Teams: Weighing group tactics in evolution. *Science* 273: 739–740. (News perspective.)

Wilson, D. F., and E. Sober. 1994. Reintroducing group selection to the human behavioral sciences. *Behavioral Brain Sciences* 17: 585–609.

Wilson, D. S., and L. A. Dugatkin. 1997. Group selection and assortative interactions. *American Naturalist* 149: 336–351.

Citations

Abbott, I., L. K. Abbott, and P. R. Grant. 1977. Comparative ecology of Galápagos ground finches (*Geospiza* Gould): Evaluation of the importance of floristic diversity and interspecific competition. *Ecological Monographs* 47: 151–184.

Audesirk, G., and T. Audesirk. 1993. *Biology: Life on Earth.* New York: Macmillan.

Behe, M. 1996. *Darwin's Black Box: The Biochemical Challenge to Evolution.* New York: Free Press/Simon and Schuster.

Boag, P. T. 1983. The heritability of external morphology in Darwin's ground finches (*Geospiza*) on Isla Daphne Major, Galápagos. *Evolution* 37: 877–894.

Boag, P. T., and P. R. Grant. 1978. Heritability of external morphology in Darwin's finches. *Nature* 274: 793–794.

Boag, P. T., and P. R. Grant. 1981. Intense natural selection in a population of Darwin's finches (Geospizinae) in the Galápagos. *Science* 214: 82–85.

Bowman, R. I. 1961. Morphological differentiation and adaptation in the Galápagos finches. *University of California Publications in Zoology* 58: 1–302.

Brusca, R. C., and G. J. Brusca. 1990. *Invertebrates.* Sunderland, MA: Sinauer.

Darwin, C. 1859. *On the Origin of Species by Means of Natural Selection.* London: John Murray.

Dawkins, R. 1986. *The Blind Watchmaker.* Essex: Longman Scientific.

Dawkins, R. 1994. The eye in a twinkling. *Nature* 368: 690–691.

Dobzhansky, T. 1973. Nothing in biology makes sense except in the light of evolution. *American Biology Teacher* 35: 125–129.

Dodson, E. O. 1960. *Evolution: Process and Product.* New York: Reinhold Publishing.

Easterbrook, G. 1997. Science and God: A warming trend? *Science* 277: 890–893.

Endo, H., D. Yamagiwa, Y. Hayashi, H. Koie, Y. Yamaya, and J. Kimura. 1999. Role of the giant panda's 'pseudo-thumb.' *Nature* 397: 309–310.

Futuyma, D. J. 1983. *Science on Trial: The Case for Evolution.* New York: Pantheon.

Giancoli, D. C. 1995. *Physics: Principles with Applications.* Englewood Cliffs, NJ: Prentice Hall.

Gibbs, H. L., and P. R. Grant. 1987. Oscillating selection on Darwin's finches. *Nature* 327: 511–513.

Gish, D. T. 1978. *Evolution: The Fossils Say No!* San Diego: Creation-Life Publishers.

Goldsmith, T. H. 1990. Optimization, constraint, and history in the evolution of eyes. *Quarterly Review of Biology* 65: 281–322.

Gould, S. J. 1977. *Ever Since Darwin: Reflections in Natural History.* New York: W. W. Norton.

Gould, S. J. 1980. *The Panda's Thumb.* New York: W. W. Norton.

Gould, S. J. 1983. *Hen's Teeth and Horse's Toes.* New York: W. W. Norton.

Grant, B. R. 1985. Selection on bill characters in a population of Darwin's finches: *Geospiza conirostris* on Isla Genovesa, Galápagos. *Evolution* 39: 523–532.

Grant, B. R., and P. R. Grant. 1989. *Evolutionary Dynamics of a Natural Population.* Chicago: University of Chicago Press.

Grant, B. R., and P. R. Grant. 1993. Evolution of Darwin's finches caused by a rare climatic event. *Proceedings of the Royal Society of London,* Series B 251: 111–117.

Grant, P. R. 1981a. Speciation and adaptive radiation on Darwin's finches. *American Scientist* 69: 653–663.

Grant, P. R. 1981b. The feeding of Darwin's finches on *Tribulus cistoides* (L.) seeds. *Animal Behavior* 29: 785–793.

Grant, P. R. 1991. Natural selection and Darwin's finches. *Scientific American* October: 82–87.

Grant, P. R. 1999. *Ecology and Evolution of Darwin's Finches,* 2nd ed. Princeton: Princeton University Press.

Grant, P. R., and B. R. Grant. 1995. Predicting microevolutionary responses to directional selection on heritable variation. *Evolution* 49: 241–251.

Grant, P. R., B. R. Grant, J. N. M. Smith, I. J. Abbott, and L. K. Abbott. 1976. Darwin's finches: Population variation and natural selection. *Proceedings of the National Academy of Sciences, USA* 73: 257–261.

Holden, C. 1995. Alabama schools disclaim evolution. *Science* 270: 1305.

Kaiser, J. 1995. Dutch debate tests on evolution. *Science* 269: 911.

Keeton, W. T. 1972. *Biological Science.* New York: W. W. Norton.

Kitcher, P. 1982. *Abusing Science: The Case Against Creationism.* Cambridge, MA: MIT Press.

Krontiris, T. G. 1995. Minisatellites and human disease. *Science* 269: 1682–1683.

Leng, E. R. 1962. Results of long-term selection for chemical composition in maize and their significance in evaluating breeding systems. *Zeitschrift für Pflanzenzüchtung* 47: 67–91.

Mayr, E. 1980. Prologue. In Mayr, E., and W. B. Provine, eds., *The Evolutionary Synthesis.* Cambridge, MA: Harvard University Press.

Mayr, E. 1991. *One Long Argument: Charles Darwin and the Genesis of Modern Evolutionary Thought.* Cambridge, MA: Harvard University Press.

National Public Radio. 1995. Evolution disclaimer to be placed in Alabama textbooks. Morning Edition, Transcript #1747, Segment #13.

Nilsson, D.-E., and S. Pelger. 1994. A pessimistic estimate of the time required for an eye to evolve. *Proceedings of the Royal Academy of London,* Series B 256: 53–58.

Packer, C., and A. E. Pusey. 1983. Adaptations of female lions to infanticide by incoming males. *American Naturalist* 121: 716–728.

Packer, C., and A. E. Pusey. 1984. Infanticide in carnivores. Pp. 31–42 in G. Hausfater and S. B. Hrdy, eds. *Infanticide.* New York: Aldine Publishing Company.

Petren, K., B. R. Grant, and P. R. Grant. 1999. A phylogeny of Darwin's finches based on microsatellite DNA length variation. *Proceedings of the Royal Society of London,* Series B 266: 321–329.

Price, T. D., P. R. Grant, H. L. Gibbs, and P. T. Boag. 1984. Recurrent patterns of natural selection in a population of Darwin's finches. *Nature* 309: 787–789.

Provine, W. B. 1971. *The Origins of Theoretical Population Genetics.* Chicago: University of Chicago Press.

Quiring, R., U. Walldorf, U. Kloter, and W. J. Gehring. 1994. Homology of the *eyeless* gene of *Drosophila* to the *small eye* gene in mice and *aniridia* in humans. *Science* 265: 785–789.

Root-Bernstein, R. S. 1995. "Darwin's Rib." *Discover* (September) 38–41.

Salvini-Plawen, L. v., and E. Mayr. 1977. On the evolution of photoreceptors and eyes. *Evolutionary Biology* 10: 207–263.

Schmidt, K. 1996. Creationists evolve new strategy. *Science* 273: 420–422.

Scott, E. C. 1994. The struggle for the schools. *Natural History* 7: 10–13.

Scott, E. C. 1998. Two kinds of materialism. *Free Inquiry* 18: 20.

Swinney, S. 1994. "Evolution: Fact or Fiction." Kansas City, MO: 1994 Staley Lecture Series, KLJC Audio Services.

Willson, M. F. 1984. *Vertebrate Natural History.* Philadelphia: Saunders.

CHAPTER 4

Mutation and Genetic Variation

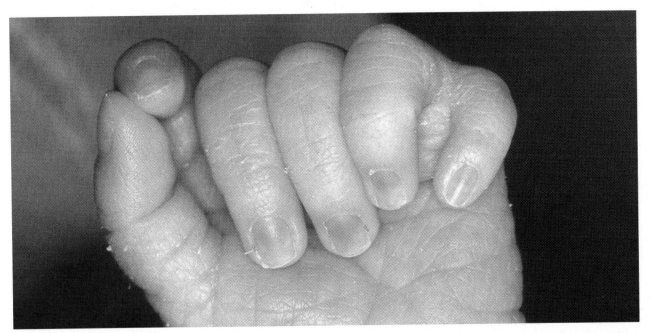

This individual has a mutation that leads to the development of six fingers on each hand. (Science Photo Library/Photo Researchers, Inc.)

MUTATIONS ARE THE RAW MATERIAL OF EVOLUTION. WITHOUT MUTATION there are no new genes, no new alleles, and eventually, no evolution. Mutation is the ultimate source of the heritable variation acted upon by natural selection and other evolutionary processes.

This chapter has two goals: to investigate the mechanisms responsible for generating new alleles and new genes, and to explore how biologists quantify the amount of genetic variation that exists in natural populations. We begin by reviewing how single-base mutations and other types of small-scale changes occur in DNA sequences. These processes produce new alleles. Later in the chapter we consider larger-scale changes that can produce new genes, change the organization of individual chromosomes, or alter the number of chromosome sets in a species. The chapter closes by considering how researchers analyze genetic variation within species.

The chapter does not attempt an encyclopedic review of all mutations that can affect gene sequences and organization, however. The roster of mutation types, especially at the level of chromosomes, is simply too large. Instead, we focus on the subset of mutations that have the greatest evolutionary impact (Table 4.1).

Table 4.1 **Types of mutation with significant evolutionary impact**

This table summarizes the types of mutation reviewed in this chapter.

Name	Description	Cause	Significance
Point mutation	Base-pair substitutions in DNA sequences	Chance errors during DNA synthesis or during repair of damaged DNA	Creates new alleles
Chromosome inversion	Flipping of a chromosome segment, so that the order of genes along the chromosome is altered	Breaks in DNA caused by radiation	Alleles inside the inversion are "locked together" into a unit
Gene duplication	Duplication of a short stretch of DNA, creating an additional copy of a gene	Unequal crossing over during meiosis (see Fig. 4.3)	The "extra" gene is free to mutate and perhaps gain new function
Polyploidy	Addition of a complete set of chromosomes	Errors in meiosis or (in plants) mitosis	Can create new species

4.1 Where New Alleles Come From

The instructions for making and running an organism are encoded in its hereditary material—the molecule called deoxyribonucleic acid, or DNA. As Figure 4.1a shows, DNA is made up of smaller molecules called deoxyribonucleotides. The four deoxyribonucleotides found in DNA are similar in structure: Each contains the 5-carbon sugar called deoxyribose, a phosphate group, and a distinctive nitrogen-containing base. The four bases in DNA belong to two discrete chemical groups: Cytosine and thymine are pyrimidines, while adenine and guanine are purines. The four deoxyribonucleotides are routinely abbreviated to C, T, A, and G.

Figure 4.1b illustrates how these molecules are linked into long strands by phosphodiester bonds that form between the 5′ carbon of one deoxyribonucleotide and the 3′ carbon of another. A single strand of DNA, then, consists of a sequence of bases attached to a sugar-phosphate "backbone." In cells, however, DNA normally consists of two such strands. These are wound around one another in the double helix diagrammed in Figure 4.1c. This structure is stabilized by hydrogen bonds that form between the bases on either strand. Due to the geometry of the bases and the amount of space available inside the helix, hydrogen bonds only form when adenine and thymine (A—T) or guanine and cytosine (G—C) bases line up on opposite strands. These purine–pyrimidine combinations are called complementary base pairs. As Figure 4.1d shows, three hydrogen bonds form between G and C, but only two are made between A and T.

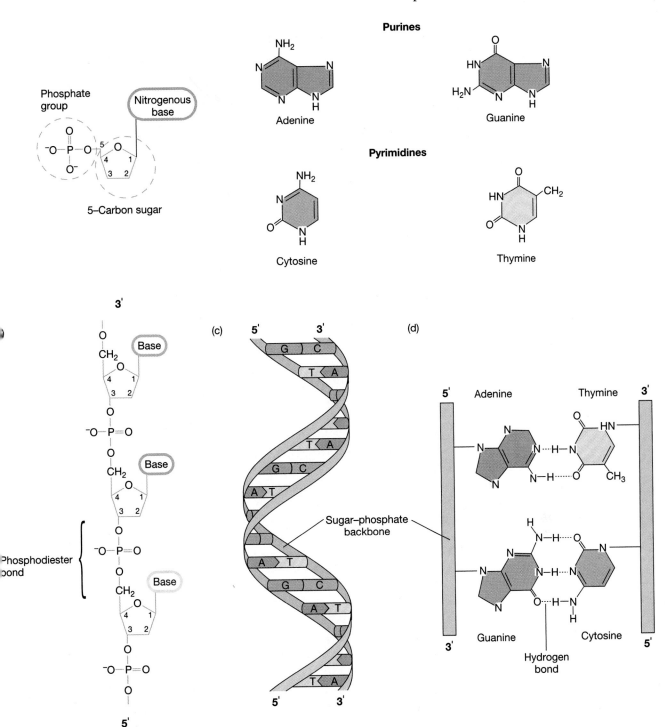

Figure 4.1 **The structure of the genetic material** (a) The diagram on the left shows the generalized form of a nucleotide. Note that each carbon atom in the sugar is numbered, and that the hydrogen and oxygen atoms bonded to these carbons are not shown. The diagrams on the right show the structure of the four nitrogen-containing bases. (b) Nucleotides are linked into long chains by phosphodiester bonds between the 5′ carbon on one nucleotide and the 3′ carbon on another. (c) When complementary bases on opposite DNA strands form hydrogen bonds, the molecule twists into a double helix like the one shown here. (d) Adenine and thymine form two hydrogen bonds; cytosine and guanine form three.

The Nature of Mutation

Once James Watson and Francis Crick (1953) had deduced the double-helical structure of DNA shown in Figure 4.1c, they immediately realized that complementary base pairing provided a mechanism for copying the hereditary material. As Figure 4.2 illustrates, one strand serves as the template for making a copy of the other strand. In 1960, Arthur Kornberg succeeded in isolating the first of several proteins, called DNA polymerases, that are responsible for copying the DNA in cells.

In the late 1950s and early 1960s, a series of experiments succeeded in clarifying how the sequence of bases in DNA encodes information and how the genetic information is transformed into the proteins that make and run cells. The central result was that DNA is transcribed into messenger RNA (mRNA), which is then translated into protein (Figure 4.3a). Researchers established that the genetic code is read in triplets called codons. They also deciphered which amino acid is specified by each of the 64 different codons (Figure 4.3b). Because only 20 amino acids need to be specified by the 64 codons, the genetic code is highly redundant—meaning that the same amino acid can be specified by more than one codon.

These results inspired an explicitly molecular view of the gene and mutation. Genes became defined as stretches of DNA that code for a distinct RNA or protein product. Alleles became defined as versions of the same gene that differ in their base sequence. Mutations were understood as changes in the base sequence of DNA.

A mutation is a change in the base sequence of DNA.

To drive this point home, consider the first mutation ever characterized on a molecular level: the change in human hemoglobin that results in the sometimes-fatal disease sickle-cell anemia. Hemoglobin is the oxygen-carrying protein found in red blood cells. In 1949, Linus Pauling's lab reported that people suffering from sickle-cell anemia had a form of hemoglobin different from that of people without the disease. In 1958, Vernon Ingram showed that the difference between normal and sickle-cell hemoglobin was due to a single amino acid change at position number 6 in the protein chain, which is 146 amino acids long. Instead of having glutamic acid at this position, the sickling allele has valine. Further work established that the amino acid replacement is caused by a single base substitution in the hemoglobin gene. The mutant allele has an adenine instead of a thymine at nu-

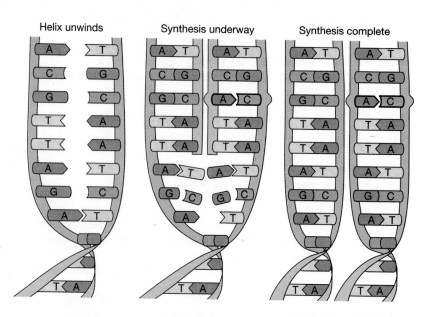

Figure 4.2 DNA forms a template for its synthesis Because of complementary base pairing, each strand in a DNA molecule forms a template for the synthesis of the complementary strand. If DNA polymerase inserts the wrong base, as in the strand at the far right, it results in a mismatched pair that must be repaired.

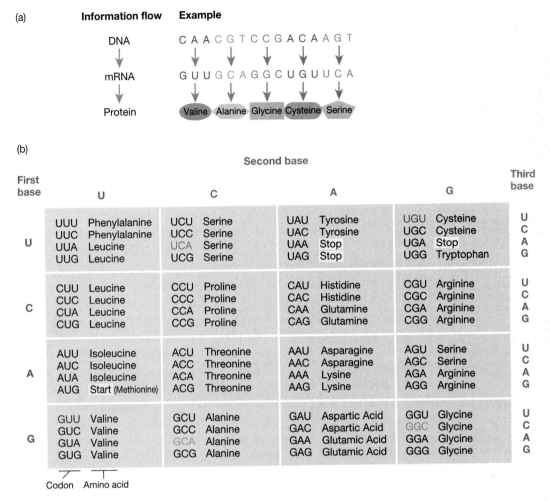

Figure 4.3   In organisms, information flows from DNA to RNA to proteins   (a) In cells, the sequence of bases in DNA is transcribed to a sequence of bases in a strand of messenger RNA (mRNA), which is then translated into a sequence of amino acids in a protein. Note that RNA contains a nitrogenous base called uracil instead of thymine. An adenine in DNA specifies a uracil in RNA. (b) This is the genetic code. Each of the 64 mRNA codons shown here specifies an amino acid or the start or end of a transcription unit. Note that in many instances, changing the third base in a codon does not change the message.

cleotide 2 in the codon for amino acid 6. A change like this is called a **point mutation**, because it alters a single point in the base sequence of a gene.

Point Mutations

Point mutations are single-base substitutions in DNA caused by one of two processes: random errors in DNA synthesis, or random errors in the repair of sites damaged by chemical mutagens or high-energy radiation. Both types of changes result from reactions catalyzed by DNA polymerase.

If DNA polymerase mistakenly substitutes a purine (A or G) for another purine, or a pyrimidine (T or C) for another pyrimidine during normal synthesis or the synthesis that occurs during a repair, the point mutation is called a **transition** (Figure 4.4). If a purine is substituted for a pyrimidine or a pyrimidine for a purine, the mutation is called a **transversion**. Of the two kinds of point mutation, transitions are far more common. They routinely outnumber transversions by at least 2:1.

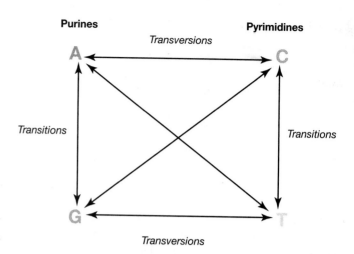

Figure 4.4   **Transitions and transversions**

The leading hypothesis to explain this observation is that transitions cause much less disruption in the DNA helix during synthesis, so are less likely to be recognized as an error and therefore less likely to be immediately corrected.

If either type of base substitution occurs in the coding region of a gene, the mutation changes the codon read by the protein, called RNA polymerase, that synthesizes RNA from the DNA template. For example, the substitution of an A for a T in the gene for hemoglobin is a transversion that changes the message in codon number 6. Look back at the genetic code in Figure 4.3b, and note that changes in the first or second position of a codon almost always change the amino acid specified by the resulting mRNA. But because of the redundancy in the genetic code, changes in the third position frequently produce no change at all.

Point mutations that result in an amino acid change are called **replacement** (or **nonsynonymous**) **substitutions**; those that result in no change are called **silent site** (or **synonymous**) **substitutions**. Both types of point mutations create new alleles. Now the question becomes, How do these new alleles affect the fitness of organisms?

Point mutations are single-base substitutions in DNA. They are classified in two ways: as transitions or transversions and as replacement or silent substitutions.

The Fitness Effects of Mutations

Silent site substitutions in DNA do not affect the phenotype of the organism because they do not alter gene products. As a result, silent site mutations are not subject to natural selection based on protein or RNA function. Alleles that have no effect on fitness are said to be **neutral**.

But what about replacement substitutions, which *do* produce a change in protein structure? Because they change the organism's phenotype, replacement substitutions are exposed to natural selection. For example, the sickle–cell mutation produces a dramatic change in phenotype. The mutant hemoglobin molecules tend to crystallize, forming long fibers. Hemoglobin is found inside red blood cells, and when the molecule crystallizes it distorts the normally disc-shaped cells into the sickled cells pictured in Figure 4.5. The sickled cells tend to get stuck in capillaries. This blocks the flow of blood, deprives tissues of oxygen, and causes severe pain. Sickled red cells are also more fragile than normal cells and more rapidly destroyed. This continuous loss of red blood cells causes anemia.

The sickling and anemia are most severe in people homozygous for the mutant allele, because all of their hemoglobin molecules are prone to crystallization. Heterozygous people get some sickling, particularly when the concentration of dissolved

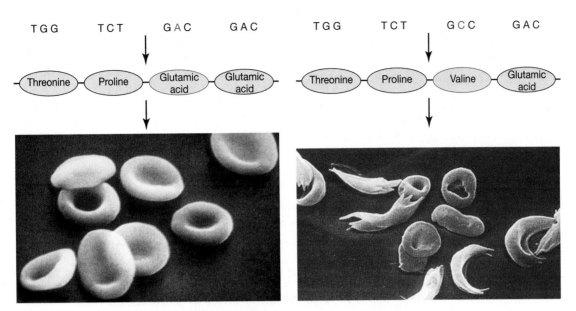

Figure 4.5   Normal and sickling forms of human red blood cells   The diagram on the left shows a short section near the start of the DNA and protein sequence of normal hemoglobin; the photo on the left shows normal red blood cells. The diagram on the right shows the same section of the DNA and protein sequence of a mutant hemoglobin; the photo on the right shows the sickled red blood cells that result from this mutation. (Photos from Photo Researchers, Inc.)

oxygen in their blood gets low. It would appear, then, that the allele has a strong adverse affect on the fitness of individuals. Natural selection should quickly eliminate the mutant alleles from the population.

The situation is not this simple, however. People who have one copy of the normal allele and one copy of the mutant allele enjoy an unexpected benefit: They are resistant to malaria. The resistance apparently results because in heterozygotes, red blood cells containing malaria parasites are much more prone to sickling than unparasitized cells. This means that red cells containing parasites are selectively destroyed. In environments where malaria is common, resistance to malaria is so valuable that heterozygotes have higher fitness than either kind of homozygote. The mutant allele is thus beneficial in environments where malaria is common, but deleterious in environments where malaria is rare. The genetic basis of sickle-cell anemia provides an example of heterozygote superiority. We will discuss heterozygote superiority in more detail in Chapter 5.

To summarize, the sickle-cell mutation created a new allele that is beneficial in some environments and deleterious in others. This is unusual, because the overwhelming majority of replacement substitutions create new alleles that have little to no effect on fitness (Keightley and Caballero 1997; García-Dorado 1997). It is not surprising that many of the random changes in the amino acid sequences of proteins do not improve their ability to function, because most proteins have been under selection for millions of years. We would not expect a random change to improve a protein's function any more than we would expect a random change in a computer's circuitry to improve processing performance. It is important, though, to recognize that both replacement and silent substitutions produce a wide range of effects on fitness—from highly deleterious to neutral to beneficial—and that the fitness effects of alleles depend on their environment. We will return to these points in Chapters 5 and 18.

In coding sequences, the fitness effects of replacement substitutions range from highly deleterious to beneficial. Most mutations have very small effects on fitness.

Mutation Rates

How often are new alleles formed? Many of our best data on mutation rates are for a class of changes known as **loss-of-function mutations**. In these types of mutations, the lack of a normal protein product leads to an easily recognizable phenotype. For example, researchers may survey a large human population and count the incidence of an autosomal-dominant syndrome like Achondroplasia (dwarfism) or an X-linked recessive disorder like Hemophilia A (in which blood clotting is impaired). The idea is to pick a trait that is easy to detect and whose transmission genetics allow researchers to identify new mutations. For example, an individual with Achondroplasia, neither of whose parents has the condition, must represent a new mutation. From data like these, a researcher can report mutation rates in units of per gene per generation.

The problem with this method is that loss-of-function mutations result from any process that inactivates a gene. As Figure 4.6 shows, genes can be knocked out by base-pair substitutions that produce a chain-terminating codon or a dysfunctional amino acid sequence. They can also be knocked out by the insertion of a mobile genetic element, chromosome rearrangements, or a disruption in the reading sequence of codons caused by the addition or deletion of one or two base pairs (these are called frameshift mutations). Further, many interesting mutations (most replacement substitutions, for example) are not detectable when researchers assess offspring phenotypes because their effects are less subtle than a loss of function. Because of these difficulties, most existing data seriously underestimate the actual rate at which mutations occur.

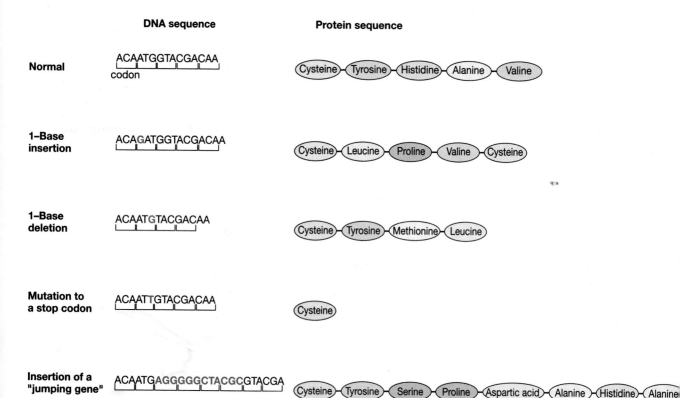

Figure 4.6   Loss-of-function mutations "Knock-out" mutants result from any event that inactivates a gene. Note that the insertion or deletion of a single base changes all subsequent codons in a gene, creating a dysfunctional protein.

Even with these limitations, we can still say some interesting things about mutation rates. For example, consider the data in Table 4.2 on rates and frequencies of loss-of-function mutations and other changes with major effects. The mutation rates reported are very low on a per-gene basis. But there are so many loci in organisms (at least 60,000 in humans, for example) that perhaps 10% of all gametes carry a phenotypically detectable mutation. This is a large percentage, considering that the reported rates undoubtedly underestimate the number of

Table 4.2 **Variation in mutation rates among genes and species**

(a) Rates of mutation to recessive phenotypes among genes in corn. L. J. Stadler (1942) bred a large number of corn plants and scored offspring for a series of recessive conditions.

Gene	Number of gametes tested	Number of mutations found	Average number of mutations per million gametes	Mutation rate (frequency per gamete)
$R \rightarrow r$	554,786	273	492.0	4.9×10^{-4}
$I \rightarrow i$	265,391	28	106.0	1.1×10^{-4}
$Pr \rightarrow pr$	647,102	7	11.0	1.1×10^{-5}
$Su \rightarrow su$	1,678,736	4	2.4	2.4×10^{-6}
$Y \rightarrow y$	1,745,280	4	2.2	2.2×10^{-6}
$Sh \rightarrow sh$	2,469,285	3	1.2	1.2×10^{-6}
$Wx \rightarrow wx$	1,503,744	0	0.0	0.0

(b) These data, summarizing mutation rates for a variety of genes and species, are taken from R. Sager and F. J. Ryan, *Heredity*. New York: John Wiley, 1961.

Organism	Mutation	Value	Units
Bacteriophage T2 (bacterial virus)	Lysis inhibition $r \rightarrow r^+$	1×10^{-8}	*Rate:* mutant genes per gene replication
	Host range $h^+ \rightarrow h$	3×10^{-9}	
Escherichia coli (bacterium)	Lactose fermentation $lac \rightarrow lac^+$	2×10^{-7}	
	Histidine requirement $his^- \rightarrow his^+$	4×10^{-8}	*Rate:* mutant cells per cell division
	$his^+ \rightarrow his^-$	2×10^{-6}	
Chlamydomonas reinhardtii (alga)	Streptomycin sensitivity $str^s \rightarrow str^r$	1×10^{-6}	
Neurospora crassa (fungus)	Inositol requirement $inos^- \rightarrow inos^+$	8×10^{-8}	*Frequency:* per asexual spore
	Adenine requirement $ad^- \rightarrow ad^+$	4×10^{-8}	
Drosophila melanogaster (fruit fly)	Eye color $W \rightarrow w$	4×10^{-5}	
Mouse	Dilution $D \rightarrow d$	3×10^{-5}	
Human to autosomal dominants	Huntington's chorea	1×10^{-6}	
	Nail-patella syndrome	2×10^{-6}	
	Epiloia (predisposition to a type of brain tumor)	$4–8 \times 10^{-6}$	*Frequency:* per gamete
	Multiple polyposis of large intestine	$1–3 \times 10^{-5}$	
	Achondroplasia (dwarfism)	$4–12 \times 10^{-5}$	
	Neurofibromatosis (predisposition to tumors of nervous system)	$3–25 \times 10^{-5}$	
to X-linked recessives	Hemophilia A	$2–4 \times 10^{-5}$	
	Duchenne's muscular dystrophy	$4–10 \times 10^{-5}$	
in bone-marrow tissue-culture cells	Normal $\rightarrow$ azaguanine resistance	7×10^{-4}	*Rate:* mutant cells per cell division

replacement substitutions and thus new alleles. One message of these data sets is that it is conceivable, or even probable, that the majority of all offspring carry at least one new allele somewhere in their genome.

A second message in these data concerns variation in mutation rates. Rates of phenotypically detectable mutations vary by 500-fold among genes within species (Table 4.2a), and by as much as five orders of magnitude, or 100,000-fold, among species (Table 4.2b). An obvious question is, why?

Why Are Mutation Rates Variable?

The rate at which new alleles are produced varies at three levels: among individuals within populations, among genes within individuals, and among species. According to the research done to date, it appears that different mechanisms may be responsible for the variation observed at each level.

Variation Among Individuals

Mutation rate varies among individuals for two reasons: Alleles of DNA polymerase can vary in their error rate, and the alleles involved in repairing damaged DNA can vary in their efficiency.

Frances Gillin and Nancy Nossal (1976a, b) were responsible for documenting that DNA polymerases vary in their accuracy. They did this by investigating single-base substitutions in the DNA polymerase of bacteriophage T4 (a virus that parasitizes bacteria). Some of the mutations Gillin and Nossal isolated decreased the rate at which polymerase made errors during DNA replication, and reduced the overall mutation rate. Other mutations in polymerase increased the error rate, and heightened the overall mutation rate. In a key finding, they also determined that the more error-prone polymerase mutants were significantly faster than the more accurate form of the enzyme. This finding implies that there is a trade-off between the speed and accuracy of DNA replication.

Mutation rates vary among individuals because of variation in the base sequences of DNA polymerase and DNA repair loci.

Point mutation rates also depend on how efficiently mistakes are corrected. Repair of mismatched bases on complementary strands can take place after synthesis or after DNA has been damaged by chemical mutagens or radiation. Research on mismatch repair has been intense because mutations in the genes responsible for repair have been implicated in aging and in the development of certain cancers. There are several different mismatch repair systems, and in mammals at least 30 different proteins are involved (Mellon et al. 1996). At least some of the repair systems are highly conserved; mismatch repair genes in humans were first identified through their homology with genes in yeast and the bacterium *Escherichia coli* (Friedberg et al. 1995). In *E. coli* and *Salmonella enteritidis,* mutations in these loci produce strains with mutation rates 100 to 1000 times higher than normal (LeClerc et al. 1996). The general message of these studies is that the efficiency of DNA mismatch repair, like the error rate of DNA polymerase, is a trait with heritable variation.

Variation Among Species

The data in Table 4.2b suggest that mutation rates vary among species. Fruit flies, mice, and humans, for example, appear to have lower mutation rates than viruses and bacteria. John Drake (1991) has published similar data implying that mutation rates vary widely among viruses, bacteria, and yeast. One problem with these studies, however, is that they do not directly compare mutation rates for homologous genes. As a result, it is not clear whether the differences observed are due to rate variation among genes or among species.

Edward Klekowski and Paul Godfrey (1989) solved this problem by studying the rate of mutation to albinism in the mangrove *Rhizophora mangle,* and comparing it to the rate of mutation to albinism in well-studied domesticated species like barley and buckwheat. Albinism in plants occurs because of loss-of-function mutations in the genes responsible for the synthesis of chlorophyll. Klekowski and Godfrey chose the mangrove as their study organism because it is a long-lived tree with an unusual trait: The seedlings germinate on the parent. To estimate a mutation rate, then, the researchers could count the number of albino offspring germinating on normal parents. Their data showed that the rate was 25 times greater in mangroves than the rate previously calculated for mutations to albinism in barley and buckwheat.

Why the difference? Klekowski and Godfrey's explanation was inspired by the realization that, in plants, germline cells differentiate late in development. (In animals, germline and somatic cells separate early in development. As a result, mutations that occur in the somatic tissues of animals are not passed on to offspring.) In large, long-lived plants like mangroves, somatic cells in stems and shoots accumulate mutations through many somatic cell divisions before differentiating as germline tissue and undergoing meiosis. As a result, long-lived plants should have higher mutation rates per generation than short-lived plants. Klekowski and Godfrey's data are consistent with this prediction, because barley and buckwheat are annuals and small in size. The result suggests an interesting generalization: Generation time may be a key factor influencing variation in mutation rates among species.

Mutation rates may vary among species because of differences in the number of cell divisions that take place prior to gamete formation.

Variation Among Genes

Compared to variation among individuals and species, we know much less about why mutation rates vary among genes. Even so, two strong generalizations have emerged from studies on DNA repair systems: Coding regions are repaired much more efficiently than noncoding regions (Bohr et al. 1985), and several of the repair systems work on transcriptionally active genes only. As a result, accuracy appears to be greatest where mutations could be most damaging.

Mutation rates vary among loci because the most transcriptionally active genes are repaired most efficiently.

4.2 Where New Genes Come From

The creation of new alleles is fairly straightforward, but where do new genes come from? As with novel alleles, several kinds of mutations can create new genes. We will review only a subset. **Gene duplications** are probably the most important source of new genes. Duplications result from a phenomenon known as unequal cross-over, diagrammed in Figure 4.7. **Unequal cross-over** is a chance mistake caused by the proteins involved in managing recombination (crossing over) during meiosis.

As Figure 4.7 shows, one of the products of unequal cross-over is a redundant stretch of DNA. The genome now has an extra copy of the sequences located in the duplicated segment. Because the parent copy still produces a normal product, the redundant sequences are free to accumulate mutations without consequences to the phenotype. The new sequence might even change function over time, thereby becoming a new locus. This is an important point. Because it creates additional DNA,

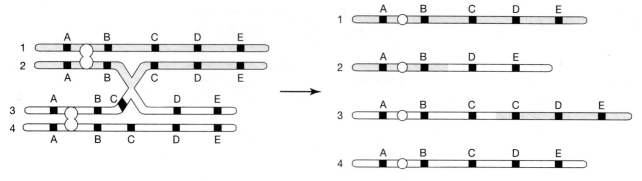

Figure 4.7 **Unequal cross-over and the origin of gene duplications** The letters and bars on each chromosome in the diagram indicate the location of loci; the open circles indicate the location of the centromere. The chromosomes on the left have synapsed, but cross-over has occurred at nonhomologous points. As a result, one of the cross-over products has a duplication of gene C and one a deletion of gene C. Unequal cross-over events like this are thought to be the most common mechanism for producing gene duplications.

gene duplication is the first mechanism we have encountered that results in entirely new possibilities for gene function. The globin gene family provides a superb example of how duplicated genes diverge in function.

Gene Duplication Events in the Globin Gene Family

In humans, the globin gene family consists of two major clusters of loci that code for the protein subunits of hemoglobin. The groups are the α–like cluster on chromosome 16 and the β–like cluster on chromosome 11 (α and β are the Greek letters alpha and beta). A completed hemoglobin molecule is made up of an iron-binding heme group surrounded by four protein subunits—two coded by loci from the α–like cluster and two coded by loci from the β–like cluster.

The data plotted in Figure 4.8 show that each locus in the α- and β-like families is expressed at a different time in development. In first-trimester human em-

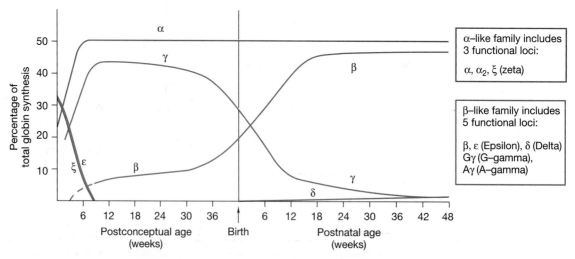

α–like family includes 3 functional loci:

α, α₂, ξ (zeta)

β–like family includes 5 functional loci:

β, ε (Epsilon), δ (Delta) Gγ (G–gamma), Aγ (A–gamma)

Figure 4.8 **Timing of expression differs among members of the globin gene families** This graph shows changes in the expression of globin genes from the α and β families in humans, during pregnancy and after birth. In embryos, hemoglobin is made up of ζ-globin from the α-like gene cluster and ε-globin from the β-like gene cluster. In the fetus, hemoglobin is made up of α-globin from the α-like gene cluster and δ-globin from the β-like gene cluster. In adults, hemoglobin is made up of α-globin from the α-like gene cluster and β-globin from the β-like gene cluster. Each of these hemoglobins has important functional differences.

bryos, for example, hemoglobin is made up of two ζ (zeta) chains and two ε (epsilon) chains, while in adults it is made up of two α chains and two β chains (recall that the sickle-cell mutation occurs in one of the β chains). Different combinations of globin polypeptides result in hemoglobin molecules with important functional differences. For example, fetal hemoglobin has a higher affinity for oxygen molecules than adult hemoglobin. This enhances oxygen transfer from the mother to the embryo.

The globin-family loci are thought to be a product of gene duplication events. The hypothesis is supported by the high structural similarity of transcription units among loci, including the remarkable correspondence in the length and position of their exons and introns diagrammed in Figure 4.9. The logic behind this claim is that it is extremely unlikely that such high structural resemblance could occur in loci that do not share a recent common ancestor. The duplication hypothesis is also supported by the observation of high sequence similarity among globin loci, as well as similarity in function.

The general model, then, is that an ancestral sequence was duplicated several times during the course of vertebrate evolution. In several of these new loci, mutations changed the function of the protein product in a way that was favored by natural selection, leading to the formation of the gene family. Because the α- and β-like clusters also contain nonfunctional loci called **pseudogenes**, which are not transcribed, biologists infer that some duplicated loci were rendered functionless by mutation.

Duplicated loci can (1) retain their original function and provide an additional copy of the parent locus, (2) gain a new function through mutation and selection, or (3) become functionless pseudogenes.

Figure 4.9

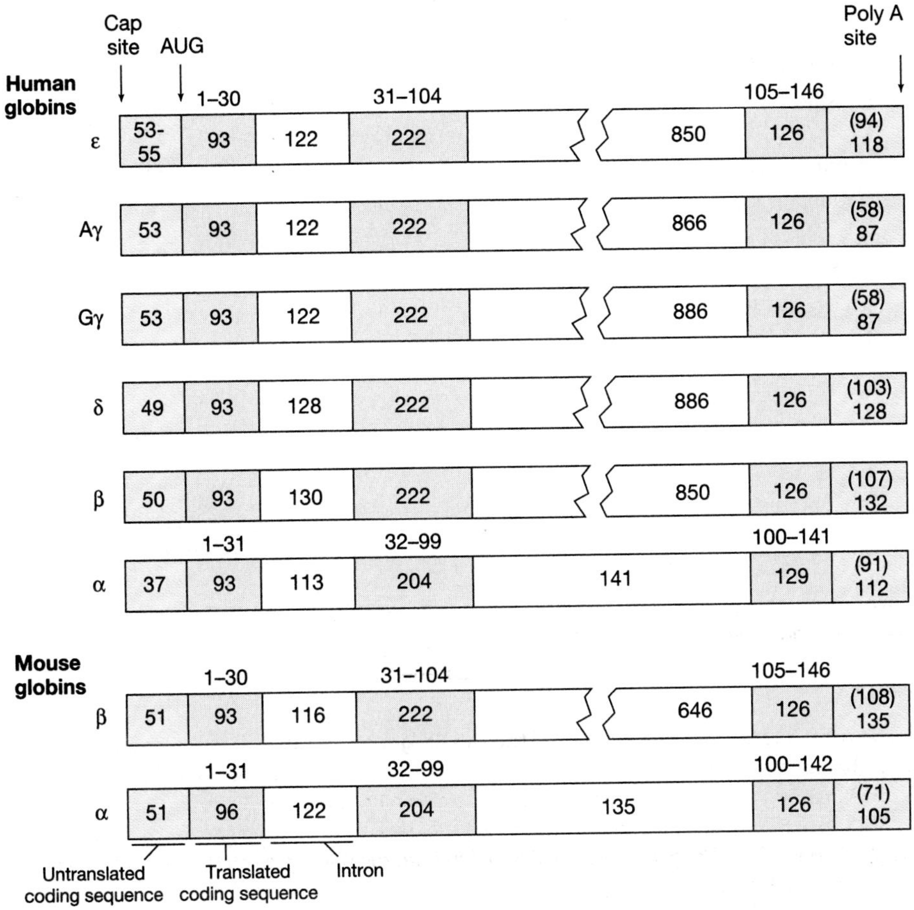

Figure 4.9 Transcription units in the globin gene family In these diagrams, the yellow-orange boxes represent coding sequences that are untranslated, the greenish boxes stand for coding sequences that are translated, and the white segments signify introns. The numbers inside the boxes denote the number of nucleotides present in the primary transcript, while the numbers above the boxes give the amino acid positions in the resulting polypeptide. AUG is the start codon. The lengths and positions of introns and exons in loci throughout the α- and β-like clusters are virtually identical.

The gene families listed in Table 4.3 share several important features with the globin loci: They contain structurally homologous genes with similar functions, clustered together on the same chromosome and accompanied by an occasional pseudogene. It is important to note, however, that not all gene duplications result in loci with different functions. In some important cases, like rRNA genes, multiple copies of the same gene have an identical or nearly identical base sequence, and produce a product with the same function.

Other Mechanisms for Creating New Genes

In addition to duplication, there are other mechanisms that can create new genes or radically new functions for duplicated genes. One example—called overprinting—results from point mutations that produce new start codons and new reading frames for translation. Paul Keese and Adrian Gibbs (1992) investigated the phenomenon in the tymoviruses, which cause mosaic disease in a variety of plants. The tiny genome of one tymovirus, turnip yellow mosaic virus, consists of three genes. Two of these overlap, meaning that they are translated from different reading frames in the same stretch of nucleotides. Keese and Gibbs estimated the phylogeny of five tymoviruses and nine close relatives based on amino acid sequences in their replicase protein (Figure 4.10), and found that the tymoviruses form their

---

Table 4.3   Some gene families

In this table, the "Number of duplicate genes" column refers to the number of loci in various gene families. These loci are presumed to be the result of duplication events. They have high sequence homology, code for products with closely related functions, and are often clustered close to one another on the same chromosome.

Family	Number of duplicate genes
Loci found in many organisms	
Actins	5–30
Tubulins (*a* and *b*)	5–15
Myosin, heavy chain	5–10
Histones	100–1000
Keratins	> 20
Heat-shock proteins	3
Insects	
Eggshell proteins (silk moth and fruit fly)	> 50
Vertebrates	
Globins (many species)	
α-like	1–5
β-like	≥ 50
Ovalbumin (chicken)	3
Vitellogenin (frog, chicken)	5
Immunoglobulins, variable regions (many species)	> 500
Transplantation antigens (mouse and human)	50–100

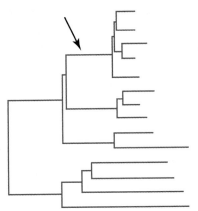

Turnip yellow mosaic virus
Kennedya yellow mosaic tymovirus
Eggplant mosaic tymovirus
Ononis yellow mosaic tymovirus
Erysimum latent tymovirus
Potato X potexvirus
White clover mosaic potexvirus
Narcissus mosaic potexvirus
Apple chlorotic leafspot closterovirus
Potato M carlavirus
Alfalfa mosaic alfamovirus
Sindbis
Tobacco mosaic tobamovirus
Beet necrotic yellow vein furovirus

Figure 4.10   Estimated phylogeny of the tymoviruses and their relatives   Of the species represented in this figure, only the tymoviruses have overprinted genes. This implies that the mutation which led to an overprinted gene occurred somewhere along the branch indicated by the arrow. From Keese and Gibbs (1992).

own branch on the phylogeny. The tymoviruses are also the only species in the phylogeny with an overlapping gene overprinted on the replicase gene.

Based on these data, Keese and Gibbs propose that the replicase gene is ancestral, and that the overlapping gene was created in the common ancestor of the tymoviruses. Their hypothesis is that a mutation created a new start codon, in a different reading frame, in the stretch of nucleotides encoding the replicase protein. They note that evolution at the new locus is likely to be tightly constrained, because any mutation that improves the function of the overlapping protein would probably be deleterious to the function of the replicase protein. Based on their survey of the literature on viral genomes, they also propose that overprinting has been a common mechanism for creating new genes during viral evolution.

Charles Langley and colleagues have investigated the origin of new genes by yet another mechanism. The ancestral gene they studied, found in fruit flies from the genus *Drosophila,* codes for the enzyme alcohol dehydrogenase (*Adh*). This locus is located on chromosome 2. Langley et al. (1982) discovered a similar locus on chromosome 3 in two (and only two) species of flies, *D. teissieri* and *D. yakuba.* Jeffs and Ashburner (1991) sequenced this chromosome 3 locus and found that it lacks the introns found in the *Adh* gene on chromosome 2. Jeffs and Ashburner propose that the new locus on chromosome 3 was created when a messenger RNA from the *Adh* gene was reverse transcribed, and the resulting complementary DNA (cDNA) was inserted into chromosome 3. As we will see in Chapter 18, this mechanism of gene duplication is not unusual. Reverse transcriptase is common in the nuclei of eukaryotic cells.

The question now becomes, Does this new locus have some function, or is it merely a pseudogene? Long and Langley (1993) sequenced the DNA in the chromosome 3 locus from a number of individuals in both *D. teissieri* and *D. yakuba,* with the goal of analyzing alleles of the new locus that had arisen by point mutation. They discovered that most of the alleles differed from each other only in silent site substitutions. This implies that natural selection is acting to conserve the amino acid sequence of a protein encoded by the new locus. In contrast, the common pattern in pseudogenes is that replacement substitutions are as common as silent site substitutions. As a result, Long and Langley concluded that the new locus is a functional gene. They named it *jingwei,* after the protagonist in a Chinese reincarnation myth.

Long and Langley were able to isolate mRNA transcribed from the *jingwei* gene. Upon sequencing the mRNA, they found that the gene contains additional exons

In many genomes, reverse transcription of mRNAs and insertion of the resulting DNA at a new location is an important source of new genes.

not found in its *Adh* ancestor. These additional exons were apparently annexed from a flanking region of chromosome 3 after the *Adh* reverse transcript was inserted. *Jingwei* is thus a hybrid locus, stitched together from pieces of genes on two different chromosomes. Although this mechanism of gene duplication sounds exotic, it illustrates a very general point: Genomes are dynamic. The amount, location, and makeup of the genetic material change through time.

4.3 Chromosome Alterations

A wide variety of changes can occur in the gross morphology of chromosomes. Some of these mutations affect only gene order and organization; others produce duplications or deletions that affect the total amount of genetic material. They can also involve the entire DNA molecule or just segments. Here we focus on two types of chromosome alterations that are particularly important in evolution.

Inversions

Chromosome inversions involve much larger stretches of DNA than the mutation types reviewed in Sections 4.1 and 4.2. They also produce very different consequences. Inversions result from a multistep process that starts when ionizing radiation causes two double-strand breaks in a chromosome. After breakage, a chromosome segment can detach, flip, and reanneal in its original location. As Figure 4.11 shows, gene order along the chromosome is now inverted.

What is the evolutionary impact? Inversions affect a phenomenon known as genetic **linkage**. Linkage is the tendency for alleles of different genes to assort together at meiosis. For obvious reasons, genes on the same chromosome tend to be more tightly linked (that is, more likely to be inherited together) than genes on nonhomologous chromosomes. Similarly, the closer together genes are on the same chromosome, the tighter the linkage. Crossing over at meiosis, on the other hand, breaks up allele combinations and reduces linkage (see Chapter 7).

Because inverted sequences cannot align properly with their normal homolog during synapsis, a crossing-over event that takes place within an inversion results in the duplication or loss of chromosome regions and the production of dysfunctional gametes. When inversions are heterozygous, successful crossing-over

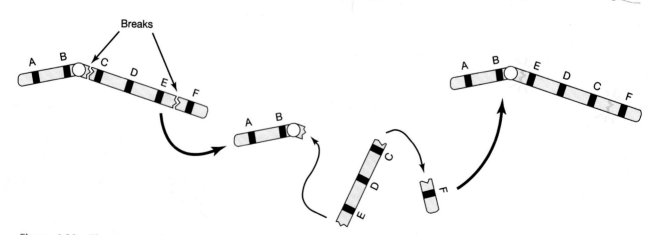

Figure 4.11 **Chromosome inversion** Inversions result when a chromosome segment breaks in two places, flips, and reanneals. Note that after the event, the order of the genes labeled C, D, and E is inverted.

events are extremely rare. The result is that alleles inside the inversion are locked so tightly together that they are inherited as a single "supergene."

Inversions are common in *Drosophila*—the most carefully studied of all insects. Are they important in evolution? Consider a series of inversions found in populations of *Drosophila subobscura*. This fruit fly is native to Western Europe, North Africa, and the Middle East, and has six chromosomes. Five of these chromosomes are polymorphic for at least one inversion (Prevosti et al. 1988), meaning that chromosomes with and without the inversions exist. Biologists have known since the 1960s that the frequencies of these inversions vary regularly with latitude and climate. This type of regular change in the frequency of an allele or an inversion over a geographic area is called a **cline**. Several authors have argued that different inversions must contain specific combinations of alleles that function well together in cold, wet weather or hot, dry conditions. But is the cline really the result of natural selection on the supergenes? Or could it be an historical accident, caused by differences in the founding populations long ago?

A natural experiment has settled the issue. In 1978 *D. subobscura* showed up in the New World for the first time, initially in Puerto Montt, Chile, and then four years later in Port Angeles, Washington, USA. Several lines of evidence argue that the North American population is derived from the South American one. For example, of the 80 inversions present in Old World populations, precisely the same subset of 19 is found in both Chile and Washington State. Also, *Drosophila* are frugivores, Chile is a major fruit exporter, and Port Angeles is a seaport. Within a few years of their arrival on each continent, the *D. subobscura* populations had expanded extensively along each coast and developed the same clines in inversion frequencies found in the Old World (Figure 4.12). The clines are even correlated with the same general changes in climate type: from wet marine environments, to Mediterranean climates, to desert and dry steppe habitats (Prevosti et al. 1988; Ayala et al. 1989). This is strong evidence that the clines result from natural selection, and are not due to historical accident.

Which genes are locked in the inversions, and how do they affect adaptation to changes in climate? In the lab, *D. subobscura* lines that are bred for small body size tend to become homozygous for the inversions found in the dryer, hotter part of the range (Prevosti 1967). Recent research has confirmed that pronounced and parallel clines in body size exist in fly populations from North America and Europe (Huey et al. 2000). These results hint that alleles inside the inversions affect body size, with natural selection favoring large flies in cold, wet climates and small flies in hot, dry areas. Research into this natural experiment is continuing. In the meantime, the fly study illustrates a key point about inversions: They are an important class of mutations because they affect selection on groups of alleles. We will return to the topic of selection on multiple loci in Chapter 7.

Inversions change gene order and lessen the frequency of crossing over...

...as a result, the alleles found inside inversions tend to be inherited as a unit.

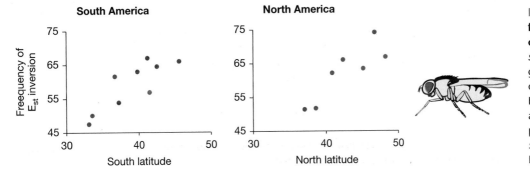

South America

Freequency of E_st inversion

South latitude

North America

North latitude

Figure 4.12 Inversion frequencies form clines in *Drosophila subobscura* These graphs plot the frequency of an inversion called E_st in South American and North American populations of *Drosophila subobscura*. From data in Prevosti et al. 1988.

Polyploidy

The final type of mutation that we will examine occurs at the largest scale possible: entire sets of chromosomes. Instead of being haploid (*n*) or diploid (2*n*), **polyploid** organisms can be tetraploid (4*n*) up to octoploid (8*n*) or higher.

Polyploidy is common in plants and rare in animals. Nearly half of all angiosperm (flowering plant) species are polyploid, as are the vast majority of the ferns. But in animals, polyploidy is rare. It occurs in taxa like earthworms and some flatworms where individuals contain both male and female gonads and can self-fertilize (these species are called self-compatible hermaphrodites). It is also present in groups that are capable of producing offspring without fertilization, through a process called parthenogenesis. In some species of beetles, sow bugs, moths, shrimp, goldfish, and salamanders, a type of parthenogenesis occurs that can lead to chromosomal doubling.

In plants, polyploidy can result from several different events. Perhaps the most frequent is errors at meiosis that result in diploid gametes (Ramsey and Schemske 1998). When plants produce diploid gametes, one of two things happens. If individuals that produce diploid gametes contain both male and female reproductive structures and self-fertilize, a tetraploid (4*n*) offspring can result (see Figure 4.13a). If this offspring self-fertilizes when it matures, or if it mates with a tetraploid sibling that produces diploid gametes, a population of tetraploids can become established.

Alternatively, individuals that produce diploid gametes can mate with normal individuals that produce haploid gametes. As Figure 4.13b shows, this type of mating results in a triploid offspring. Triploid individuals have poor fertility, however. Because their homologous chromosomes are present in an odd number, they cannot synapse correctly during meiosis. As a result, the majority of the gametes produced by triploids end up with the wrong number of chromosomes (see the uppermost histogram in Figure 4.13b). But the bottom histogram of Figure 4.13b shows that if triploid individuals self-fertilize, most of the offspring that result are tetraploid. These data show that the few offspring that escape from the "triploid block" can go on to establish viable populations of tetraploids.

Polyploidy is important because it can result in new species being formed. To understand why, imagine the outcome of matings between individuals in a tetraploid population, established by one of the mechanisms described above, and the parental diploid population. If individuals from the two populations mate, their triploid offspring are semisterile. But if tetraploid individuals continue to self-fertilize or mate among themselves, fully fertile tetraploid offspring will result. In this way, natural selection should favor polyploids that are reproductively isolated from their parent population. If the diploid and tetraploid populations became genetically isolated, they would be considered a separate species.

It is also important to recognize that doubled chromosome sets, like the duplicated individual genes analyzed earlier in the chapter, are free to gain new function as a result of mutation and natural selection. Polyploidy is a key source of genetic variation because it produces hundreds or thousands of duplicated loci.

What is the mutation rate to polyploidy in plants? Justin Ramsey and Douglas Schemske (1998) answered this question by calculating how frequently the two major mechanisms of tetraploid formation occur. To estimate how frequently diploid gametes combine to form tetraploid offspring (the route to polyploidy summarized in Figure 4.13a), they surveyed published studies on the rate of diploid

Populations of polyploid individuals are often isolated, genetically, from their parental species.

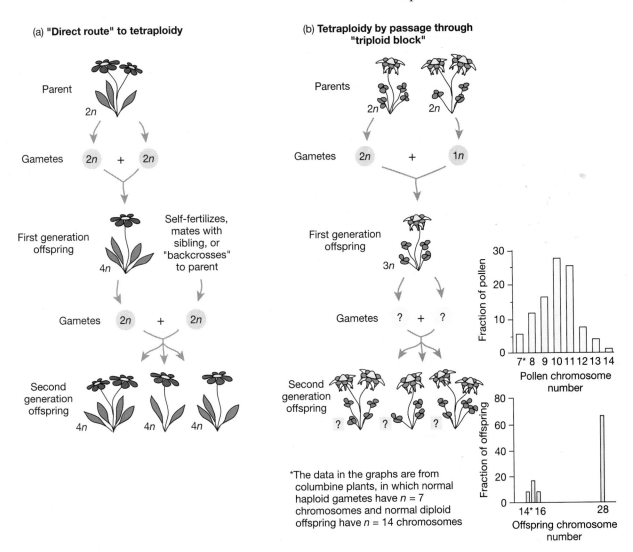

Figure 4.13   Mechanisms for producing tetraploid individuals in plants   See text for explanation.

gamete formation in flowering plants. Because the data in the literature suggested that diploid gametes are produced at an average frequency of 0.00465 in most flowering plant species, the frequency of tetraploids produced by this route should be $0.00465 \times 0.00465 = 2.16 \times 10^{-5}$. In each generation, then, this mechanism of polyploid formation occurs in about 2 out of every 10,000 offspring produced by a typical flowering plant species. Ramsey and Schemske pursued the same strategy to estimate the frequency at which triploid offspring arise and go on to produce tetraploid descendants. (This is the route to polyploidy summarized in Figure 4.13b.) Using published data sets on the frequency of each step in the sequence of events leading to polyploid formation by this mechanism, they calculated that tetraploids are produced at a frequency of at least 1.16×10^{-5} each generation.

The overall message of the Ramsey and Schemske study is striking: In flowering plants, polyploid formation occurs about as frequently as point mutations in individual loci. Along with replacement substitutions, gene duplications, and chromosome inversions, polyploidy is an important source of genetic variation in natural populations.

In plants, polyploidy occurs often enough to be considered an important type of mutation.

4.4 Measuring Genetic Variation in Natural Populations

In the previous three sections of this chapter, we discussed the processes that generate new alleles, genes, and chromosomes. These processes create the genetic variation that is the raw material for evolution. In this last section, we turn to the methods biologists use to measure the amount of genetic variation present in natural populations.

Traditionally, biologists thought that allelic variation in populations would be limited...

We will focus on measurements of allelic variation at individual loci. Before looking at data on genetic variation in populations, however, it is worth considering how much variation we might expect to find. The classical view was that populations should contain little genetic variation. The reasoning behind this view was that among the alleles possible at any given locus, one should be better than all the others. Natural selection should preserve the one allele most conducive to survival and reproduction, and eliminate the rest. The one best allele was called the wild type; any other alleles present were considered mutants.

...but research has revealed that it is actually extensive.

As we will see, modern methods for assessing genetic variation have revealed that the classical view was mistaken. Starting with pioneering work by Harris (1966) and Lewontin and Hubby (1966), evolutionary biologists have looked at the proteins encoded by alleles, and at the DNA of the alleles themselves. The deeper biologists have looked, the more genetic variation they have found. Today, evolutionary biologists recognize that natural populations harbor substantial genetic variation.

Determining Genotypes

To measure the diversity of alleles at a particular locus, we must determine the genotypes of individuals. For some loci, it is possible to infer the genotypes of individuals from their phenotypes. For example, intestinal schistosomiasis is a human disease caused by infection with the parasitic flatworm *Schistosoma mansoni*. Several lines of evidence indicate that susceptibility to infection by *S. mansoni* is strongly influenced by a single locus on chromosome 5, called SM1. (For a review, see Online Mendelian Inheritance in Man 1999.) Laurent Abel and colleagues (1991) analyzed the pedigrees of 20 Brazilian families, and found that their data were consistent with a model in which SM1 has two codominant alleles. Individuals homozygous for one of the alleles are susceptible, whereas individuals homozygous for the other allele are resistant. Heterozygotes have intermediate resistance. In areas where everyone is exposed to water contaminated with *S. mansoni,* it is possible, with reasonable accuracy, to infer a person's genotype from the intensity of his or her infection. Abel and colleagues estimated that in the Brazilian population they studied, about 60% of the people were homozygous resistant, about 5% were homozygous susceptible, and about 35% were heterozygous.

In contrast to SM1, for most loci it is difficult or impossible to infer the genotypes of individuals simply by noting their phenotypes. As a result, most biologists studying allelic diversity look directly at the proteins encoded by alleles, or at the DNA of the alleles themselves. There are a variety of methods for doing so, most of which rely on gel electrophoresis. Gel electrophoresis uses a slab of gelatin-like material and an electric field to separate molecules by size, mass, and electric charge. (See Box 4.1.)

BOX 4.1 Gel electrophoresis

Gel electrophoresis is a widely used technique for assessing the amount of genetic variation in populations. At heart, electrophorsesis is simply a method of sorting molecules. A basic electrophoresis setup appears in Figure 4.14a. The gel itself is a porous slab of gelatin-like material made of any of a number of ingredients, including starch, agarose, or polyacrylamide. At one end of the gel, or sometimes in the center, is

(a)

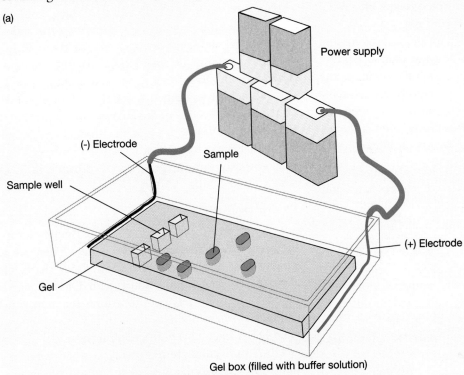

(b)

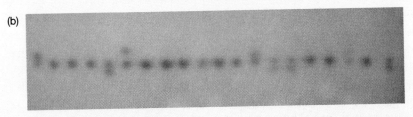

(c)

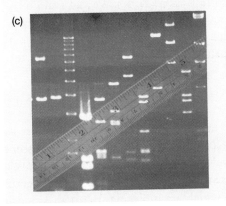

Figure 4.14 *Gel electrophoresis* (a) The diagram shows the minimal equipment needed for electrophoresis. In the setup shown, the power supply is simply five 9-volt batteries snapped together to make a single 45-volt battery. Researchers typically use commerical power supplies with variable voltage, timers, etc. (b) This photograph shows the result of electrophoresis of proteins. The gel in the photo has been stained for the PGM enzyme. If an individual has two forms of the enzyme, two bands appear in the same lane Because we assume that the alternative forms are the products of different alleles (Feder et al. 1989a), we can infer that an individual with two bands is a heterozygote. This gel indicates that three different alleles exist, and that 8 of the 20 flies in this sample are heterozygotes at the PGM locus. (Jeff Feder, University of Notre Dame) (c) This photograph shows the result of electrophoresis of DNA fragments. The DNA fragments in this gel have been stained with ethidium bromide, which makes them visible in ultraviolet light. Smaller fragments are closer to the bottom of the gel. (National Institutes of Health/Custom Medical Stock Photo, Inc.)

BOX 4.1 Continued

a series of slots, or wells. A researcher fills each well with a solution containing a mixture of molecules to be sorted. The researcher bathes the gel in a buffer solution, which keeps the gel moist and conducts electricity. A power supply connected to the electrodes creates an electric field across the gel.

Most biological molecules, including proteins and DNA, are electrically charged when in solution. Because they are charged, they move through the gel under the influence of the electric field. Negatively charged molecules, for example, move toward the positive electrode. The speed at which a molecule moves through the gel is determined by a number of factors, including these:

1. The ratio of the molecule's electric charge to the molecule's mass. Molecules with higher charge and lower mass move more quickly.

2. The molecule's physical size. Smaller molecules fit more easily through the pores in the gel, and therefore move more quickly.

If the mixture placed in a well contains molecules with different charge-to-mass ratios, and/or different sizes, the different molecules will separate from each other as they move at different speeds through the gel.

Electrophoresis of proteins

Suppose there are two alleles at a locus encoding an enzyme. Recall that enzymes are proteins, and that proteins are chains of amino acids. Imagine that our two alleles encode versions of the enzyme that have different amino acids at a few positions. These distinct versions of the enzyme, encoded by alleles at the same locus, are called allozymes. If one allozyme has a negatively charged amino acid where the other has a neutral or positively charged one, then the two versions of the protein will have different net electric charges. They will move at different speeds through an electrophoresis gel.

To determine an individual's genotype at our enzyme locus, we can extract a sample of the individual's proteins, and separate them on an electrophoresis gel. We then place the gel in a bath containing a substrate for a chemical reaction catalyzed by the enzyme in question, and a stain that binds to a product of the chemical reaction. This bath will stain the gel only in places where the enzyme we are studying has ended up. If the gel yields just one stained spot, then our individual contains just one version of the enzyme. Therefore, the individual must be a homozygote. If the gel yields two stained spots, then the individual contains two versions of the enzyme and is thereby a heterozygote. We can run protein samples from several individuals next to each other on the same gel and then compare the pattern of spots, or bands, in each lane (Figure 4.14b).

Electrophoresis of DNA

Suppose there are two alleles at a locus. By definition, the alleles have different DNA sequences. There are a variety of electrophoresis-based methods that will allow us to distinguish individuals with different genotypes. All of them rely on procedures for preparing the DNA wherein alleles with different sequences yield DNA fragments with different sizes.

DNA molecules are negatively charged when in solution, primarily because of the phosphate group on each nucleotide. All DNA molecules have approximately the same charge-to-mass ratio, regardless of their length. However, smaller DNA molecules move faster through an electrophoresis gel. If we run a mixture of DNA fragments on a gel, the fragments will sort themselves by size. If we render the fragments visible, perhaps by staining them or making them fluorescent, then we will see a band on the gel corresponding to each fragment size (Figure 4.14c). We can run DNA prepared from several different individuals next to each other on the gel. Individuals with different genotypes give different patterns of bands. See the main text for an example.

Our example of how researchers use electrophoresis to determine genotypes concerns a gene in humans called *CC-CKR-5*. This gene, located on chromosome 3, encodes a protein called C-C chemokine receptor-5, often abbreviated CCR5. CCR5 is a cell surface protein found on white blood cells. As its name suggests, CCR5's function is to bind chemokines, which are molecules released as signals by other immune system cells. When a white blood cell is stimulated by chemokines binding to its receptors, the cell moves into inflamed tissues to help fight an infection. What makes CCR5 particularly interesting is that it is also exploited as a coreceptor by most sexually transmitted strains of HIV-1.

As we mentioned in Chapter 1, HIV-1 virions use a protein of their own, called Env, to infiltrate host cells. Env appears to work by first binding to a cell surface protein called CD4, and then binding to CCR5. When Env binds to CCR5, it initiates the fusion of the viral envelope with the host cell's membrane. This fusion delivers the viral core into the host cell's cytoplasm.

In 1996, Rong Liu and colleagues discovered allelic variation at the *CCR5* locus that influences susceptibility to infection by sexually transmitted strains of HIV-1. Liu and colleagues were studying two individuals who remained uninfected despite multiple unprotected sexual encounters with partners known to be HIV-positive. The researchers discovered that these individuals were homozygous for a 32-base pair deletion in a coding region of the gene for CCR5. As a result of the deletion, the encoded protein is severely shortened, and nonfunctional. Lacking CCR5 on their surface, the cells of deletion homozygotes offer no handles to HIV-1 virions that must bind to CCR5 to initiate an infection.

We will call the functional allele *CCR5+*, or just +, and the allele with the 32-base pair deletion *CCR5-Δ32*, or just *Δ32*. Individuals with genotype +/+ are susceptible to infection with HIV-1, individuals with genotype +/Δ32 are susceptible, but may progress to AIDS more slowly, and individuals with genotype *Δ32/Δ32* are resistant to most sexually transmitted strains of the virus.

Upon learning of the *CCR5-Δ32* allele, AIDS researchers immediately wanted to know how common it is. Michel Samson and colleagues (1996), who discovered the allele independently, developed a genotype test that works as follows. Researchers first extract DNA from a sample of the subject's cells. Then the researchers use a polymerase chain reaction (PCR) to make many copies of a region of the gene, several hundred base pairs long, that contains the site of the 32-base pair deletion. (PCR duplicates a targeted sequence many times over by employing a test-tube DNA replication system in combination with specifically tailored primer sequences that direct the DNA polymerase to copy just the locus of interest.) Finally, the researchers cut the duplicated DNA sequences with a restriction enzyme, and run the resulting fragments on an electrophoresis gel.

The results appear in Figure 4.15. Both alleles yield two DNA fragments. The fragments from a *CCR5-+* allele are 332- and 403-base pairs long. The fragments from a *CCR5-Δ32* allele are 332- and 371-base pairs long. Homozygotes have just two bands in their lane on the gel, whereas heterozygotes have three bands.

Several laboratories have completed surveys of *CCR5* genotypes in various indigenous populations from around the world. Data excerpted from a survey by Jeremy Martinson and colleagues (1997) appear in Table 4.4.

Calculating Allele Frequencies

We have noted that a pressing question concerning the *CCR5-Δ32* allele is, How common is it? To answer this question precisely, we need to use the data on genotypes in Table 4.4 to calculate the frequency of the *Δ32* allele in the various populations tested. The frequency of an allele is its fractional representation among all the alleles present in a population.

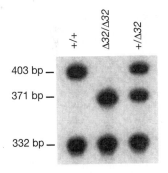

Figure 4.15 Determining CCR5 genotypes by electrophoresis of DNA. Each lane of this gel contains DNA fragments prepared from the *CCR5* alleles of a single individual. The locations of the dark spots, or bands, on the gel indicate the sizes of the fragments. Each genotype yields a unique pattern of bands. From Samson et al. (1996). Reprinted with permission from Nature. © 1996, Macmillan Magazines Ltd.

Table 4.4   Diversity of *CCR5* genotypes in various populations

Population	Number of people tested	Number with each genotype			Allele frequency (%)	
		+/+	+/Δ32	Δ32/Δ32	CCR5-+	CCR5-Δ32
Europe						
Ashkenazi	43	26	16	1	79.1	20.9
Iceland	102	75	24	3	85.3	14.7
Britain	283	223	57	3		
Spain: Basque	29	24	5	0		
Italy	91	81	10	0		
Ireland	44	40	4	0		
Greece	63	60	3	0		
Middle East						
Caucasus: Daghestan	110	96	14	0		
Saudi Arabia	241	231	10	0		
Yemen	34	34	0	0		
Asia						
Russia: Udmurtia	46	38	7	1		
Pakistan	34	32	2	0		
Punjab	34	33	1	0		
Bengal	25	25	0	0		
Hong Kong	50	50	0	0		
Filipino	26	26	0	0		
Mongolia	59	59	0	0		
Thailand	101	100	1	0		
Borneo	151	151	0	0		
Africa						
Nigeria	111	110	1	0		
Central African Repub.	52	52	0	0		
Kenya	80	80	0	0		
Ivory Coast	87	87	0	0		
Zambia	96	96	0	0		
Kalahari San	36	36	0	0		
Oceania						
New Guinea Coast	96	96	0	0		
French Polynesia	94	94	0	0		
Aboriginal Australian	98	96	2	0		
Guam	59	58	1	0		
Fiji	17	17	0	0		
Americas						
Nuu-Chah-Nulth	38	37	1	0		
Mexican (Huicholes)	52	52	0	0		
Brazilian Amerindian	98	98	0	0		
Jamaica	119	119	0	0		

As an example, we will calculate the frequency of the *Δ32* allele in the Ashkenazi population in Europe, from the data in the first row of Table 4.4. The simplest way to calculate allele frequencies is to count allele copies. Martinson and colleagues tested 43 individuals. Each individual carries 2 allele copies, so the researchers tested a total of 86 allele copies. Of these 86 allele copies, 18 were copies of the *Δ32* allele: one from each of the 16 heterozygotes, and 2 from the single homozygote. Thus the frequency of the *Δ32* allele in the Ashkenazi sample is

To estimate the amount of genetic variation in a population, researchers compute the frequencies of each allele present.

$$\frac{18}{86} = 0.209$$

or 20.9%. We can check our work by calculating the frequency of the + allele. It is

$$\frac{(52 + 16)}{86} = 0.791$$

or 79.1%. If our calculations are correct, the frequencies of the two alleles should sum to one, which they do.

An alternative method of figuring the allele frequencies in the Ashkenazi population is to calculate them from the genotype frequencies. Martinson and colleagues tested 43 individuals, so the genotype frequencies are as follows:

+/+	+/Δ32	Δ32/Δ32
$\frac{26}{43} = 0.605$	$\frac{16}{43} = 0.372$	$\frac{1}{43} = 0.023$

The frequency of the *Δ32* allele is the frequency of *Δ32/Δ32* plus half the frequency of +/*Δ32*:

$$0.023 + \frac{1}{2}(0.372) = 0.209$$

This is the same value we got by the first method.

We have filled in the allele frequencies for the first two rows in Table 4.4. We leave it to readers to calculate the allele frequencies for the rest of the populations listed in the table, and to note the locations of the various populations on a world map. Readers who do so will discover an intriguing pattern. The *CCR5-Δ32* allele is common in populations of Northern European extraction, with frequencies as high as 21%. As we move away from northern Europe, both to the east and to the south, the frequency of the *Δ32* allele declines. Outside of Europe, the Middle East, and western Asia, the *Δ32* allele is virtually absent. We will return to this pattern in Chapters 5 and 7.

Documenting allele frequencies in a variety of populations can reveal interesting patterns.

How Much Genetic Diversity Exists in a Typical Population?

Since the mid-1960s, evolutionary biologists have used gel electrophoresis of enzymes to assess genetic diversity in populations representing hundreds of species of plants and animals. Data from two studies appear in Figure 4.16.

J. G. Oakeshott and colleagues (1982) studied allelic diversity at the alcohol dehydrogenase locus in fruit flies. Alcohol dehydrogenase, or Adh, breaks down ethanol, the poisonous active ingredient in wine, beer, and, most important to fruit flies, rotting fruit. There are two electrophoretically distinguishable allozymes of Adh: Adh^F and Adh^S. The F and S are short for fast and slow, the speeds at which the allozymes move through an electrophoresis gel. Oakeshott and colleagues

If more than one allele exists at a particular locus, a population is said to be polymorphic at that locus.

determined the frequencies of the two Adh allozymes in 34 Australian fly populations (Figure 4.16a). This survey showed that almost all fly populations are **polymorphic** at the Adh locus. That is, nearly all populations harbor both alleles. The map in Figure 4.16a also reveals a pattern that is repeated in Europe and North America: Adh^S is generally at higher frequency at low latitudes (that is, closer to the equator), whereas Adh^F is at higher frequency at high latitudes. The significance of this pattern is unclear, although it may relate to the fact that Adh^S is more stable at higher temperatures.

Dennis Powers and colleagues (1991, 1998) studied allelic diversity at the lactate dehydrogenase-B locus in populations of the mummichog (*Fundulus heteroclitus*), a

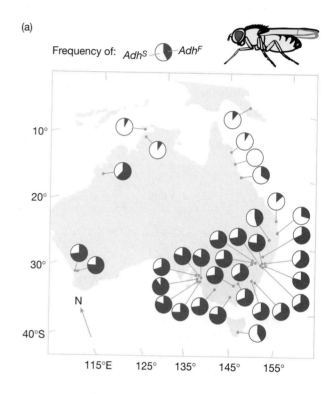

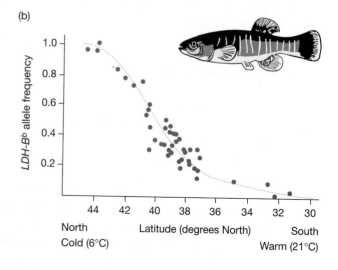

Figure 4.16 Gel electrophoresis of enzymes reveals allelic diversity in natural populations (a) The pie diagrams on this map show the frequencies of two alleles of alcohol dehydrogenase in Australian populations of fruit flies: Adh^F (black) and Adh^S (white). From Oakeshott et al. (1982), Copyright © 1991, Evolution. Reprinted by permission. (b) This scatterplot shows the frequency of the Ldh-B^b allele as a function of latitude in populations of the mummichog fish (*Fundulus heteroclitus*) along the east coast of the United States. Ldh-B^b is one of two electrophoretically distinguishable alleles of lactate dehydrogenase-B; the other is Ldh-B^a. Reprinted with permission from Powers et al. (1991). © 1991, by Annual Reviews, www.AnnualReviews.org.

5- to 10-cm-long fish that lives in inlets, bays, and estuaries along the Atlantic coast of North America. Lactate dehydrogenase-B, or Ldh-B, is an enzyme that converts lactate to pyruvate; it is important in both glucose production and aerobic metabolism. There are two electrophoretically distinguishable allozymes of Ldh-B: $Ldh-B^a$, and $Ldh-B^b$. Powers and colleagues determined the frequencies of the two Ldh-B allozymes in mummichog populations from Maine to Georgia. This survey shows that most populations are polymorphic. Furthermore, as the scatterplot in Figure 4.16b shows, there is a strong geographic pattern: $Ldh-B^b$ is at higher frequency in northern populations, while $Ldh-B^a$ is at higher frequency in southern populations. This pattern makes sense, because $Ldh-B^b$ has higher catalytic efficiency at low temperatures, whereas $Ldh-B^a$ has higher catalytic efficiency at high temperatures.

To draw general conclusions from studies like those reviewed in the preceding two paragraphs, we need to summarize data on allelic diversity across loci within populations. There are two commonly used summary statistics: the mean heterozygosity, and the percentage of polymorphic loci. The mean heterozygosity can be interpreted in two equivalent ways: as the average frequency of heterozygotes across loci, or as the fraction of loci that are heterozygous in the genotype of the average individual. The percentage of polymorphic loci is the fraction of loci in a population that have at least two alleles.

Electrophoretic studies of enzymes have demonstrated that most natural populations harbor substantial genetic variation. Figure 4.17 summarizes data on mean heterozygosities from invertebrates, vertebrates, and plants. As a broad generalization, in a typical natural population, between 33 and 50% of the enzyme loci are polymorphic, and the average individual is heterozygous at 4 to 15% of its loci (Mitton 1997).

Analysis of protein variation suggest that in a typical population, between a third and a half of all coding loci are polymorphic...

Methods that directly examine the DNA of alleles are even more powerful at revealing genetic diversity. This is because not every change in the DNA sequence at a locus produces an electrophoretically distinguishable protein. Among the most intensively studied loci to date is that of the gene associated with cystic fibrosis in humans. This locus, on chromosome 7, encodes a protein called the cystic fibrosis transmembrane conductance regulator (CFTR). CFTR is a cell surface protein expressed in the mucus membrane lining of the intestines and lungs. Gerald Pier and colleagues (1997) demonstrated that one of CFTR's key functions is to enable the cells of the lung lining to ingest and destroy *Pseudomonas aeruginosa* bacteria. Individuals homozygous for loss-of-function mutations in the CFTR gene have cystic fibrosis. They suffer chronic infections with *P. aeruginosa,* eventually leading to severe lung damage. Molecular geneticists have examined the DNA sequence in the CFTR alleles of more than 15,000 cystic fibrosis patients, for a total of more than 30,000 copies of disease alleles. They have discovered over 500 different loss-of-function mutations at this one locus (Figure 4.18). We will return to the CFTR gene in Chapter 5.

...while early surveys of DNA sequence variation suggest that polymorphism may be even more extensive.

Why Are Populations Genetically Diverse?

As we noted at the beginning of this section, the classical view of genetic diversity, under which little diversity was expected in most populations, was clearly wrong. So how can we explain the substantial diversity present in most populations? Two

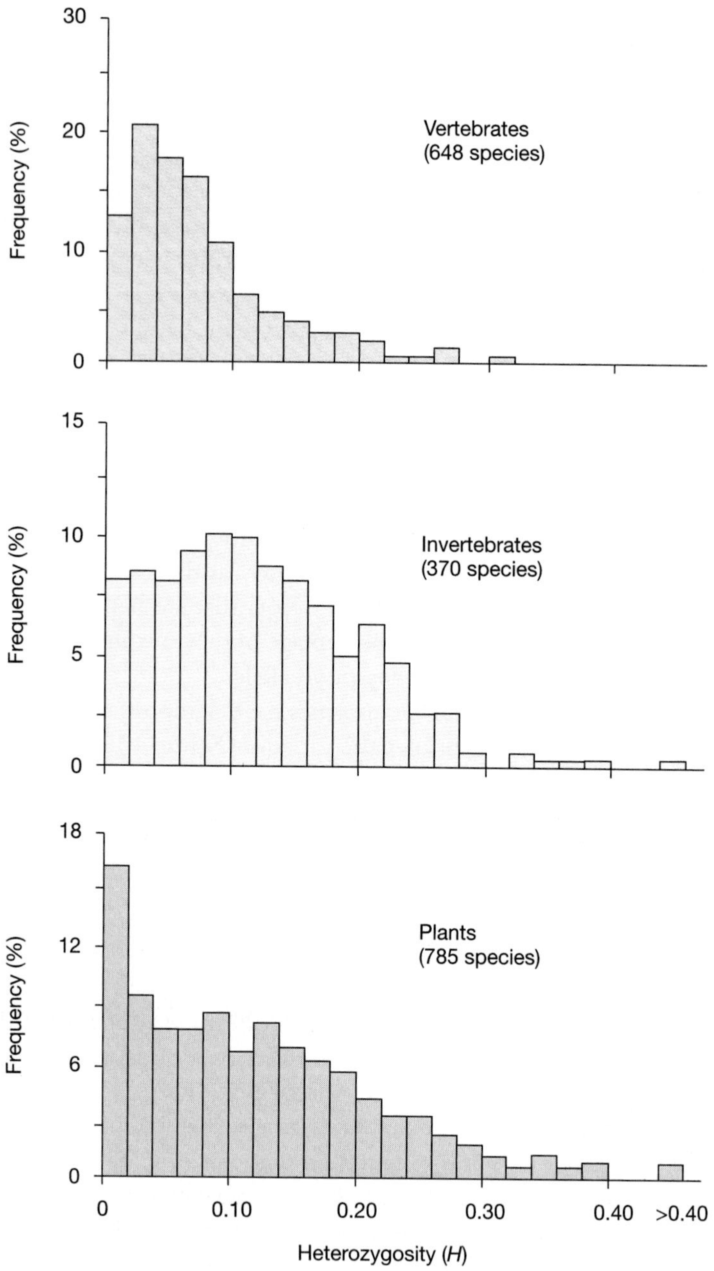

Figure 4.17 Electrophoresis of enzymes reveals that most populations harbor considerable genetic diversity These histograms show the distribution of enzyme heterozygosities among species of animals and plants. For example, about 7% of all plant species have a heterozygosity between 0.08 and 0.10. Heterozygosity can be interpreted in two ways: as the mean percentage of individuals heterozygous per locus, or as the mean percentage of loci heterozygous per individual. From Fig. 2.2, p. 19, of Avise (1994). © 1994, Chapman and Hall. Reprinted by permission of Kluwer Academic Publishers.

modern views have replaced the classic theory. According to the balance, or selectionist theory, genetic diversity is maintained by natural selection—in favor of rare individuals, in favor of heterozygotes, or in favor of different alleles at different times and places. According to the neutral theory, most of the alleles at most polymorphic loci are functionally and selectively equivalent. In effect, genetic diversity is maintained because it is not eliminated by selection. We will consider the selectionist and neutral theories in more detail in Chapters 5, 7, and 18.

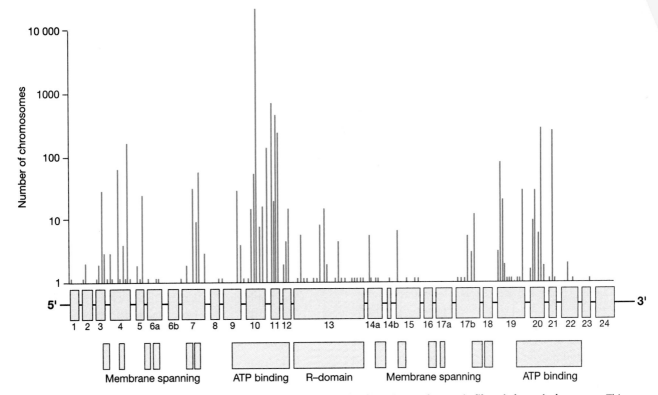

Figure 4.18 Sequencing studies have revealed enormous genetic diversity at the cystic fibrosis locus in humans This graph shows the abundance and location of the loss-of-function mutations discovered in an examination of over 30,000 disease-causing alleles at the cystic fibrosis locus. The histogram shows the number of copies of each mutation found. The locus map below it, in which the boxes represent exons, shows the location of each mutation within the CFTR gene. The boxes at the bottom of the graph give the functions of the coding regions of the gene. From Fig. 2, p. 395, in Tsui (1992). Copyright © 1992, Elsevier Science. Reprinted with permission of Elsevier Science.

Summary

Mutations range from single base-pair substitutions to the duplication of entire chromosome sets, and vary in impact from no amino acid sequence change to single amino acid changes to gene creation and genome duplication.

Point mutations result from errors made by DNA polymerase during DNA synthesis or errors made by DNA repair enzymes after sequences have been damaged by chemical mutagens or radiation. Point mutations in first and second positions of codons frequently result in replacement substitutions that lead to changes in the amino acid sequence of proteins. Point mutations in third positions of codons usually result in silent substitutions that do not lead to changes in the amino acid sequence of proteins. Point mutations create new alleles.

Mutation rates vary both among genes within genomes and among species. Both DNA polymerase and the many loci involved in mismatch repair exhib-

it heritable variation. As a result, mutation rate is a trait that can respond to natural selection and other evolutionary processes.

The most common sources of new genes are duplication events that result from errors during crossing over. A duplicated gene can diverge from its parent sequence and become a new locus with a different function, or a nonfunctional pseudogene. New genes can also arise when mRNAs are reverse-transcribed and inserted into the genome in a new location.

Chromosome alterations form a large class of mutations. Chromosome inversions have interesting evolutionary implications because they reduce the frequency of recombination between loci within the inversion. As a result, alleles within inversions tend to be inherited as a group instead of independently. Polyploidy is a condition characterized by duplication of an entire chromosome

Polyploidy is common in plants, and is important because polyploid individuals are genetically isolated from the population that gave rise to them.

Evolutionary biologists typically measure allelic diversity in populations by using gel electrophoresis to look directly at the proteins encoded by alleles or at the DNA of the alleles themselves. Such studies have revealed that most natural populations contain substantial genetic diversity.

Now that we know something about where alleles and genes come from, and about the genetic diversity present in most populations, we are ready to shift our focus and ask a different question: What determines the fate of these new alleles and genes in a population? This is the subject of Chapter 5 and Chapter 6.

Questions

1. The evolutionary biologist Graham Bell (1997) has said, "Most mutations are not very deleterious. The assault on adaptedness is not carried out primarily by a storm of mutations that kill or maim, but rather by a steady drizzle of mutations with slight or inappreciable effects on health and vigor" (Bell 1997). This statement is supported by classical experiments in fruit flies and other organisms. Yet most known human mutations cause severe disease (for example, see Table 4.2b). Is it possible that mutations in humans are qualitatively different from mutations in other organisms? Or has our traditional perception of mutations as highly deleterious been colored by intensive studies on a small subset of human mutations? For a gene like the β-globin gene, how would you go about determining how often mutations with small effects occur?

2. Schlager & Dickie (1971) set out to determine the rate of coat-color mutations in mice. They spent six years studying five coat-color genes in over seven million mice, examining thousands of brother–sister matings from 28 inbred strains. For each gene they studied two mutation rates: (1) the rate at which a normal gene mutated to a form resulting in loss of function, and (2) the rate at which a mutant gene would then mutate back to the normal form. For example, in 67,395 tested crosses, the "albino" gene mutated from normal (colored) to nonfunctional (albino) just three times, for a mutation rate of 44.5×10^{-6}. Interestingly, in all the coat-color genes, the back-mutation rates (e.g., from albino to colored) were typically around 2.5×10^{-6}, which was always lower than the rates for loss of function. Think about the different mutations that can all cause loss of function of a single gene, versus the mutations that can cause regain of function. Why were the mutation rates for loss of function always higher than the back-mutation rates for regain of function?

3. Voelker, Schaffer, & Mukai (1980) studied 1000 lines of flies for 220 generations to estimate the mutation rate of a certain protein. In 3,111,598 crosses, they found 16 flies with new replacement substitution mutations in that protein (detected by a slight change in its electrical charge), a mutation rate of 5.1×10^{-6}. However, only 4 of these mutations actually altered protein function; the remaining 12 did not detectably affect protein function. If Voelker et al. had simply been measuring loss of function, would their estimate of mutation rate have been lower or higher? If they had been able to measure silent site substitutions as well, would their estimate of mutation rate have been lower or higher? Do you think that by measuring changes in protein charge, they were able to measure all of the replacement substitutions that occurred? What do you think is the most informative measure of mutation rate?

4. In this chapter, we introduced the consequences of mutations in two sorts of traits: changes in phenotypic traits such as hemoglobin structure, and changes in mutation rate itself. To clarify the distinction between these two kinds of traits, examine the following list. Which of these proteins can affect mutation rate itself? Which do not affect mutation rate, but instead affect some other trait of the organism?

Protein	*Example of mutation in the protein*
• β-globin	• Increased tendency to sickle
• Mismatch repair proteins	• Increased repair of damaged DNA
• Melanin (coat-color protein)	• Red coat instead of black coat
• Growth hormone	• Dwarfism or gigantism
• DNA polymerase	• Increased speed and decreased accuracy during DNA replication

5. The discovery of "overprinting" shows that it is possible for one stretch of DNA to code for two entirely different, and functional, proteins. Let's examine this unlikely phenomenon further. Suppose we discover a tiny gene, 12 base pairs long, that codes for a tiny polypeptide just 3 amino acids long:
   - DNA ACUGCUGUCUAA
   - Amino acids thr-ala-val-stop

Now suppose this organism would benefit greatly if it had another little polypeptide composed of leu-leu-ser. Would this be possible if the organism started transcribing the gene from the second base pair? Look back at the genetic code in Fig. 4.3b to figure this out. Suppose further that the organism would benefit even more if instead of leu-leu-ser, it had pro-leu-ser. What mutations would be necessary to do this, and would they destroy the amino acid sequence of the original protein shown above? In general, what sort of mutations can occur that will not alter the original protein, but will allow changes in amino acids to occur in the other, "overprinted" protein?

6. The amino acid sequences encoded by the red and green visual pigment genes found in humans are 96% identical (Nathans et al. 1986). These two loci are found close together on the X chromosome, while the locus for the blue pigment is located on chromosome 7. Among primates, only Old World monkeys, the great apes, and humans have a third pigment gene—New World monkeys have only one X-linked pigment gene. Comment on the following three hypotheses:

   - One of the two visual pigment loci on the X chromosome originated in a gene duplication event.
   - The gene duplication event occurred after New World and Old World monkeys had diverged from a common ancestor, which had two visual pigment genes.
   - Human males with a mutated form of the red or green pigment gene experience the same color vision of our male primate ancestors.

7. Chromosome number can evolve by smaller-scale changes than duplication of entire chromosome sets. For example, domestic horses have 64 chromosomes per diploid set while Przewalski's horse, an Asian subspecies, has 66. Przewalski's horse is thought to have evolved from an ancestor with $2n = 64$ chromosomes. The question is, Where did its extra chromosome pair originate? It seems unlikely that an entirely new chromosome pair was created *de novo* in Przewalski's horse. To generate a hypothesis explaining the origin of the new chromosome in Przewalski's horse, examine the adjacent figure.

The drawing shows how certain chromosomes synapse in the hybrid offspring of a domestic horse–Przewalski's horse mating (Short et al. 1974). The remaining chromosomes show a normal 1:1 pairing.

Do you think this sort of gradual change in chromosome number involves a change in the actual number of genes present, or just rearrangement of the same number of genes?

8. If you have not already done so, complete Table 4.4 by calculating the frequencies of the *CCR5-+* and *CCR5-Δ32* alleles in each population. Can you suggest any hypotheses to explain the global distribution of the CCR-Δ32 allele? What additional questions are raised by the data presented in the table? List as many as you can. Then, pick one and describe a research project that might answer it.

9. We have seen that in plants, generation time can affect the number of mutations seen in the offspring—individual plants that had long lifespans had fruits with more mutations than individual plants with short lifespans. This is apparently because in plants, numerous cell divisions of somatic cells precede the production of gamete cells.

   a. Do you think that the same might be true in animals—could generation time affect accumulation of mutations in the gametes of *individual* animals? Could generation time affect accumulation of mutations *per year* in a *population* of animals? Why or why not?

   b. In mammals, sperm cells are produced by parent cells (spermatogonia) that undergo constant cell division throughout life, whereas egg cells are produced only during fetal development. Do you think the average number of mutations per gamete might differ in males vs. females? Why or why not? How could you test this theory? Look up

Shimmin, L. C., B. H.-J. Chang, W.-H. Li. 1993. Male-driven evolution of DNA sequences. *Nature* 362:745–747.

Exploring the Literature

10. The directed-mutation hypothesis has been the most controversial topic in recent research on mutation. This hypothesis, inspired by experimental work on the bacterium *Escherichia coli,* maintains that organisms can generate specific types of mutations in response to particular environmental challenges. For example, if the environment grew hotter over time, the hypothesis maintains that organisms would respond by specifically generating mutations in genes involved in coping with hot temperatures.

This implies that mutations do not occur randomly, but are directed by the environment. Look up the following papers to learn more about the controversy:

Cairns, J., J. Overbaugh, and S. Miller. 1988. The origin of mutants. *Nature* 335: 142–145.

Foster, P. L., and J. M. Trimarchi. 1994. Adaptive reversion of a frameshift mutation in *Escherichia coli* by simple base deletions in homopolymeric runs. *Science* 265: 407–409.

Galitski, T., and J. R. Roth. 1995. Evidence that F plasmid transfer replication underlies apparent adaptive mutation. *Science* 268: 421–423.

Radicella, J. P., P. U. Park, and M. S. Fox. 1995. Adaptive mutation in *Escherichia coli*: A role for conjugation. *Science* 268: 418–420.

Rosenberg, S. M., S. Longerich, P. Gee, and R. S. Harris. 1994. Adaptive mutations by deletions in small mononucleotide repeats. *Science* 265: 405–407.

Sniegowski, P. D., and R. E. Lenski. 1995. Mutation and adaptation: The directed mutation controversy in evolutionary perspective. *Annual Review of Ecology and Systematics* 26: 553–578.

11. Some evolutionary geneticists have suggested that the genetic code has been shaped by natural selection to minimize the deleterious consequences of mutations. For an entry into the literature on this issue, see

Knight, R. D., S. J. Freeland, and L. F. Landweber. 1999. Selection, history and chemistry: The three faces of the genetic code. *Trends in Biochemical Sciences* 24: 241–247.

Freeland S. J., and L. D. Hurst. 1998. Load minimization of the genetic code: History does not explain the pattern. *Proceedings of the Royal Society London,* Series B 265: 2111–2119.

Freeland S. J., and L. D. Hurst. 1998. The genetic code is one in a million. *Journal of Molecular Evolution* 47: 238–248.

Citations

Abel, L., F. Demenais, et al. 1991. Evidence for the segregation of a major gene in human susceptibility/resistance to infection by *Schistosoma mansoni*. *American Journal of Human Genetics* 48: 959–970.

Avise, John C. 1994. *Molecular Markers, Natural History and Evolution*. New York: Chapman & Hall.

Ayala, F. J., L. Serra, and A. Prevosti. 1989. A grand experiment in evolution: The *Drosophila subobscura* colonization of the Americas. *Genome* 31: 246–255.

Bell, G. 1997. *Selection: The Mechanism of Evolution*. New York: Chapman & Hall.

Bohr, V. A., C. A. Smith, D. S. Okumoto, and P. C. Hanawalt. 1985. DNA repair in an active gene: Removal of pyrimidine dimers from the DHRF gene of CHO cells is much more efficient than in the genome overall. *Cell* 40: 359–369.

Drake, J. W. 1991. A constant of rate of spontaneous mutation in DNA-based microbes. *Proceedings of the National Academy of Sciences, USA* 88: 7160–7164.

Feder, J. L., C. A. Chilcote, and G. L. Bush. 1989. Inheritance and linkage relationships of allozymes in the apple maggot fly. *Journal of Heredity* 80: 277-283.

Friedberg, E. C., G. C. Walker, and W. Siede. 1995. *DNA Repair and Mutagenesis*. Washington D.C.: ASM Press.

García-Dorado, A. 1997. The rate and effects distribution of viability mutation in *Drosophila*: minimum distance estimation. *Evolution* 51: 1130–1139.

Gillin, F. D., and N. G. Nossal. 1976a. Control of mutation frequency by bacteriophage T4 DNA polymerase I. The ts CB120 antimutator DNA polymerase is defective in strand displacement. *Journal of Biological Chemistry* 251: 5219–5224.

Gillin, F. D., and N. G. Nossal. 1976b. Control of mutation frequency by bacteriophage T4 DNA polymerase II. Accuracy of nucleotide selection by L8 mutator, CB120 antimutator, and wild type phage T4 DNA polymerases. *Journal of Biological Chemistry* 251: 5225–5232.

Harris, H. 1966. Enzyme polymorphisms in man. *Proceedings of the Royal Society London,* Series B 164: 298–310.

Huey, R. B., G. W. Gilchrist, M. L. Carlson, D. Berrigan, and L. Serra. 2000. Rapid evolution of a geographic cline in size in an introduced fly. *Science* 287: 308–309

Ingram, V. M. 1958. How do genes act? *Scientific American* 198: 68–76.

Jeffs, P., and M. Ashburner. 1991. Processed pseudogenes in *Drosophila*. *Proceedings of the Royal Society of London,* Series B 244: 151–159.

Keese, P. K., and A. Gibbs. 1992. Origins of genes: "Big bang" or continuous creation? *Proceedings of the National Academy of Sciences, USA* 89: 9489–9493.

Keightley, P. D., and A. Caballero. 1997. Genomic mutation rates for lifetime reproductive output and lifespan in *Caenorhabditis elegans*. *Proceedings of the National Academy of Sciences, USA* 94: 3823–3827.

Klekowski, E. J., Jr., and P. J. Godfrey. 1989. Aging and mutation in plants. *Nature* 340: 389–391.

Langley, C. H., E. Montgomery, and W. F. Quattlebaum. 1982. Restriction map variation in the *Adh* region of *Drosophila*. *Proceedings of the National Academy of Sciences, USA* 78: 5631–5635.

LeClerc, J. E., B. Li, W. L. Payne, and T. A. Cebula. 1996. High mutation frequencies among *Escherichia coli* and *Salmonella* pathogens. *Science* 274: 1209–1211.

Lewontin, R. C., and J. L. Hubby. 1966. A molecular approach to the study of genetic heterozygosity in natural populations. II. Amount of variation and degree of heterozygosity in natural populations of *Drosophila pseudoobscura*. *Genetics* 54: 595–609.

Liu, R., W. A. Paxton, et al. 1996. Homozygous defect in HIV-1 coreceptor accounts for resistance in some multiply-exposed individuals to HIV-1 infection. *Cell* 86: 367–377.

Long, M., and C. H. Langley. 1993. Natural selection and the origin of *jingwei*, a chimeric processed functional gene in *Drosophila*. *Science* 260: 91–95.

Martinson, J. J., N. H. Chapman, et al. 1997. Global distribution of the CCR5 gene 32-base-pair deletion. *Nature Genetics* 16: 100–103.

Mellon, I., D. K. Rajpal, M. Koi, C. R. Boland, and G. N. Champe. 1996. Transcription-coupled repair deficiency and mutations in the human mismatch repair genes. *Science* 272: 557–560.

Mitton, J. B. 1997. *Selection in Natural Populations*. Oxford: Oxford University Press.

Nathans, J., D. Thomas, and D. S. Hogness. 1986. Molecular genetics of human color vision: The genes encoding blue, green, and red pigments. *Science* 232: 193–202.

Oakeshott, J. G., J. B. Gibson, et al. 1982. Alcohol dehydrogenase and glycerol-3-phosphate dehydrogenase clines in *Drosophila melanogaster* on different continents. *Evolution* 36: 86-96.

Online Mendelian Inheritance in Man, OMIM(TM). 1999. Johns Hopkins University, Baltimore, MD. MIM Number: 181460. World Wide Web URL: http://www.ncbi.nlm.nih.gov/omim/

Pauling, L., H. A. Itano, S. J. Singer, and I. C. Wells. 1949. Sickle-cell anemia, a molecular disease. *Science* 110: 543–548.

Pier, G. B., M. Grout , and T. S. Zaidi. 1997. Cystic fibrosis transmembrane conductance regulator is an epithelial cell receptor for clearance of *Pseudomonas aeruginosa* from the lung. *Proceedings of the National Academy of Science, U.S.A.* 94: 12088–12093.

Powers, D. A., T. Lauerman, et al. 1991. Genetic mechanisms for adapting to a changing environment. *Annual Review of Genetics* 25: 629–659.

Powers, D. A., P. M. Schulte, D. Crawford, and L. DiMichele. 1998. Evolutionary adaptations of gene structure and expression in natural populations in relation to a changing environment: A multidisciplinary approach to address the million-year saga of a small fish. *The Journal of Experimental Zoology* 282: 71–94.

Prevosti, A. 1967. Inversion heterozygosity and selection for wing length in *Drosophila subobscura*. *Genetical Research Cambridge* 10: 81–93.

Prevosti, A., G. Ribo, L. Serra, M. Aguade, J. Balaña, M. Monclus, and F. Mestres. 1988. Colonization of America by *Drosophila subobscura:* Experiment in natural populations that supports the adaptive role of chromosomal-inversion polymorphism. *Proceedings of the National Academy of Sciences, USA* 85: 5597–5600.

Ramsey, J., and D. W. Schemske. 1998. Pathways, mechanisms, and rates of polyploid formation in flowering plants. *Annual Review of Ecology and Systematics* 29: 467–501.

Samson, M., F. Libert, et al. 1996. Resistance to HIV-1 infection in caucasian individuals bearing mutant alleles of the CCR5 chemokine receptor gene. *Nature* 382: 722–725.

Schlager, G., and M.M. Dickie. 1971. Natural mutation rates in the house mouse. Estimates for 5 specific loci and dominant mutations. *Mutation Research* 11: 89–96.

Short, R. V., A.C. Chandley, R. C. Jones, and W. R. Allen. 1974. Meiosis in interspecific equine hybrids. II. The Przewalski horse/domestic horse hybrid. *Cytogenetics and Cell Genetics* 13: 465–478.

Stadler, L. J. 1942. Some observations on gene variability and spontaneous mutation. Spragg Memorial Lectures. East Lansing: Michigan State College.

Tsui, L.-C. 1992. The spectrum of cystic fibrosis mutations. *Trends in Genetics* 8: 392–398.

Voelker, R. A., H. E. Schaffer, and T. Mukai. 1980. Spontaneous allozyme mutations in *Drosophila melanogaster:* Rate of occurrence and nature of the mutants. *Genetics* 94: 961–968.

Watson, J. D., and F. H. C. Crick 1953. A structure for deoxyribose nucleic acid. *Nature* 171: 737–738.

CHAPTER 5

Mendelian Genetics in Populations I: Selection and Mutation as Mechanisms of Evolution

A population of mice, including newborns, juveniles, and adults. (C. C. Lockwood/Animals Animals/Earth Scenes)

Most people are susceptible to HIV. Their best hope of avoiding infection is to avoid contact with the virus. There are, however, a few individuals who remain uninfected despite repeated exposure. In 1996, AIDS researchers discovered that at least some of the variation in susceptibility to HIV has a genetic basis (see Chapters 1 and 4). The gene responsible encodes a cell surface protein called CCR5. CCR5 is exploited by most sexually transmitted strains of HIV-1 as a means of infiltrating white blood cells. There is a mutant allele of the CCR5 gene, called *CCR5-Δ32*, with a 32-base-pair deletion that destroys the encoded protein's ability to function. Individuals who inherit two copies of this allele have no CCR5 on the surface of their white blood cells, and are therefore highly resistant to HIV-1. The fact that individuals homozygous for *CCR5-Δ32* are much less likely to contract AIDS raises a question: Will the AIDS epidemic cause an increase in the frequency of the *Δ32* allele in human populations?

Consider, too, this question. In the 1927 case of *Buck v. Bell,* the United States Supreme Court upheld by a vote of eight to one the state of Virginia's sterilization statute. Drafted on the advice of eugenicists, the law was intended to improve the genetic quality of future generations by allowing the forced sterilization of individuals afflicted with hereditary forms of insanity, feeblemindedness, and other mental defects. The court's decision in *Buck v. Bell* reinvigorated a compulsory sterilization movement dating from 1907 (Kevles 1995). By 1940, thirty states had enacted sterilization laws, and by 1960 over 60,000 people had been sterilized without their consent (Reilly 1991; Lane 1992). In hindsight, the evidence that these individuals suffered from hereditary diseases was weak. If the genetic assumptions had been correct, would sterilization have been an effective means of reducing the incidence of undesirable traits?

And, finally, consider this question. Cystic fibrosis is among the most common serious genetic diseases among people of European ancestry, affecting approximately 1 newborn in 2500. Cystic fibrosis is inherited as an autosomal recessive trait (see Chapter 4). Affected individuals suffer chronic infections with the bacterium *Pseudomonas aeruginosa* and ultimately sustain severe lung damage (Pier et al., 1997). At present, most individuals with cystic fibrosis live into their thirties or forties (Elias et al. 1992), but until recently few survived to reproductive age. In spite of the fact that cystic fibrosis was lethal for most of human history, in some populations as many as 4% of individuals are carriers. How can alleles that cause a lethal genetic disease remain this common?

The questions posed in the preceding paragraphs all concern forces that influence the frequencies of alleles in populations. Such questions can be addressed using the tools of **population genetics**. Population genetics, the subject of Chapters 5 and 6, integrates Darwin's theory of evolution by natural selection with Mendelian genetics (for a history, see Provine 1971). The crucial insight of population genetics is that changes in the relative abundance of traits in a population can be tied to changes in the relative abundance of the alleles that influence them. From a population-genetic perspective, evolution is a change across generations in the frequencies of alleles. Population genetics provides the theoretical foundation for much of our modern understanding of evolution.

5.1 Mendelian Genetics in Populations: The Hardy–Weinberg Equilibrium Principle

Before we can hope to predict whether the AIDS epidemic will cause an increase in the frequency of the *CCR5-Δ32* allele in human populations, we need to understand how the allele will behave without the AIDS epidemic. In other words, we need to develop a null model for the behavior of genes in populations. This null model should specify, under the simplest possible assumptions, what will happen across generations to the frequencies of alleles and genotypes. The model should apply not just to humans, but to any population of organisms that are both diploid and sexual.

A population is a group of interbreeding individuals and their offspring (Figure 5.1). The crucial events in the life cycle of a population are these: Adults produce gametes, the gametes combine to make zygotes, and the zygotes grow up to become the next generation of adults. We want to track the fate, across generations, of

Population genetics begins with a model of what happens to allele and genotype frequencies in an idealized population. Once we know how Mendelian genes behave in the idealized population, we will be able to explore how they behave in real populations.

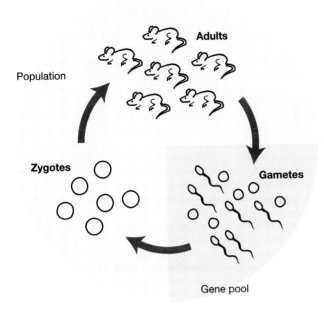

Figure 5.1   **The life cycle of an imaginary population of mice, highlighting the stages that will be important in our development of population genetics**

Mendelian genes in such a population. We want to know whether a particular allele or genotype will become more common or less common over time, and why.

Imagine that the mice in Figure 5.1 have in their genome a particular locus, the A locus, with two alleles: *A* and *a*. We can begin tracking these alleles at any point in the life cycle. We will then follow them through one complete turn of the cycle, from one generation to the next, to see if their frequencies change.

A Numerical Example

Our task of following alleles will be simpler if we start with the gametes produced by the adults when they mate. We will assume that the adults choose their mates at random. A useful mental trick is to picture the process of random mating happening like this: We take all the eggs and sperm produced by all the adults in the population and mix them together in a barrel. This barrel is known as the gene pool. Each sperm then swims about at random until it collides with an egg to make a zygote. Something rather like this actually happens in sea urchins and other marine organisms that simply release their gametes onto the tide. For other organisms, like mice and humans, it is obviously a simplification.

The adults in our mouse population are diploid, so each carries two alleles for the A locus. But the adults made their eggs and sperm by meiosis. Following Mendel's law of segregation, each gamete received just one allele for the A locus. Imagine that 60% of the eggs and sperm received allele *A,* and 40% received allele *a*. In other words, the frequency of allele *A* in the gene pool is 0.6, and the frequency of allele *a* is 0.4 (Figure 5.2).

What happens when eggs meet sperm? For example, what fraction of the zygotes they produce will have genotype *AA*? Figure 5.2 shows the four possible combinations of egg and sperm, the zygotes they produce, and a calculation specifying the probability of each. For example, if we pick an egg to watch at random, there is a 60% chance that it will have genotype *A*. When a sperm comes along

Starting with the eggs and sperm that constitute the gene pool, our model tracks alleles through zygotes and adults and into the next generation's gene pool.

Figure 5.2 Random mating in the gene pool of our model mouse population produces zygotes with predictable genotype frequencies

A gene pool with allele frequencies of 0.6 and 0.4...

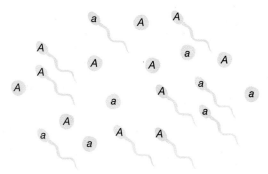

...yields zygotes with genotype frequencies of 0.36, 0.48, and 0.16

Egg		Sperm		Zygote	Probability
A	&	A	→	AA	0.6 x 0.6 = 0.36
A	&	a	→	Aa	0.6 x 0.4 = 0.24
a	&	A	→	aA	0.4 x 0.6 = 0.24
a	&	a	→	aa	0.4 x 0.4 = 0.16

(The rows Aa and aA are bracketed) = 0.48

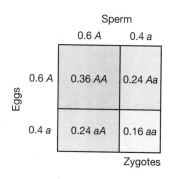

Sperm

	0.6 A	0.4 a
0.6 A	0.36 AA	0.24 Aa
0.4 a	0.24 aA	0.16 aa

Eggs

Zygotes

AA		Aa		aa		Total
0.36	+	0.48	+	0.16	=	1.0

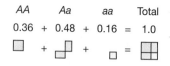

Figure 5.3 A geometrical representation of the genotype frequencies produced by random mating The fractions along the left and top edges of the box represent the frequencies of *A* and *a* eggs and sperm in the gene pool. The fractions inside the box represent the genotype frequencies among zygotes formed by random encounters between gametes in the gene pool.

to fertilize the egg, there is a 60% chance that the sperm will have genotype *A*. The probability that we will witness the production of an *AA* zygote is therefore

$$0.6 \times 0.6 = 36 \qquad \text{(see Box 5.1)}$$

If we watched the formation of all the zygotes, 36% of them would have genotype *AA*. The calculations in Figure 5.2 show that random mating in the gene pool produces zygotes in the following proportions:

AA	*Aa*	*aa*
0.36	0.48	0.16

(The *Aa* category includes heterozygotes produced by combining either an *A* egg with an *a* sperm or an *a* egg with an *A* sperm.) Notice that

$$0.36 + 0.48 + 0.16 = 1$$

This confirms that we have accounted for all of the zygotes. Figure 5.3 shows a geometrical representation of the same calculations.

We now let the zygotes grow to adulthood, and we let the adults produce gametes to make the next generation's gene pool. Will the frequencies of alleles *A* and *a* in the new gene pool be different from what they were before?

We can calculate the frequency of allele *A* in the new gene pool as follows. Because adults of genotype *AA* constitute 36% of the population, they will make 36% of the gametes. All of these gametes carry allele *A*. Likewise, adults of genotype *Aa* constitute 48% of the population, and will make 48% of the gametes. Half of these gametes carry allele *A*. So the total fraction of the gametes in the gene pool that carry allele *A* is

BOX 5.1 Combining probabilities

The combined probability that two independent events will occur together is equal to the product of their individual probabilities. For example, the probability that a tossed penny will come up heads is $\frac{1}{2}$. The probability that a tossed nickel will come up heads is also $\frac{1}{2}$. If we toss both coins together, the outcome for the penny is independent of the outcome for the nickel. Thus the probability of getting heads on the penny and heads on the nickel is

$$\frac{1}{2} \times \frac{1}{2} = \frac{1}{4}$$

The combined probability that either of two mutually exclusive events will occur is the sum of their individual probabilities. When rolling a die we can get a one or a two (among other possibilities), but we cannot get both at once. Thus, the probability of getting either a one or a two is

$$\frac{1}{6} + \frac{1}{6} = \frac{1}{3}$$

$$0.36 + \left(\frac{1}{2}\right) 0.48 = 0.6$$

Figure 5.4 shows this calculation graphically. The figure also shows a calculation establishing that the fraction of the gametes in the gene pool that carry allele a is 0.4. Notice that

$$0.6 + 0.4 = 1$$

This confirms that we have accounted for all of the gametes. Figure 5.5 shows a geometrical representation of the same calculations.

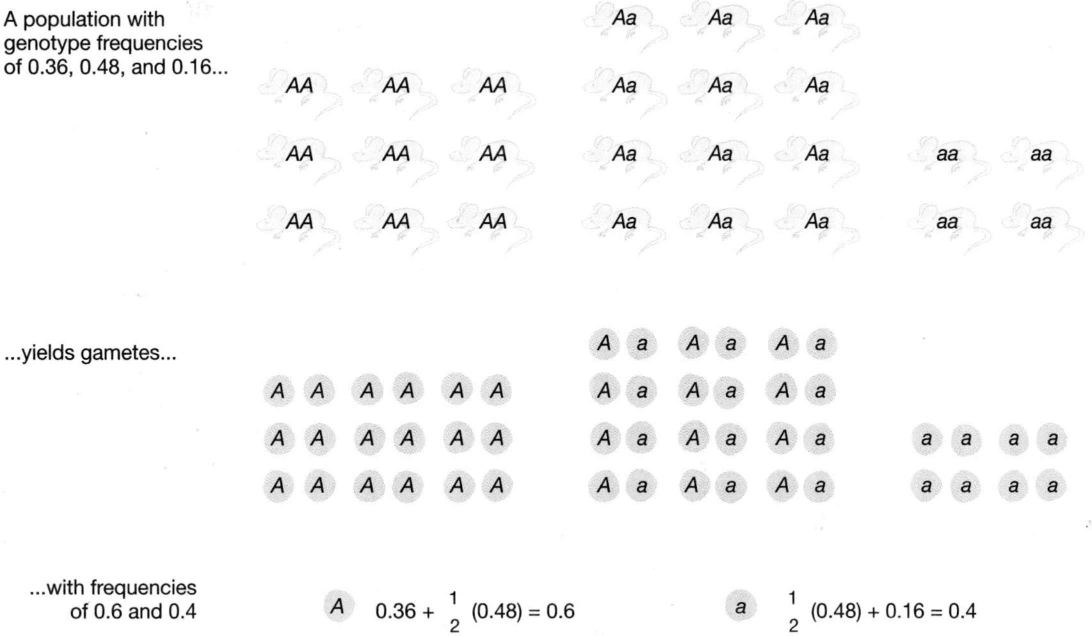

A population with genotype frequencies of 0.36, 0.48, and 0.16...

...yields gametes...

...with frequencies of 0.6 and 0.4

$A \quad 0.36 + \frac{1}{2}(0.48) = 0.6$

$a \quad \frac{1}{2}(0.48) + 0.16 = 0.4$

Figure 5.4 When the adults in our model mouse population make gametes, they produce a gene pool in which the allele frequencies are identical to the ones we started with a generation ago

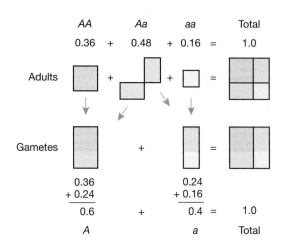

Figure 5.5 A geometrical representation of the allele frequencies produced when adults in our model population make gametes The area of each box represents the frequency of an adult or gamete genotype. Note that half the gametes produced by *Aa* adults carry allele *A*, and half carry allele *a*.

Numerical examples show that in our idealized population, allele frequencies remain constant from one generation to the next.

We have come full circle, and arrived right where we began. We started with allele frequencies of 60% for *A* and 40% for *a* in our population's gene pool. We followed the alleles through zygotes and adults and into the next generation's gene pool. The allele frequencies in the new gene pool are still 60% and 40%. The allele frequencies for *A* and *a* in our population are thus in equilibrium: They do not change from one generation to the next. The population does not evolve.

The first biologist to work a numerical example, tracing the frequencies of Mendelian alleles from one generation to the next in an ideal population, was G. Udny Yule in 1902. He started with a gene pool in which the frequencies of two alleles were 0.5 and 0.5, and showed that in the next generation's gene pool the allele frequencies were still 0.5 and 0.5. (Readers should reproduce his calculations as an exercise.)

Like us, Yule concluded that the allele frequencies in his imaginary population were in equilibrium. Yule's conclusion was both ground breaking and correct, but he took it a bit too literally. He had worked only one example, and he believed that allele frequencies of 0.5 and 0.5 represented the only possible equilibrium state for a two–allele system. For example, Yule believed that if a single *A* allele appeared as a mutation in a population whose gene pool otherwise consisted only of *a*'s, then the *A* allele would automatically increase in frequency until it constituted one half of the gene pool. Yule argued this claim during the discussion that followed a talk given in 1908 by R. C. Punnett (of Punnett-square fame). Punnett thought that Yule was wrong, but he did not know how to prove it.

We have already demonstrated, of course, that Punnett was correct in rejecting Yule's claim. Our calculations showed that a population with allele frequencies of 0.6 and 0.4 is in equilibrium too. What Punnett wanted, however, is a general proof. This proof should show that any allele frequencies, so long as they sum to 1, will remain unchanged from one generation to the next.

Punnett took the problem to his mathematician friend G. H. Hardy, who produced the proof in short order (Hardy 1908). Hardy simply repeated the calculations that Yule had performed, using variables in place of the specific allele frequencies that Yule had assumed. Hardy's calculation of the general case indeed showed that any allele frequencies will be in equilibrium.

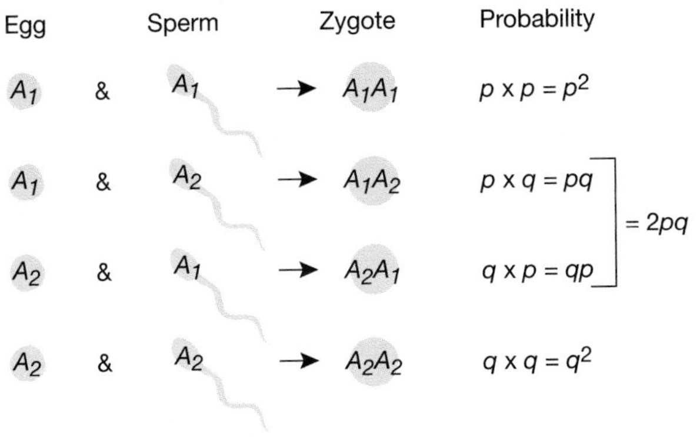

Egg   Sperm   Zygote   Probability

A_1 & A_1 $\rightarrow$ A_1A_1 $p \times p = p^2$

A_1 & A_2 $\rightarrow$ A_1A_2 $p \times q = pq$

A_2 & A_1 $\rightarrow$ A_2A_1 $q \times p = qp$

$\left. \begin{array}{c} \\ \\ \end{array} \right\} = 2pq$

A_2 & A_2 $\rightarrow$ A_2A_2 $q \times q = q^2$

Figure 5.6   The general case for random mating in the gene pool of our model mouse population

The General Case

For our version of Hardy's general case, we will again work with an imaginary population. We are concerned with a single locus with two alleles: A_1 and A_2. We use capital letters with subscripts because we want our calculation to cover cases in which the alleles are codominant as well as cases in which they are dominant and recessive. The three possible diploid genotypes are A_1A_1, A_1A_2, and A_2A_2.

As in our numercial example, we will start with the gene pool, and follow the alleles through one complete turn of the life cycle. The gene pool will contain some frequency of A_1 gametes and some frequency of A_2 gametes. We will call the frequency of A_1 in the gene pool p and the frequency of A_2 in the gene pool q. There are only two alleles in the population, so

$$p + q = 1$$

The first step is to let the gametes in the gene pool combine to make zygotes. Figure 5.6 shows the four possible combinations of egg and sperm, the zygotes they produce, and a calculation specifying the probability of each. For example, if we pick an egg to watch at random, the chance is p that it will have genotype A_1. When a sperm comes along to fertilize the egg, the chance is p that the sperm will have genotype A_1. The probability that we will witness the production of an A_1A_1 zygote is therefore

$$p \times p = p^2$$

If we watched the formation of all the zygotes, p^2 of them would have genotype A_1A_1. The calculations in Figure 5.6 show that random mating in our gene pool produces zygotes in the following proportions:

$$\begin{array}{ccc} \mathbf{A_1A_1} & \mathbf{A_1A_2} & \mathbf{A_2A_2} \\ p^2 & 2pq & q^2 \end{array}$$

Figure 5.7 shows a geometrical representation of the same calculations. The figure also shows that

$$p^2 + 2pq + q^2 = 1$$

This confirms that we have accounted for all the zygotes. The same result can be demonstrated algebraically by substituting $(1 - p)$ for q in the expression $p^2 + 2pq + q^2$, then simplifying.

The challenge now is to prove algebraically that there was nothing special about our numerical examples. Any allele frequencies will remain constant from generation to generation.

Sperm

	fr(A_1) = p	fr(A_2) = q
Eggs fr(A_1) = p	fr(A_1A_1) = p^2	fr(A_1A_2) = pq
fr(A_2) = q	fr(A_2A_1) = qp	fr(A_2A_2) = q^2

Zygotes

A_1A_1		A_1A_2		A_2A_2		Total
p^2	+	$2pq$	+	q^2	=	1.0
☐	+	⬚	+	☐	=	⊞

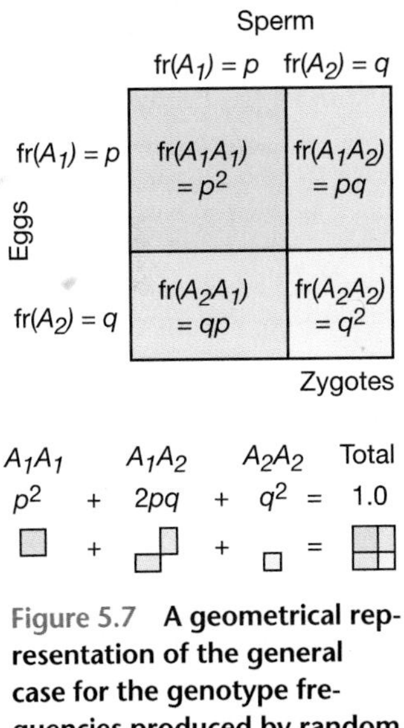

Figure 5.7   A geometrical representation of the general case for the genotype frequencies produced by random mating   The variables along the left and top edges of the box represent the frequencies of A and a eggs and sperm in the gene pool. The expressions inside the box represent the genotype frequencies among zygotes formed by random encounters between gametes in the gene pool.

We have gone from the allele frequencies in the gene pool to the genotype frequencies among the zygotes. We now let the zygotes grow up to become adults, and let the adults produce gametes to make the next generation's gene pool.

We can calculate the frequency of allele A_1 in the new gene pool as follows. Because adults of genotype A_1A_1 constitute a proportion p^2 of the population, they will make p^2 of the gametes. All of these gametes carry allele A_1. Likewise, adults of genotype A_1A_2 constitute a proportion $2pq$ of the population, and will make $2pq$ of the gametes. Half of these gametes carry allele A_1. So the total fraction of the gametes in the gene pool that carry allele A_1 is

$$p^2 + \left(\frac{1}{2}\right)2pq = p^2 + pq$$

We can simplify the expression on the right by substituting $(1 - p)$ for q. This gives

$$p^2 + pq = p^2 + p(1 - p)$$
$$= p^2 + p - p^2$$
$$= p$$

Figure 5.8 shows this calculation graphically. The figure also shows a calculation establishing that the fraction of the gametes in the gene pool that carry allele A_2 is q. We assumed at the outset that p and q sum to 1, so we know that we have accounted for all of the gametes.

Our model has shown that our idealized population does not evolve. This conclusion is known as the Hardy–Weinberg equilibrium principle.

Once again we have come full circle, and arrived back where we started. We started with allele frequencies of p and q in our population's gene pool. We followed the alleles through zygotes and adults and into the next generation's gene pool. The allele frequencies in the new gene pool are still p and q. The allele frequencies p and q can be stable at any values at all between 0 and 1, as long as they sum to 1. In other words, *any* allele frequencies will be in equilibrium, not just $p = q = 0.5$ as Yule thought.

This is a profound result. At the beginning of the chapter we defined evolution as change in allele frequencies in populations. The calculations we just performed show, given simple assumptions, that in populations following the rules of Mendelian genetics, allele frequencies do not change.

We have presented this result as the work of Hardy (1908). It was derived independently by Wilhelm Weinberg (1908) and has become known as the

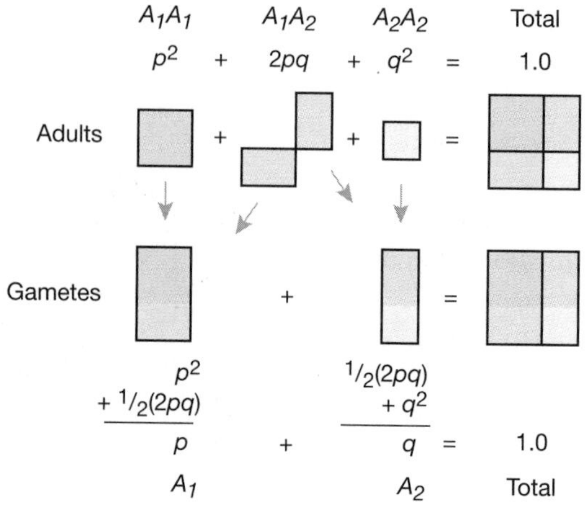

Figure 5.8   A geometrical representation of the general case for the allele frequencies produced when adults in our model population make gametes   The area of each box represents the frequency of an adult or gamete genotype.

Hardy–Weinberg equilibrium principle. (Some evolutionary biologists refer to it as the Hardy–Weinberg–Castle equilibrium principle, because William Castle [1903] worked a numerical example and stated the general equilibrium principle nonmathematically five years before Hardy and Weinberg explicitly proved the general case [see Provine 1971].) The Hardy–Weinberg equilibrium principle yields two fundamental conclusions:

- **Conclusion 1:** The allele frequencies in a population will not change, generation after generation.
- **Conclusion 2:** If the allele frequencies in a population are given by p and q, the genotype frequencies will be given by p^2, $2pq$, and q^2.

We get an analogous result if we generalize the analysis from the two-allele case to the usual case of a population containing many alleles at a locus (see Box 5.2).

What Use Is the Hardy–Weinberg Equilibrium Principle?

It may seem puzzling that in a book about evolution we have devoted so much space to a proof that apparently shows that evolution does not happen. What makes the Hardy–Weinberg equilibrium principle useful is that it rests on a specific set of simple assumptions. When one or more of these assumptions is violated, the Hardy–Weinberg conclusions no longer hold.

We left most of the assumptions unstated when we developed our null model for how Mendelian alleles behave in populations. We can now state them explicitly. The crucial assumptions are:

1. **There is no selection.** All members of our model population survived at equal rates and contributed equal numbers of gametes to the gene pool. When this assumption is violated—when individuals with some genotypes survive and reproduce at higher rates than others—the frequencies of alleles may change from one generation to the next.

2. **There is no mutation.** In the model population, no copies of existing alleles were converted by mutation into other existing alleles, and no new alleles were

The Hardy–Weinberg equilibrium principle becomes useful when we list the assumptions we made about our idealized population. By providing a set of explicit conditions under which evolution does not happen, the Hardy–Weinberg analysis identifies the forces that can cause evolution in real populations.

BOX 5.2   The Hardy–Weinberg equilibrium principle with more than two alleles.

Imagine a single locus with several alleles. We can call the alleles A_i, A_j, A_k, and so on, and we can represent the frequencies of the alleles in the gene pool with the variables p_i, p_j, p_k, and so on. The formation of a zygote with genotype A_iA_i requires the union of an A_i egg with an A_i sperm. Thus the frequency of any homozygous genotype A_iA_i is p_i^2. The formation of a zygote with genotype A_iA_j requires either the union of an A_i egg with an A_j sperm, or an A_j egg with an A_i sperm. Thus, the frequency of any heterozygous genotype A_iA_j is $2p_ip_j$.

For example, if there are three alleles with frequencies p_1, p_2, and p_3, such that

$$p_1 + p_2 + p_3 = 1$$

then the genotype frequencies are given by

$$(p_1 + p_2 + p_3)^2 = p_1^2 + p_2^2 + p_3^2 + 2p_1p_2 + 2p_1p_3 + 2p_2p_3$$

and the allele frequencies do not change from generation to generation.

created. When this assumption is violated, and, for example, some alleles have higher mutation rates than others, allele frequencies may change from one generation to the next.

3. **There is no migration.** No individuals moved into or out of the model population. When this assumption is violated, and individuals with some alleles move into or out of the population at higher rates than individuals with other alleles, allele frequencies may change from one generation to the next.

4. **There were no chance events** that caused individuals with some genotypes to pass more of their alleles to the next generation than others. We avoided this type of random event by assuming that the eggs and sperm in the gene pool collided with each other at their actual frequencies of p and q, with no deviations caused by chance. Another way to state this assumption is that the model population was infinitely large. When this assumption is violated, and by chance some individuals contribute more alleles to the next generation than others, allele frequencies may change from one generation to the next. This kind of allele frequency change is called **genetic drift**.

5. **Individuals choose their mates at random.** We explicitly set up the gene pool to let gametes find each other at random. In contrast to assumptions 1 through 4, when this assumption is violated—when, for example, individuals prefer to mate with other individuals of the same genotype—allele frequencies do not change from one generation to the next. Genotype frequencies may change, however. Such shifts in genotype frequency, in combination with a violation of one of the other four assumptions, can influence the evolution of populations.

By furnishing a list of specific ideal conditions under which populations will not evolve, the Hardy–Weinberg equilibrium principle identifies the set of forces that can cause evolution in the real world. This is the sense in which the Hardy–Weinberg equilibrium principle serves as a null model. Biologists can measure allele and genotype frequencies in nature, and determine whether the Hardy–Weinberg conclusions hold. A population in which conclusions 1 and 2 hold is said to be in **Hardy–Weinberg equilibrium**. If a population is not in Hardy–Weinberg equilibrium—if the allele frequencies change from generation to generation or if the genotype frequencies cannot, in fact, be predicted by multiplying the allele frequencies—then one or more of the Hardy–Weinberg model's assumptions is being violated. Such a discovery does not, by itself, tell us which assumptions are being violated, but it does tell us that further research may be rewarded with interesting discoveries.

In the following sections of Chapter 5, we consider how violations of assumptions 1 and 2 affect the two Hardy–Weinberg conclusions, and we explore empirical research on selection and mutation as forces of evolution. In Chapter 6, we consider violations of assumptions 3, 4, and 5.

Changes in the Frequency of the *CCR5-Δ32* Allele

We began this chapter by asking whether we can expect the frequency of the *CCR5-Δ32* allele to change in human populations. Now that we have developed a null model for how Mendelian alleles behave in populations, we can give a partial answer. As long as individuals of all CCR5 genotypes survive and reproduce at equal rates, and as long as no mutations convert some CCR5 alleles into others, and as long as no one moves from one population to another, and as long as populations are infinitely large, and as long as people choose their mates at random, then no, the frequency of the *CCR5-Δ32* allele will not change.

This answer is, of course, thoroughly unsatisfying. It is unsatisfying because none of the assumptions will be true in any real population. We asked the question in the first place precisely because we expect *Δ32/Δ32* individuals to survive the AIDS epidemic at higher rates than individuals with either of the other two genotypes. In the next two sections, we will see that our null model, the Hardy–Weinberg equilibrium principle, provides a framework that will allow us to assess with precision the importance of differences in survival.

5.2 Selection

When we worked with a model population to derive the Hardy–Weinberg equilibrium principle, first on our list of assumptions was that all individuals survive at equal rates and contribute equal numbers of gametes to the gene pool. Systematic violations of this assumption are examples of **selection**. Selection happens when individuals with particular phenotypes survive to reproductive age at higher rates than individuals with other phenotypes, or when individuals with particular phenotypes produce more offspring during reproduction than individuals with other phenotypes. The bottom line in either kind of selection is differential reproductive success: Some individuals have more offspring than others. Selection can lead to evolution when the phenotypes that exhibit differences in reproductive success are heritable—that is, when certain phenotypes are associated with certain genotypes.

First on the list of assumptions about our idealized population was that individuals survive at equal rates and have equal reproductive success. We now explore what happens to allele frequencies when this assumption is violated.

Population geneticists often assume that phenotypes are determined strictly by genotypes. They might, for example, think of pea plants as being either tall or short, such that individuals with the genotypes *TT* and *Tt* are tall and individuals with the genotype *tt* are short. Such a view is at least roughly accurate for some traits, including the examples we use in this chapter.

When phenotypes fall into discrete classes that appear to be determined strictly by genotypes, we can think of selection as if it acts directly on the genotypes. We can then assign a particular level of lifetime reproductive success to each genotype. In reality, most phenotypic traits are not, in fact, strictly determined by genotype. Pea plants with the genotype *TT,* for example, vary in height. This variation is due to genetic differences at other loci and to differences in the environments in which the pea plants grew. We will consider such complications in Chapter 7. For the present, however, we adopt the simple view.

When we think of selection as if it acts directly on genotypes, its defining feature is that some genotypes contribute more alleles to future generations than others. In other words, there are differences among genotypes in fitness.

Our task in this section is to incorporate selection into the Hardy–Weinberg analysis. We begin by asking whether selection can change the frequencies of alleles in the gene pool from one generation to the next. In other words, can violation of the no-selection assumption lead to a violation of conclusion 1 of the Hardy–Weinberg equilibrium principle?

Adding Selection to the Hardy–Weinberg Analysis: Changes in Allele Frequencies

We start with a numerical example that shows that selection can indeed change the frequencies of alleles. Imagine that in our population of mice there is a locus, the B locus, that affects the probability of survival. Assume, as we did for the A locus in Figure 5.2, that the frequency of allele B_1 in the gene pool is 0.6 and the frequency of allele B_2 is 0.4 (Figure 5.9). After random mating, we get genotype frequencies for B_1B_1, B_1B_2, and B_2B_2, of 0.36, 0.48, and 0.16. The rest of our calculations will be simpler if we give the population of zygotes a finite size, so imagine that there are 1,000 zygotes:

$$B_1B_1 \quad B_1B_2 \quad B_2B_2$$
$$360 \qquad 480 \qquad 160$$

These zygotes are represented by a bar graph in the figure. We will follow the individuals that develop from these zygotes as they grow to adulthood. Those that survive will breed to produce the next generation's gene pool.

We incorporate selection by stipulating that the genotypes differ in their rates of survival. All of the B_1B_1 individuals survive, 75% of the B_1B_2 individuals survive, and 50% of the B_2B_2 individuals survive. As shown in Figure 5.9, there are now 800 adults in the population:

$$B_1B_1 \quad B_1B_2 \quad B_2B_2$$
$$360 \qquad 360 \qquad 80$$

The frequencies of the three genotypes among the adults are as follows:

$$B_1B_1 \qquad\qquad B_1B_2 \qquad\qquad B_2B_2$$
$$360/800 \qquad 360/800 \qquad 80/800$$
$$= 0.45 \qquad\quad = 0.45 \qquad\quad = 0.1$$

When these adults produce gametes, the frequency of allele B_1 in the new gene pool is equal to the frequency of B_1B_1 among the surviving adults, plus half the

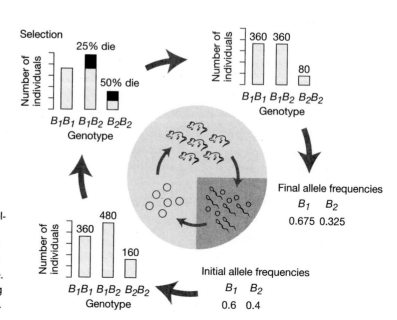

Figure 5.9 **Selection can cause allele frequencies to change across generations** This figure follows our model mouse population from one generation's gene pool to the next generation's gene pool. The bar graphs show the number of individuals of each genotype in the population at any given time. Selection, in the form of differences in survival among juveniles, causes the frequency of allele B_1 to increase.

frequency of B_1B_2. This calculation, and that for the frequency of allele B_2, are as follows:

$$
\begin{array}{cc}
\boldsymbol{B_1} & \boldsymbol{B_2} \\
0.45 + \left(\dfrac{1}{2}\right)0.45 & \left(\dfrac{1}{2}\right)0.45 + 0.1 \\
= 0.675 & = 0.325
\end{array}
$$

The frequency of allele B_1 has risen by an increment of 7.5 percentage points. The frequency of allele B_2 has dropped by the same amount.

Violation of the no-selection assumption has resulted in violation of conclusion 1 of the Hardy–Weinberg analysis. The population has evolved in response to selection.

We used strong selection to make a point in our numerical example. Rarely in nature are differences in survival rates large enough to cause such dramatic change in allele frequencies in a single generation. If selection continues for many generations, however, even small changes in allele frequency in each generation can add up to substantial changes over the long run. Figure 5.10 illustrates the cumulative change in allele frequencies that can be wrought by selection. The figure is based on a model population similar to the one we used in the preceding numerical example, except that the initial allele frequencies are 0.01 for B_1 and 0.99 for B_2. The yellow line shows the change in allele frequencies when the survival rates are 100% for B_1B_1, 90% for B_1B_2, and 80% for B_2B_2. The frequency of allele B_1 rises from 0.01 to 0.99 in less than 100 generations. Under weaker selection schemes, the frequency of B_1 rises more slowly, but still inexorably. (See Box 5.3 for a general algebraic treatment incorporating selection into the Hardy–Weinberg analysis.)

A numerical example shows that when individuals with some genotypes survive at higher rates than individuals with other genotypes, allele frequencies can change from one generation to the next. In other words, our model shows that natural selection causes evolution.

Empirical Research on Allele Frequency Change by Selection

Douglas Cavener and Michael Clegg (1981) documented a cumulative change in allele frequencies over many generations in a laboratory-based natural selection experiment on the fruit fly (*Drosophila melanogaster*). Fruit flies, like most other animals, make an enzyme that breaks down ethanol, the poisonous active ingredient in beer, wine, and rotting fruit. This enzyme is called alcohol dehydrogenase, or ADH. Cavener and Clegg worked with populations of flies that had two alleles at the ADH locus: Adh^F and Adh^S. (The F and S refer to whether the protein encoded by the allele moves quickly or slowly through an electrophoresis gel [see Box 4.1 in Chapter 4]).

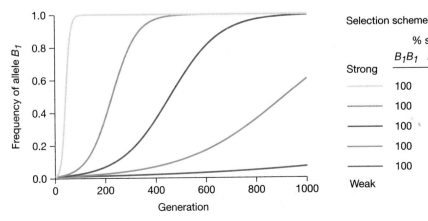

Selection scheme

	% surviving		
	B_1B_1	B_1B_2	B_2B_2
Strong			
	100	90.0	80.0
	100	98.0	96.0
	100	99.0	98.0
	100	99.5	99.0
	100	99.8	99.6
Weak			

Figure 5.10   Persistent selection can produce substantial changes in allele frequencies over time   Each curve shows the change in allele frequency over time under a particular selection intensity.

BOX 5.3 A general treatment of selection

Here we develop equations that predict allele frequencies in the next generation, given allele frequencies in this generation and the fitnesses of the different genotypes. We start with a population that has a gene pool in which allele A_1 is at frequency p and allele A_2 is at frequency q. We allow gametes to pair at random to make zygotes of genotypes A_1A_1, A_1A_2, and A_2A_2 at frequencies p^2, $2pq$, and q^2, respectively.

We incorporate selection by imagining that A_1A_1 zygotes survive to adulthood at rate w_{11}, A_1A_2 zygotes survive at rate w_{12}, and A_2A_2 zygotes survive at rate w_{22}. All individuals that survive produce the same number of offspring. Therefore, a genotype's survival rate is proportional to the genotype's lifetime reproductive success, or fitness. We thus refer to the survival rates as fitnesses. The average fitness for the whole population, $\overline{w}$, is given by the expression:

$$\overline{w} = p^2 w_{11} + 2pq w_{12} + q^2 w_{22}$$

[To see this, note that we can calculate the average of the numbers 1, 2, 2, and 3 as $\frac{(1 + 2 + 2 + 3)}{4}$ or as $(\frac{1}{4} \times 1) + (\frac{1}{2} \times 2) + (\frac{1}{4} \times 3)$. Our expression for the average fitness is of the second form: We multiply the fitness of each genotype by its frequency in the population and then sum the results.]

We now calculate the genotype frequencies among the surviving adults (right before their gametes go into the gene pool). The new frequencies of the genotypes are

A_1A_1	A_1A_2	A_2A_2
$\dfrac{p^2 w_{11}}{\overline{w}}$	$\dfrac{2pq w_{12}}{\overline{w}}$	$\dfrac{q^2 w_{22}}{\overline{w}}$

(We have to divide by the average fitness in each case to ensure that the new frequencies still sum to 1.)

Finally, we let the adults breed, and calculate the allele frequencies in the gene pool:

- For the A_1 allele: A_1A_1 individuals contribute $\frac{p^2 w_{11}}{\overline{w}}$ of the gametes, all of them A_1; A_1A_2 individuals contribute $\frac{2pq w_{12}}{\overline{w}}$ of the gametes, half of them A_1. So the new frequency of A_1 is

$$\frac{p^2 w_{11} + pq w_{12}}{\overline{w}}$$

- For the A_2 allele: A_1A_2 individuals contribute $\frac{2pq w_{12}}{\overline{w}}$ of the gametes, half of them A_2; A_2A_2 individuals contribute $\frac{q^2 w_{22}}{\overline{w}}$ of the gametes, all of them A_2. So the new frequency of A_2 is

$$\frac{pq w_{12} + q^2 w_{22}}{\overline{w}}$$

Readers should confirm that the new frequencies of A_1 and A_2 sum to 1.

It is instructive to calculate the change in the frequency of allele A_1 from one generation to the next. This value, Δp, is the new frequency of allele A_1 minus the old frequency of A_1:

$$\Delta p = \frac{p^2 w_{11} + pq w_{12}}{\overline{w}} - p$$

$$= \frac{p^2 w_{11} + pq w_{12}}{\overline{w}} - \frac{p\overline{w}}{\overline{w}}$$

$$= \frac{p^2 w_{11} + pq w_{12} - p\overline{w}}{\overline{w}}$$

$$= \frac{p}{\overline{w}}(p w_{11} + q w_{12} - \overline{w})$$

The final expression is a useful one, because it shows that the change in frequency of allele A_1 is proportional to $(p w_{11} + q w_{12} - \overline{w})$. The expression $(p w_{11} + q w_{12} - \overline{w})$ is equal to the average fitness of allele A_1 when paired at random with other alleles $(p w_{11} + q w_{12})$ minus the average fitness of the population $(\overline{w})$. In other words, if the average A_1-carrying individual has higher-than-average fitness, then allele A_1 will increase in frequency.

The change in the frequency of allele A_2 from one generation to the next is

$$\Delta q = \frac{pq w_{12} + q^2 w_{22}}{\overline{w}} - q$$

$$= \frac{q}{\overline{w}}(p w_{12} + q w_{22} - \overline{w})$$

The scientists maintained two experimental populations of flies on food spiked with ethanol, and two control populations of flies on normal, nonspiked food. The researchers picked the breeders for each generation at random. This is why we are calling the project a natural selection experiment: Cavener and Clegg set up different environments for their different populations, but the researchers did not themselves directly manipulate the survival or reproductive success of individual flies.

Every several generations, Cavener and Clegg took a random sample of flies from each population, determined their ADH genotypes, and calculated the allele frequencies. The results appear in Figure 5.11. The control populations showed no large or consistent long-term change in the frequency of the Adh^S allele. The experimental populations, in contrast, showed a rapid and largely consistent decline in the frequency of Adh^S (and, of course, a corresponding increase in the frequency of Adh^F). Hardy–Weinberg conclusion 1 appears to hold in the control populations, but is clearly not in force in the experimental populations.

Can we identify for certain which of the assumptions of the Hardy–Weinberg analysis is being violated? The only difference between the two kinds of populations is that the experimentals have ethanol in their food. This suggests that it is the assumption of no selection that is being violated in the experimental populations. Flies with the Adh^F allele appear to have higher lifetime reproductive success (higher fitness) than flies with the Adh^S allele when ethanol is present in the food. Cavener and Clegg note that this outcome is consistent with the fact that alcohol dehydrogenase extracted from Adh^F homozygotes breaks down ethanol at twice the rate of alcohol dehydrogenase extracted from Adh^S homozygotes. Whether flies with the Adh^F allele have higher fitness because they have higher rates of survival or because they produce more offspring is unclear.

Empirical research on fruit flies is consistent with our conclusion that natural selection can cause allele frequencies to change.

Adding Selection to the Hardy–Weinberg Analysis: The Calculation of Genotype Frequencies

The calculations and example we have just discussed show that selection can cause allele frequencies to change across generations. Selection invalidates conclusion 1 of the Hardy–Weinberg analysis. We now consider how selection affects conclusion 2 of the Hardy–Weinberg analysis. In a population under selection, can we still calculate the genotype frequencies by multiplying the allele frequencies?

We often cannot. As before, we use a population with two alleles at a locus affecting survival: B_1 and B_2. We assume that the initial frequency of each allele in

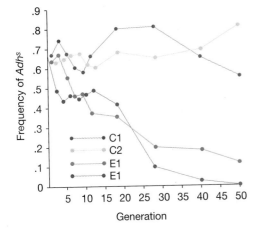

Figure 5.11 **Frequencies of the Adh^S allele in four populations of fruit flies over 50 generations** The red and yellow dots and lines represent control populations living on normal food; the blue and green dots and lines represent experimental populations living on food spiked with ethanol. From Cavener and Clegg (1981). Copyright © Evolution. Reprinted by permission.

the gene pool is 0.5 (Figure 5.12). After random mating, we get genotype frequencies for B_1B_1, B_1B_2, and B_2B_2, of 0.25, 0.5, and 0.25. The rest of our calculations will be simpler if we give the population of zygotes a finite size, so imagine that there are 1000 zygotes:

$$\begin{array}{ccc} \boldsymbol{B_1B_1} & \boldsymbol{B_1B_2} & \boldsymbol{B_2B_2} \\ 250 & 500 & 250 \end{array}$$

These zygotes are represented by a bar graph in the figure. We will follow the individuals that develop from these zygotes as they grow to adulthood. Those that survive will breed to produce the next generation's gene pool.

We incorporate selection by stipulating that the genotypes differ in their rates of survival. Fifty percent of the B_1B_1 individuals survive, all of the B_1B_2 individuals survive, and 50% of the B_2B_2 individuals survive. As shown in Figure 5.12, there are now 750 adults in the population:

$$\begin{array}{ccc} \boldsymbol{B_1B_1} & \boldsymbol{B_1B_2} & \boldsymbol{B_2B_2} \\ 125 & 500 & 125 \end{array}$$

The frequencies of the three genotypes among the adults are as follows:

$$\begin{array}{ccc} \boldsymbol{B_1B_1} & \boldsymbol{B_1B_2} & \boldsymbol{B_2B_2} \\ 125/750 & 500/750 & 125/750 \\ = 0.167 & = 0.667 & = 0.167 \end{array}$$

When these adults produce gametes, the frequencies of the two alleles in the new gene pool are

$$\begin{array}{cc} \boldsymbol{B_1} & \boldsymbol{B_2} \\ 0.167 + \left(\dfrac{1}{2}\right)0.667 & \left(\dfrac{1}{2}\right)0.667 + 0.167 \\ = 0.5 & = 0.5 \end{array}$$

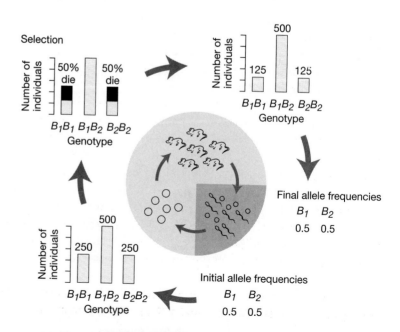

Figure 5.12   Selection can change genotype frequencies so that they cannot be calculated by multiplying the allele frequencies   When half of the homozygotes in this population die, the allele frequencies do not change. But among the survivors, there are more heterozygotes then predicted under Hardy–Weinberg equilibrium.

In spite of strong selection against homozygotes, the frequencies of the alleles have not changed; the population has not evolved.

Note, however, that violation of the no-selection assumption *has* resulted in violation of conclusion 2 of the Hardy–Weinberg analysis. We can no longer calculate the genotype frequencies among the adult survivors by multiplying the frequencies of the alleles. For example:

$$\text{Frequency of } B_1B_1 \qquad (\text{Frequency of } B_1)^2$$
$$0.167 \qquad \neq \qquad (0.5)^2 = 0.25$$

We used strong selection in our numerical example to make a point. In fact, selection is rarely strong enough to produce, in a single generation, such a large violation of Hardy–Weinberg conclusion 2. Even if it does, a single bout of random mating will immediately put the genotypes back into Hardy–Weinberg equilibrium. Nonetheless, researchers sometimes find violations of Hardy–Weinberg conclusion 2 that seem to be the result of selection.

Natural selection can also drive genotype frequencies away from the values predicted under the Hardy–Weinberg equilibrium principle.

Empirical Research on Selection and Genotype Frequencies

Our example comes from research on a serious human genetic disease known as Jaeken syndrome (also known as carbohydrate-deficient-glycoprotein syndrome type 1). Patients with Jaeken sydrome are severely developmentally disabled, with skeletal deformities and an abnormal distribution of subcutaneous fat (Matthijs et al. 1998). They have inadequate liver function, and 20% die before the age of five.

Jaeken syndrome is inherited as an autosomal recessive condition. Most cases are caused by loss-of-function mutations in a gene on chromosome 16. The gene, called *PMM2,* encodes an enzyme called phosphomannomutase (PMM). Biochemically, reduced PMM activity results in an insufficient ability to attach carbohydrates to proteins to make glycoproteins.

There are at least 24 different loss-of-function mutations in the *PMM2* gene that can cause Jaeken sydrome. Most are missense mutations; one is a single-base-pair deletion. Gert Matthijs and colleagues (1998), in research led by Jaak Jaeken, investigated whether some of these loss-of-function mutations are more serious than others. The researchers hypothesized that some mutations preserve less of PMM's catalytic activity than others, and are therefore especially severe.

The researchers performed a test of their hypothesis that was based on the Hardy–Weinberg equilibrium principle. The logic of the test runs as follows. Individuals with Jaeken syndrome are all homozygotes, in the sense that they all carry two mutant alleles. However, many carry two different loss-of-function mutations. We can think of affected individuals as being homozygous or heterozygous with respect to the specific disease alleles they carry. Within the affected individuals in a population, the different disease alleles should be in Hardy–Weinberg equilibrium with each other (see Box 5.4.). If a particular disease allele causes an especially severe loss of function, then individuals homozygous for that allele might have so little PMM activity that they would be unable to survive. Because selection would remove such homozygotes from the affected population, there will be fewer of them than we would predict by multiplying the frequencies of the different disease alleles.

The researchers determined the identity of the disease alleles present in 54 caucasian patients with Jaeken syndrome. The most common mutation they found was

BOX 5.4   Hardy–Weinberg equilibrium among different mutant alleles that cause a recessive genetic disease

Consider an autosomal recessive genetic disease. At the first level of analysis, there are two alleles, which we will call D and d. Individuals with genotype DD or Dd are phenotypically normal; dd individuals have the disease.

Let p represent the frequency of allele D, and let z represent the frequency of allele d, such that $p + z = 1$. In a population obeying the Hardy–Weinberg assumptions, the genotype frequencies are

DD	Dd	dd
p^2	$2pz$	z^2

Now, imagine that there are, in fact, two different disease alleles, d_1 and d_2. In other words, dd individuals can have genotype d_1d_1, d_1d_2, or d_2d_2. Let q represent the frequency of d_1, and let r represent the

frequency of allele d_2. Because d_1 and d_2 are the two possible versions of d, we know that

$$z = q + r$$

Thus, the frequency of affected individuals can be expressed as

$$\text{Frequency of } dd = z^2$$
$$= (q + r)^2$$
$$= q^2 + 2qr + r^2$$

The terms of this expression are the frequencies that we would predict from the Hardy–Weinberg equilibrium principle simply by multiplying the frequencies of d_1 and d_2. In other words, within the population of affected individuals, the different disease alleles are in Hardy–Weinberg equilibrium with each other.

an amino acid substitution called *R141H*. If we divide the disease alleles into those containing *R141H* and those containing other mutations, the allele frequencies in the population of 54 affected individuals are

Other	R141H
0.6	0.4

From these allele frequencies, we can calculate that if the population is in Hardy–Weinberg equilibrium, then the genotype frequencies will be

Other/Other	Other/R141H	R141H/R141H
0.36	0.48	0.16

The discovery that genotype frequencies in a population are not in Hardy–Weinberg equilibrium may be a clue that natural selection is at work.

In fact, the actual genotype frequencies among the affected indivdiuals are

Other/Other	Other/R141H	R141H/R141H
$\frac{11}{54} = 0.2$	$\frac{43}{54} = 0.8$	0

The allele and genotype frequencies among the affected individuals are in violation of conclusion 2 of the Hardy–Weinberg analysis. There is a striking deficit of homozygotes, most notably *R141H* homozygotes. The deficit of homozygotes is statistically significant (see Box 5.5.).

Jaeken and his team believe the most plausible interpretation for the absence of *R141H* homozygotes is that *R141H* is an especially severe loss-of-function mutation. Under this hypothesis, zygotes with genotype *R141H/R141H* are produced at the frequency predicted under the Hardy–Weinberg equilibrium principle, but the individuals that develop from these zygotes die before or shortly after birth. The deficit of *Other/Other* homozygotes may be due to additional severe loss-of-function mutations among the other disease alleles.

BOX 5.5 Statistical analysis of allele and genotype frequencies using the χ^2 (chi-square) test

Here we use the data from Matthijs and colleagues (1998) to illustrate one method for determining whether genotype frequencies deviate significantly from what they would be under Hardy–Weinberg equilibrium. The researchers surveyed a population of 54 individuals affected with Jaeken syndrome. The numbers of individuals with each genotype were as follows:

Other/Other	*Other/R141H*	*R141H/R141H*
11	43	0

From these numbers, we will calculate the allele frequencies of *Other* and *R141H,* and determine whether the genotype frequencies observed are those we would expect according to the Hardy–Weinberg equilibrium principle. There are five steps:

1. Calculate the allele frequencies. The sample of 54 individuals is also a sample of 108 alleles. All 22 of the alleles carried by the 11 *Other/Other* individuals are *Other,* as are 43 of the alleles carried by the 43 *Other/R141H* individuals. Thus, the frequency of *Other* alleles is

$$\frac{(22 + 43)}{108} = 0.6$$

and the frequency of allele *R141H* is

$$\frac{(43 + 0)}{108} = 0.4$$

2. Calculate the genotype frequencies expected under the Hardy–Weinberg principle, given the allele frequencies calculated in Step 1. According to the Hardy–Weinberg equilibrium principle, if the frequencies of two alleles are p and q, then the frequencies of the genotypes are p^2, $2pq$, and q^2. Thus, the expected frequencies of genotypes in a population of individuals with Jaeken syndrome are

Other/Other	*Other/R141H*	*R141H/R141H*
$(0.6)^2$	$2(0.6)(0.4)$	$(0.4)^2$
$= 0.36$	$= 0.48$	$= 0.16$

3. Calculate the expected number of individuals of each genotype under Hardy–Weinberg equilibrium. This is simply the expected frequency of each genotype multiplied by the number of individuals in the sample, 54. The expected values are

Other/Other	*Other/R141H*	*R141H/R141H*
$(0.36)(54)$	$(0.48)(54)$	$(0.16)(54)$
$= 19.44$	$= 25.92$	$= 8.64$

The numbers of individuals expected are different from the number of individuals actually observed (11, 43, and 0). The actual sample contains more heterozygotes and fewer homozygotes than expected. Is it plausible that this large a difference between expectation and reality could arise by chance? Or is the difference statistically significant? Our null hypothesis is that the difference is simply due to chance.

4. Calculate a test statistic. We will use a test statistic that was devised in 1900 by Karl Pearson. It is called the chi-square (χ^2). The chi-square is defined as

$$\chi^2 = \sum \frac{(\text{observed} - \text{expected})^2}{\text{expected}}$$

where the symbol Σ indicates a sum taken across all the classes considered. In our data there are three classes: the three genotypes. For our data set:

$$\chi^2 = \frac{(11 - 19.44)^2}{19.44} + \frac{(43 - 25.92)^2}{25.92}$$

$$+ \frac{(0 - 8.64)^2}{8.64} = 23.56$$

5. Determine whether the value of the test statistic is significant. The chi-square is defined in such a way that the chi-square gets larger as the difference between the observed and expected values gets larger. How likely is it that we could get a chi-square as large as 23.56 by chance? Most statistical textbooks have a table that provides the answer. In Zar (1996) this table is called "Critical values of the chi-square distribution."

To use this table, we need to calculate a number called the degrees of freedom for the test statistic. The number of degrees of freedom for the chi-square is equal to the number of classes minus the number of independent values we calculated from the data for use in determining the expected values. For our chi-square there are three classes: the three genotypes. We calculated two values from the data for use in determining the expected values:

BOX 5.5 Continued

the total number of individuals, and the frequency of allele *R141H*. (We also calculated the frequency of *Other* alleles, but it is not independent of the frequency of allele *R141H*, because the frequency of *Other* is one minus the frequency of *R141H*). Thus the number of degrees of freedom is 1. (Another formula for calculating the degrees of freedom in chi-square tests for Hardy–Weinberg equilibrium is

$$df = k - 1 - m$$

where *k* is the number of classes and *m* is the number of independent allele frequencies estimated from the data).

According to the table in the statistics book, the critical value of chi-square for one degree of free-

dom and $P = 0.05$ is 3.841. This means that there is a 5% chance under the null hypothesis of getting $\chi^2 \geq 3.841$. The probability under the null hypothesis of getting $\chi^2 \geq 23.56$ is therefore (considerably) less than 5%. We reject the null hypothesis, and assert that our value of chi-square is statistically significant at $P < 0.05$. (In fact, in this case $P < 0.00001$.)

The chi-square test tells us that the alleles of the *PMM2* locus in the population of individuals with Jaeken syndrome are not in Hardy–Weinberg equilibrium. This indicates that one or more of the assumptions of the Hardy–Weinberg analysis has been violated. By itself, however, it does not tell us which assumptions are being violated, or how.

This study of Jaeken syndrome is a case in which a population-genetic analysis led to a potentially important medical discovery. The analysis suggests that some PMM activity is necessary for life. Furthermore, it indicates that parents who are both carriers of *R141H* can expect a different distribution of phenotypes among their children than parents who are carriers of two different disease alleles.

Changes in the Frequency of the *CCR5-Δ32* Allele Revisited

Our exploration of natural selection has given us tools we can use to predict the future of human populations.

We are now in a position to give a more satisfying answer to the medical question we raised at the beginning of the chapter: Will the AIDS epidemic cause the frequency of the *CCR5-Δ32* allele to increase in human populations? The AIDS epidemic could, in principle, cause the frequency of the allele to increase rapidly, but at present it appears that it will probably not do so in any real population. This conclusion is based on the three model populations depicted in Figure 5.13 (See Box 5.6 for the algebra.) Each model is based on different assumptions about the initial frequency of the *CCR5-Δ32* allele and the prevalence of HIV infection. Each graph shows the predicted change in the frequency of the *Δ32* allele over 40 generations, or approximately 1000 years of evolution.

The model population depicted in Figure 5.13a provides a scenario in which the frequency of the *Δ32* allele could increase rapidly. In this scenario, the initial frequency of the *CCR5-Δ32* allele is 20%. One quarter of the individuals with genotype +/+ or +/*Δ32* contract AIDS and die without reproducing, whereas all of the *Δ32/Δ32* individuals survive. The 20% initial frequency of *Δ32* is approximately equal to the highest frequency reported for any population, a sample of Ashkenazi Jews studied by Martinson et al. (1997). The mortality rates approximate the situation in Botswana, Namibia, Swaziland, and Zimbabwe, where up to 25% of individuals between the ages of 15 and 49 are infected with HIV (UN-AIDS 1998). In this model population, the frequency of the *Δ32* allele increases by as much as a few percentage points each generation. By the end of 40 generations, the allele is at a frequency of virtually 100%. Thus, in a human population that combined the highest reported frequency of the *Δ32* allele with the highest reported rates of infection, the AIDS epidemic could cause the frequency of the allele to increase rapidly.

At present, however, no known population combines a high frequency of the *Δ32* allele with a high rate of HIV infection. In northern Europe, many populations have *Δ32* frequencies between 0.1 and 0.2 (Martinson et al. 1997; Stephens et al. 1998), but HIV infection rates are well under 1% (UNAIDS 1998). A model population reflecting these conditions is depicted in Figure 5.13b. The initial frequency of the *Δ32* allele is 0.2, and 0.5% of the *+/+* and *+/Δ32* individuals contract AIDS and die without reproducing. The frequency of the *Δ32* allele hardly changes at all. Selection is too weak to cause appreciable evolution in such a short time.

In parts of sub-Saharan Africa, as many as a quarter of all individuals of reproductive age are infected with HIV. However, the *Δ32* allele is virtually absent (Martinson et al. 1997). A model population reflecting this situation is depicted in Figure 5.13c. The initial frequency of the *Δ32* allele is 0.01, and 25% of the *+/+* and *+/Δ32* individuals contract AIDS and die without reproducing. Again, the frequency of the *Δ32* allele hardly changes at all. When the *Δ32* allele is at low frequency, most copies are in heterozygotes. Because heterozygotes are susceptible to infection, these copies are hidden from selection.

The analysis we have just described is based on a number of simplifying assumptions. For example, we have assumed that all HIV-infected individuals die without reproducing, and that the death rate is the same in heterozygotes as in *+/+* homozygotes. In reality, although heterozygotes are susceptible to HIV infection, they appear to progress more slowly to AIDS (Dean et al. 1996). As a result, the fitness of heterozygotes may actually be higher than that of *+/+* homozygotes. We challenge our readers to explore the evolution of human populations under a variety of selection schemes, to see how strongly our simplifying assumptions affect the predicted course of evolution.

5.3   Patterns of Selection

At the start of the chapter we asked whether a compulsory sterilization law could achieve its eugenic goal of reducing the incidence of a genetic disease. Before attempting to provide an answer, it will be helpful to consider how the details of Mendelian genetics at a particular locus might affect the course of evolution. For example, does the rate of evolution in response to selection against a particular allele depend on whether the allele is dominant or recessive? Does the rate of evolution depend on whether the allele is common or rare?

Selection on Recessive and Dominant Alleles

Data collected by Peter Dawson (1970) illustrate how recessiveness and dominance affect the course of evolution. Dawson had been studying a laboratory colony of flour beetles (*Tribolium castaneum*), and had identified a gene we will call the l locus. This locus has two alleles: *+* and *l*. Individuals with genotype *+/+* or *+/l* are phenotypically normal, whereas individuals with genotype *l/l* do not survive. In other words, *l* is a recessive lethal allele.

Dawson collected heterozygotes from his flour beetle colony and used them to establish two new experimental populations. Because all the founders were heterozygotes,

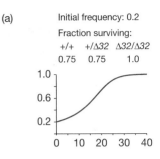

(a) Initial frequency: 0.2
Fraction surviving:
+/+   +/Δ32   Δ32/Δ32
0.75   0.75   1.0

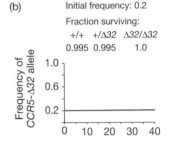

(b) Initial frequency: 0.2
Fraction surviving:
+/+   +/Δ32   Δ32/Δ32
0.995 0.995   1.0

Frequency of CCR5-Δ32 allele

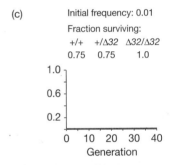

(c) Initial frequency: 0.01
Fraction surviving:
+/+   +/Δ32   Δ32/Δ32
0.75   0.75   1.0

Generation

Figure 5.13   Predicted change in allele frequencies at the CCR5 locus due to the AIDS epidemic under three different scenarios   (a) When the initial frequency of the *CCR5-Δ32* allele is high and a large fraction of the population becomes infected with HIV, the allele frequencies can change rapidly. However, no real population combines these characteristics. (b) In European populations allele frequencies are high, but only a small fraction of individuals become infected. (c) In parts of Africa there are high infection rates, but allele frequencies are low.

BOX 5.6 Predicting the frequency of the *CCR5-Δ32* allele in future generations

Let q_g be the frequency of the *CCR5-Δ32* allele in the present generation. Based on Box 5.3, we can write an equation predicting the frequency of the allele in the next generation, given estimates of the survival rates (fitnesses) of individuals with each genotype. The equation is

$$q_{g+1} = \frac{(1 - q_g)q_g w_{+\Delta} + q_g^2 w_{\Delta\Delta}}{(1 - q_g)^2 w_{++} + 2(1 - q_g)q_g w_{+\Delta} + q_g^2 w_{\Delta\Delta}}$$

where q_{g+1} is the frequency of the *Δ32* allele in the next generation, w_{++} is the fitness of individuals

homozygous for the normal allele, $w_{+\Delta}$ is the fitness of heterozygotes, and $w_{\Delta\Delta}$ is the fitness of individuals homozygous for the *CCR5-Δ32* allele.

After choosing a starting value for the frequency of the *Δ32* allele, we plug it and the estimated fitnesses into the equation to generate the frequency of the *Δ32* allele after one generation. We then plug this resulting value into the equation to get the frequency of the allele after two generations, and so on.

the initial frequency of the two alleles was 0.5 in both populations. Because *l/l* individuals have zero fitness, Dawson expected his populations to evolve toward ever lower frequencies of the *l* allele and ever higher frequencies of the *+* allele. Dawson used the equations derived in Box 5.3 and the method described in Box 5.6 to make a quantitative prediction of the course of evolution. He then let his two populations evolve for a dozen generations, each generation measuring the frequencies of the two alleles.

Empirical research on flour beetles shows that predictions made with population genetic models are accurate, at least under laboratory conditions.

The results appear in Figure 5.14. Dawson's data match his theoretical predictions closely. At first, the frequency of the recessive lethal allele declined rapidly (Figure 5.14a). By the second generation it had dropped from 0.5 to about 0.25. As evolu-

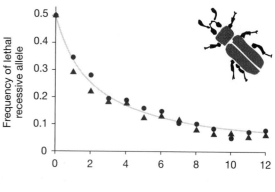

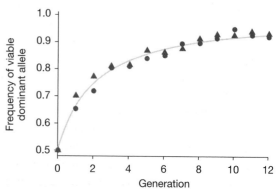

Figure 5.14 Evolution in laboratory populations of flour beetles (a) The decline in frequency of a lethal recessive allele (red symbols) matches the theoretical prediction (gray curve) almost exactly. As the allele becomes rare, the rate of evolution slows dramatically. (b) This graph plots the increase in frequency of the corresponding dominant allele. Redrawn from Dawson (1970).

tion progressed, however, further reductions in the frequency of the lethal allele came more slowly. Between generations 10 and 12 the frequency did not drop at all. Dawson's experiment demonstrates that the theory of population genetics, in spite of its simplifying assumptions, allows us to accurately predict the course of evolution—at least under controlled conditions in the lab.

The experiment also shows that dominance and allele frequency interact to determine the rate of evolution. When a recessive allele is common (and a dominant allele is rare), evolution by natural selection is rapid. In contrast, when a recessive allele is rare, and a dominant allele is common, evolution by natural selection is slow.

The Hardy–Weinberg equilibrium principle explains why. First imagine a recessive allele that is common: Its frequency is, say, 0.95. The dominant allele thus has a frequency of 0.05. By multiplying the allele frequencies, we can calculate the genotype frequencies:

Natural selection is most potent as a force of evolution when it is acting on common recessive alleles (and rare dominant alleles).

$$\begin{array}{ccc} \textbf{\textit{AA}} & \textbf{\textit{Aa}} & \textbf{\textit{aa}} \\ (0.05)^2 & 2(0.05)(0.95) & (0.95)^2 \\ = 0.0025 & = 0.095 & = 0.9025 \end{array}$$

Roughly 10% of the individuals in the population have the dominant phenotype, while 90% have the recessive phenotype. Both phenotypes are reasonably well represented, and if they differ in fitness then the allele frequencies in the next generation may be substantially different. Now imagine a recessive allele that is rare: Its frequency is 0.05. The dominant allele thus has a frequency of 0.95. The genotype frequencies are

$$\begin{array}{ccc} \textbf{\textit{AA}} & \textbf{\textit{Aa}} & \textbf{\textit{aa}} \\ (0.95)^2 & 2(0.95)(0.05) & (0.05)^2 \\ = 0.9025 & = 0.095 & = 0.0025 \end{array}$$

Approximately 100% of the population has the dominant phenotype, while approximately 0% has the recessive phenotype. Even if the phenotypes differ greatly in fitness, there are so few of the minority phenotype that there will be little change in allele frequencies in the next generation. In a random mating population, most copies of a rare recessive allele are phenotypically hidden inside heterozygous individuals. For an algebraic treatment of selection on recessive and dominant alleles see Box 5.7.

Selection on Heterozygotes and Homozygotes

When one allele is recessive and the other is dominant, the fitness of heterozygotes is equal to that of one kind of homozygote. Other scenarios are possible, of course. Often the fitness of heterozygotes is between that of the two homozygotes. This may change the rate of evolution, but it does not alter the ultimate outcome. Eventually, one allele becomes fixed in the population and the other is lost. Figure 5.10 shows several examples.

It is also possible for the fitness of heterozygotes to be superior or inferior to that of either homozygote. Heterozygote superiority and inferiority produce dramatically different outcomes.

Our first example comes from research on laboratory populations of fruit flies (*Drosophila melanogaster*) by Terumi Mukai and Allan Burdick (1959). Like Dawson, Mukai and Burdick studied evolution at a single locus with two alleles. Homozygotes for one allele were viable, whereas homozygotes for the other allele were

BOX 5.7   An algebraic treatment of selection on recessive and dominant alleles

Here we develop equations that illuminate the differences between selection on recessive versus dominant alleles. Imagine a single locus with two alleles. Let p be the frequency of the dominant allele A, and let q be the frequency of the recessive allele a.

Selection on the recessive allele

Let the fitnesses of the genotypes be given by:

w_{AA}	w_{Aa}	w_{aa}
1	1	$1 + s$

where s, called the **selection coefficient**, gives the strength of selection on homozygous recessives relative to the other genotypes. Positive values of s represent selection in favor of the recessive allele; negative values of s represent selection against the recessive allele.

Based on Box 5.3, the following equation gives the frequency of allele a in the next generation, q', given the frequency of a in this generation and the fitnesses of the three genotypes:

$$q' = \frac{pqw_{Aa} + q^2 w_{aa}}{\bar{w}} = \frac{pqw_{Aa} + q^2 w_{aa}}{p^2 w_{AA} + 2pqw_{Aa} + q^2 w_{aa}}$$

Substituting the fitness values from the table above, and $(1 - q)$ for p, and then simplifying gives

$$q' = \frac{q(1 + sq)}{1 + sq^2}$$

If a is a lethal recessive, then s is equal to -1. Substituting this value into the preceding equation gives

$$q' = \frac{q(1 - q)}{1 - q^2} = \frac{q(1 - q)}{(1 - q)(1 + q)} = \frac{q}{(1 + q)}$$

A little experimentation shows that once a recessive lethal allele becomes rare, further declines in frequency are slow. For example, if the frequency of allele a in this generation is 0.01, then in the next generation its frequency will be approximately 0.0099.

Selection on the dominant allele

Let the fitnesses of the genotypes be given by:

w_{AA}	w_{Aa}	w_{aa}
$1 + s$	$1 + s$	1

where s, the selection coefficient, gives the strength of selection on genotypes containing the dominant allele relative to homozygous recessives. Positive values of s represent selection in favor of the dominant allele; negative values of s represent selection against the dominant allele.

Based on Box 5.3, we can write an equation that predicts the frequency of allele A in the next generation, p', given the frequency of A in this generation and the fitnesses of the three genotypes:

$$p' = \frac{p^2 w_{AA} + pqw_{Aa}}{\bar{w}} = \frac{p^2 w_{AA} + pqw_{Aa}}{p^2 w_{AA} + 2pqw_{Aa} + q^2 w_{aa}}$$

Substituting the fitnesses from the table, and $(1 - p)$ for q, and then simplifying gives

$$p' = \frac{p(1 + s)}{1 + 2sp - sp^2}$$

If A is a lethal dominant, s is equal to -1. Substituting this value into the foregoing equation shows that a lethal dominant is eliminated from a population in a single generation.

Selection on recessive alleles versus selection on dominant alleles

Selection on recessive alleles and selection on dominant alleles are opposite sides of the same coin. Selection against a recessive allele is selection in favor of the dominant allele and vice versa.

Figure 5.15a (left) shows 100 generations of evolution in a model population under selection against a recessive allele and in favor of the dominant allele. At first, the frequencies of the alleles change rapidly. As the recessive allele becomes rare, however, the rate of evolution slows dramatically. When the recessive allele is rare, most copies in the population are in heterozygous individuals, where they are effectively hidden from selection.

The figure also shows (right) the mean fitness of the population (see Box 5.3) as a function of the frequency of the dominant allele. As the dominant allele goes from rare to common, the mean fitness of the population rises. Mean fitness is maximized when the favored allele reaches a frequency of 100%. Graphs of mean fitness as a function of allele frequency are often referred to as adaptive landscapes.

BOX 5.7   Continued

Figure 5.15b (left) shows 100 generations of evolution in a model population under selection in favor a recessive allele and against the dominant allele. At first, the frequencies of the alleles change slowly. The recessive allele is rare, most copies present are in heterozygotes, and selection cannot see it. However, as the recessive allele becomes common enough that a substantial fraction of homozygotes appear, the rate of evolution increases dramatically. Once the pace of

evolution accelerates, the favorable recessive allele quickly achieves a frequency of 100%. That is, the recessive allele becomes fixed in the population.

The figure also shows (right) the mean fitness of the population (see Box 5.3) as a function of the frequency of the recessive allele. As the recessive allele goes from rare to common, the mean fitness of the population rises. Mean fitness is maximized when the favored allele reaches a frequency of 100%.

(a) Selection against a recessive allele and for a dominant allele

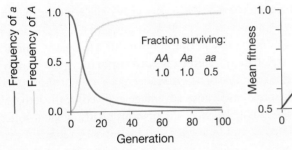
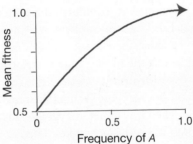

(b) Selection for a recessive allele and against a dominant allele

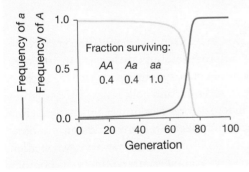
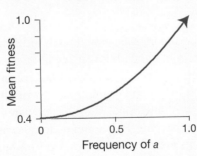

Figure 5.15   Evolution in model populations under selection on recessive and dominant alleles Graphs on the left show changes in allele frequencies over time. Graphs on the right show adaptive landscapes: changes in population mean fitness as a function of allele frequencies.

not. The researchers used heterozygotes as founders to establish two experimental populations with initial allele frequencies of 0.5. They allowed the populations to evolve for 15 generations, each generation measuring the frequency of the viable allele.

Mukai and Burdick's results appear in Figure 5.16, represented by the red symbols. As expected, the frequency of the viable allele increased rapidly over the first few generations. However, the rate of evolution slowed long before the viable allele approached a frequency of 1.0. Instead, the viable allele seemed to reach an equilibrium, or unchanging state, at a frequency of about 0.79.

To investigate further, Mukai and Burdick established two more experimental populations, this time with the initial frequency of the viable allele at 0.975. Evolution in these populations is represented by the blue symbols in Figure 5.16. Instead

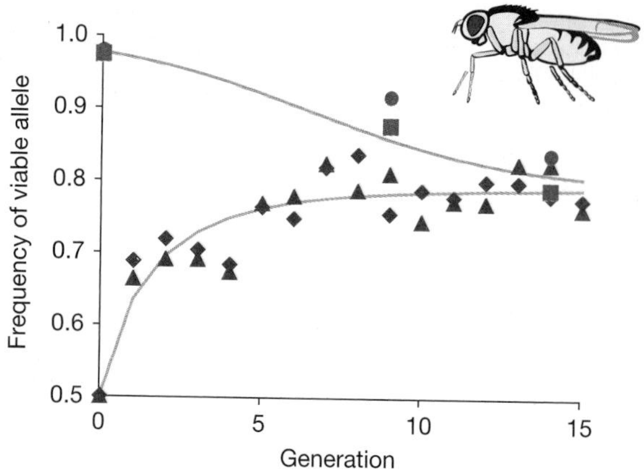

Figure 5.16 Evolution in four laboratory populations of fruit flies In homozygous state, one allele is viable and the other is lethal. Nonetheless, all four populations evolved toward an equilibrium in which both alleles are maintained. The likely explanation is that heterozygotes enjoy superior fitness to either homozygote. Drawn from data presented in Mukai and Burdick (1958).

of rising toward 1.0, the frequency of the viable allele dropped, again reaching an equilibrium near 0.79.

Note that an equilibrium frequency of 0.79 for the viable allele means that the lethal allele has an equilbrium frequency of 0.21. How could natural selection maintain a lethal allele at such a high frequency in this population? Mukai and Burdick argue that the most plausible explanation is **heterozygote superiority**, also known as **overdominance**. Under this hypothesis, heterozygotes have higher fitness than either homozygote. At equilibrium, the selective advantage enjoyed by the lethal allele when it is in heterozygotes exactly balances the obvious disadvantage it suffers when it is in homozygotes. The red and blue curves in Figure 5.16 represent evolution in a model population in which the fitnesses of the three genotypes are as follows (V represents the viable allele; L represents the lethal allele):

VV	VL	LL
0.735	1.0	0

Research on fruit flies shows that natural selection can act to maintain two alleles at a stable equilibrium. One way this can happen is when heterozygotes have superior fitness.

The theoretical curves match the data closely. By keeping a population at an equibrium in which both alleles are present, heterozygote superiority can maintain genetic diversity. For an algebraic treatment of heterozygote superiority, see Box 5.8.

Our second example, from work by G. G. Foster and colleagues (1972), demonstrates how populations evolve when heterozygotes have lower fitness than either homozygote. Foster and colleagues used fruit flies with compound chromosomes. Compound chromosomes are homologous chromosomes that have swapped entire arms, so that one homolog has two copies of one arm, and the other homolog has two copies of the other arm (Figure 5.17a,b). During meiosis, compound chromosomes may or may not segregate. As a result, four kinds of gametes are produced in equal numbers: gametes with both homologous chromosomes, gametes with just one member of the pair, gametes with the other member of the pair, and gametes with neither member of the pair (Figure 5.17c). When two flies with compound chromosomes mate with each other, one quarter of their zygotes have every chromosome arm in the correct dose and are viable. The other three quarters have too many or too few of copies of one or both chromosome arms, and are inviable (Figure 5.17d). When a fly with compound chromosomes mates with a fly with normal chromosomes, none of the zygotes they make are viable (Figure 5.17e).

It is also possible for heterozygotes to have inferior fitness.

Foster and colleagues established laboratory populations in which some of the founders had compound second chromosomes [*C(2)*] and others had normal second chromosomes [*N(2)*]. For purposes of analysis, we can treat each chromo-

(a) A normal pair of homologous chromosomes (each has one blue arm and one green arm).

(b) A pair of compound chromosomes (one has two blue arms, the other has two green arms).

(c) Gametes made by an individual with compound chromosomes may contain both chromosomes, one, or neither.

(d) When individuals with compound chromosomes mate, one quarter of their zygotes are viable.

(e) When an individual with compound chromosomes mates with an individual with normal chromosomes, none of their zygotes are viable.

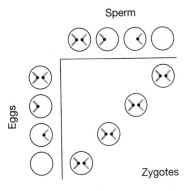

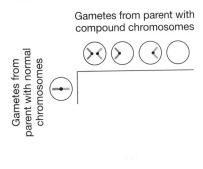

(f) Evolution in 13 populations of *Drosophila melanogaster* containing a mixture of compound second chromosomes [*C(2)*] and normal second chromosomes [*N(2)*]. The initial frequency of *C(2)* ranged from 0.71 to 0.96.

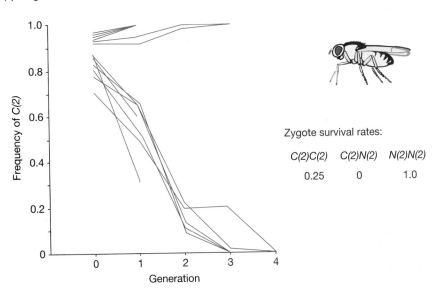

Zygote survival rates:

C(2)C(2)	C(2)N(2)	N(2)N(2)
0.25	0	1.0

Figure 5.17 **An experiment designed to show how populations evolve when heterozgyotes have lower fitness than either homozygote** The experimental design makes clever use of compound chromosomes. Redrawn with permission from Foster et al. (1972). Copyright © 1972, American Association for the Advancement of Science.

some as though it were a single allele. Thus, the founders consisted of *C(2)C(2)* homozygotes and *N(2)N(2)* homozygotes. Based on the zygote viablities we just described, the fitnesses of the genotypes in the mixed population are

C(2)C(2)	*C(2)N(2)*	*N(2)N(2)*
0.25	0	1.0

In other words, the genotypes exhibit strong **underdominance**.

BOX 5.8   Stable equilibria with heterozygote superiority and unstable equilibria with heterozygote inferiority

Here we develop algebraic and graphical methods for analyzing evolution at loci with overdominance and underdominance. Imagine a population in which allele A_1 is at frequency p and allele A_2 is at frequency q. In Box 5.3, we developed an equation describing the change in p from one generation to the next under selection:

$$\Delta p = \frac{p}{\overline{w}} (pw_{11} + qw_{12} - \overline{w})$$

$$= \frac{p}{\overline{w}} (pw_{11} + qw_{12} - p^2w_{11} - 2pqw_{12} - q^2w_{22})$$

Substituting $(1 - q)$ for p in the first and third terms in the expression in parentheses gives

$$\Delta p = \frac{p}{\overline{w}} ((1 - q)w_{11} + qw_{12}$$
$$- (1 - q)^2w_{11} - 2pqw_{12} - q^2w_{22})$$

which, after simplifying and factoring out q, becomes

$$\Delta p = \frac{pq}{\overline{w}} (w_{12} + w_{11} - qw_{11} - 2pw_{12} - qw_{22})$$

Now, by definition, the frequency of allele A_1 is at equilibrium when $\Delta p = 0$. The equation above shows that $\Delta p = 0$ when $p = 0$ or $q = 0$. These two equilibria are unsurprising. They occur when one allele or the other is absent from the population. The equation also gives a third condition for equilibrium, which is

$$w_{12} + w_{11} - qw_{11} - 2pw_{12} - qw_{22} = 0$$

Substituting $(1 - p)$ for q and solving for p gives

$$\hat{p} = \frac{w_{22} - w_{12}}{w_{11} - 2w_{12} + w_{22}}$$

where $\hat{p}$ is the frequency of allele A_1 at equilibrium. Finally, let the genotype fitnesses be as follows:

A_1A_1	A_1A_2	A_2A_2
$1 + s$	1	$1 + t$

Positive values of the selection coefficients s and t represent underdominance; negative values represent overdominance. Substituting the fitnesses into the previous equation and simplifying gives

$$\hat{p} = \frac{t}{s + t}$$

For example, when $s = -0.4$ and $t = -0.6$, heterozygotes have superior fitness, and the equilibrium frequency for allele A_1 is 0.6. When $s = 0.4$ and $t = 0.6$, heterozygotes have inferior fitness, and the equilibrium frequency for allele A_1 is also 0.6.

Another useful method for analyzing equilibria is to plot Δp as a function of p. Figure 5.18a shows such a plot for the two numerical examples we just calculated. Both curves show that $\Delta p = 0$ when $p = 0, p = 1$, or $p = 0.6$.

The curves in Figure 5.18a also allow us to determine whether an equilibrium is stable or unstable. Look at the red curve; it describes a locus with heterozygote superiority. Notice that when p is greater than 0.6, Δp is negative. This means that when the frequency of allele A_1 exceeds its equilibrium value, the population will move back towards equilibrium in the next generation. Likewise, when p is less than 0.6, Δp is positive. When the frequency of allele A_1 is below its equilibrium value, the population will move back towards equilibrium in the next generation. The "internal" equilibrium for a locus with heterozyote superiority is stable.

Figure 5.18b shows an adaptive landscape for a locus with heterozygote superiority. The graph plots population mean fitness as a function of the frequency of allele A_1. Mean fitness is low when A_1 is absent, and relatively low when A_1 is fixed. As the allele frequency moves from either direction towards its stable equilibrium, the population mean fitness rises to a maximum.

Now, look at the blue curve in Figure 5.18a. It describes a locus with heterozygote inferiority. If p rises even slightly above 0.6, p will continue to rise toward 1.0 in subsequent generations; if p falls even slightly below 0.6, p will continue to fall toward 0 in subsequent generations. The internal equilibrium for a locus with heterozygote inferiority is unstable.

Figure 5.18c shows an adaptive landscape for a locus with heterozygote inferiority. Population mean fitness is lowest when the frequency of allele A_1 is at its unstable internal equilibrium. As the allele frequency moves away from this equilibrium in either direction mean fitness rises.

BOX 5.8   Continued

A comparison of the adaptive landscape in Figure 5.18c with those in Figure 5.18b and Figure 5.15 offers a valuable insight. As a population evolves in response to selection, the mean fitness of the individuals in the population tends to rise. Selection does not, however, always maximize mean fitness in a global sense. Depending on the intial allele frequencies, the population depicted in Figure 5.18c may evolve toward either fixation or loss of A_1. If the allele becomes fixed, the population will be at a stable equilibrium, but the population's mean fitness will be substantially lower than it would be if the allele were lost.

(a) Δp as a function of p

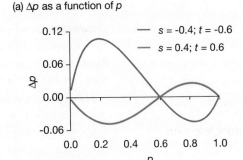

(b) Mean fitness as a function of p for overdominance

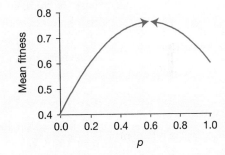

(c) Mean fitness as a function of p for underdominance

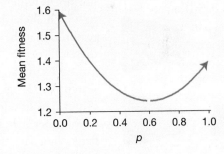

Figure 5.18   A graphical analysis of stable and unstable equilibria at loci with overdominance and underdominance   a) A plot of Δp as a function of p. (b) and (c) Adaptive landscapes.

The algebraic analysis described in Box 5.8 predicts that a mixed population will be in genetic equilibrium, with both alleles present, when the frequency of *C(2)* is exactly 0.8. This equilibrium is unstable, however. If the frequency of *C(2)* ever gets above 0.8, then it should quickly rise to 1.0. Likewise, if the frequency of *C(2)* ever dips below 0.8, it should quickly fall to zero.

Intuitively, the reason for this prediction is as follows. Heterozygotes are inviable, so the adults in the population are all homozygotes. Imagine first that *C(2)C(2)* individuals are common and *N(2)N(2)* individuals are rare. If the flies mate at random, then almost all matings will involve *C(2)C(2)* flies mating with each other, or *C(2)C(2)* flies mating with *N(2)N(2)* flies. Only very rarely will *N(2)N(2)* flies mate with their own kind. Consequently, most *N(2)N(2)* flies will have zero reproductive success, and the frequency of *C(2)* will climb to 1.0. Now imagine that there are enough *N(2)N(2)* flies present that appreciable numbers of them *do* mate with each other. These matings will produce four times as many offspring as matings between *C(2)C(2)* flies. Consequently, the frequency of *N(2)* will climb to 1.0 and the frequency of *C(2)* will fall to zero.

When heterozygotes have inferior fitness, one allele tends to go to fixation while the other allele is lost. However, different populations may lose different alleles.

Foster and colleagues set up 13 mixed populations, with *C(2)* frequencies ranging from 0.71 to 0.96, then monitored their evolution for up to four generations. The results appear in Figure 5.17f. Qualitatively, the outcome matches the theoretical prediction nicely. In populations with higher initial *C(2)* frequencies, *C(2)* quickly rose to fixation, while in populations with lower initial *C(2)* frequencies, *C(2)* was quickly lost. The exact location of the unstable equilibrium turned out to be approximately 0.9 instead of 0.8. Foster and colleagues note that their *C(2)C(2)* flies carried recessive genetic markers that the biologists had bred into them to allow for easy identification. They suggest that these markers reduced the relative fitness of the *C(2)C(2)* flies below the value of 0.25 inferred solely on the basis of their compound chromosomes. Foster et al.'s experiment demonstrates that heterozygote inferiority leads to a loss of genetic diversity within populations. By driving different alleles to fixation in different populations, however, heterozygote inferiority may help maintain genetic diversity among populations.

Frequency-Dependent Selection

We have so far looked at examples in which the pattern of selection is constant over time. When selection consistently favors a particular allele, the population evolves inexorably toward fixation of that allele and loss of the others. When selection consistently favors heterozygotes, the population evolves to a stable equilibrium at which both alleles are present. The last scenario we will examine is one in which allele frequencies in a population remain near an equilibrium, but the reason is that the direction of selection fluctuates. First, selection favors one allele, then it favors the other. This scenario is called **frequency-dependent selection**.

Our example of frequency-dependent selection comes from Michio Hori's research (1993) on the scale-eating fish, *Perissodus microlepis,* in Africa's Lake Tanganyika. As its name suggests, the scale-eating fish makes its living by biting scales off of other fish. The scale eater attacks from behind, grabs scales off the victim's flank, then darts away. Stranger still, within the species *P. microlepis,* there are right-handed (dextral) fish, whose mouths are twisted to the right, and left-handed (sinistral) fish, whose mouths are twisted to the left (Figure 5.19). Hori showed that to a first approximation, handedness is determined by a single locus with two alleles. Right-handedness is dominant over left-handedness.

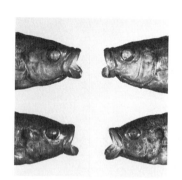

Figure 5.19 **Scale-eating fish** *(Perissodus microlepis)* **from Lake Tanganyika** (top) A right-handed (dextral) fish, shown from both sides. The mouth of this fish twists to the fish's right. (bottom) A left-handed (sinistral) fish, shown from both sides. The mouth of this fish twists to the fish's left. These two individuals belong to the same species and are members of the same population. (Dr. Michio Hori, Kyoto University, Kyoto, Japan)

Hori observed attacks on prey fish used as lures, and in addition examined scales recovered from the stomachs of scale-eating fish. These observations show that right-handed fish always attack their victim's left flank, and left-handed fish always attack their victim's right flank. (Readers can visualize the reason for this by first twisting their lips to the right or to the left, then imagining trying to bite scales off the flank of a fish.) The prey species are wary and alert, and scale eaters are successful in only about 20% of their attacks.

Hori reasoned that if right-handed scale eaters were more abundant than left-handers, then prey species would be more vigilant for attacks from the left. This would give left-handed scale eaters, who attack from the right, an advantage in their efforts to catch their prey unawares. Left-handed scale eaters would get more food than right-handers, have more offspring, and pass on more of their left-handed genes. This would increase the frequency of left-handed scale eaters in the population.

After left-handed scale eaters had become more abundant than right-handers, the prey fish would start to be more vigilant for attacks from the right. This would give right-handed scale eaters, who attack from the left, an advantage. The right-handers would get more food and have more offspring, and the frequency of right-handers in the population would increase.

The result is that left- and right-handed fish should be just about equally abundant in the population at any given time. The dominant right-handed allele should be held at a frequency of just under 0.3, and the recessive left-handed allele at a frequency of just over 0.7; under the Hardy–Weinberg equilibrium principle, these allele frequencies give phenotype frequencies of 0.5 and 0.5. This phenomenon, in which the rare phenotype is favored by natural selection, is an example of frequency-dependent selection.

Selection can also maintain two alleles in a population if each allele is advantageous when it is rare.

Hori's fish story is an elegant hypothesis, but is it true? To find out, Hori used a gill net to catch a sample of scale-eating fish in Lake Tanganyika every year or two for 11 years. The frequencies of the two phenotypes indeed appear to oscillate around 0.5 for each (Figure 5.20). In some years, slightly more than half of the fish were left-handed. Invariably, a year or two later, the pendulum had swung back, and slightly more than half of the fish were right-handed.

Is it possible that the frequencies of the two forms were just drifting at random rather than being held near 0.5 by selection? In three different years, Hori examined adult fish that were known to be breeding because they were caught in the act of brooding their young by scuba-diving scientists. The frequencies of handedness in these samples oscillated too, but the most abundant handedness among the breeders was always the opposite of the most abundant handedness in the population as a whole. (The breeders are indicated by the squares in Figure 5.20.) In other words, at any given time, the rare form seems to be doing more breeding. This is consistent with Hori's hypothesis of frequency-dependent selection.

Furthermore, Hori has evidence to support his hypothesis about the mechanism of selection. He examined bite wounds on a prey species in 1980, when left-handed

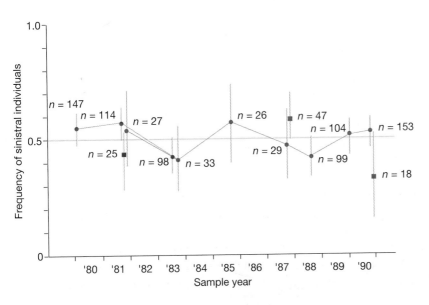

Figure 5.20 **Frequency of left-handed (sinistral) fish over time**   Circles represent scale-eating fish captured with a gill net; red versus blue circles represent fish caught at different locations. Squares (in 1981, 1987, and 1990) represent actively breeding adults, selectively captured by scuba-diving scientists. The numbers (*n*) report the sample sizes. Reprinted with permission from Hori (1993). Copyright © 1993, American Association for the Advancement of Science.

scale eaters were more common, and in 1983, when right-handed scale eaters were more common. In both years, the prey had more bite marks inflicted by whichever of the two forms was rarer at the time. This is consistent with the idea that the prey are indeed more vigilant for attacks from whichever form of scale eater is more common. It appears that Hori's hypothesis is correct and that over the long term, the allele, genotype, and phenotype frequencies in scale-eating fish are being held constant by frequency-dependent selection. Frequency-dependent selection, like heterozygote superiority, maintains genetic diversity in populations.

Compulsory Sterilization

We can use population genetic models to evaluate whether eugenic sterilization could have accomplished the aims of its proponents, had their assumptions about the heritability of traits been correct. The answer depends on the frequency of the alleles in question, and on the criteria for success.

Having discussed a variety of patterns of selection, we can now consider the evolutionary consequences of a eugenic compulsory sterilization program. The proponents of eugenic sterilization sought to reduce the fitness of particular genotypes to zero, and thereby to reduce the frequency of alleles responsible for undesirable phenotypes.

The phenotype that caught the eugenicists' attention perhaps more than any other was feeblemindedness. The Royal College of Physicians in England defined a feebleminded individual as "One who is capable of earning his living under favorable circumstances, but is incapable from mental defect existing from birth or from an early age (a) of competing on equal terms with his normal fellows or (b) of managing himself and his affairs with ordinary prudence" (see Goddard 1914). Evidence presented in 1914 by Henry H. Goddard, who was the director of research at the Training School for Feebleminded Girls and Boys in Vineland, New Jersey, convinced many eugenicists that strength of mind behaved like a simple Mendelian trait (see Paul and Spencer 1995). Normalmindedness was believed to be dominant, and feeblemindedness recessive.

A recessive genetic disease is not a promising target for a program that would eliminate it by sterilizing affected individuals. As Figure 5.14 and Figure 5.15 show, rare recessive alleles decline in frequency slowly, even under strong selection. On the other hand, eugenicists did not believe that feeblemindedness was especially rare (Paul and Spencer 1995). Indeed, they believed that feeblemindedness was alarmingly common and increasing in frequency. Edward M. East (1917) estimated the frequency of feeblemindedness at three per thousand. Henry H. Goddard reported a frequency of 2% among New York school children. Tests of American soldiers during World War I suggested a frequency of nearly 50% among white draftees.

We will assume a frequency for feeblemindedness of 1%, and reproduce a calculation reported by R. C. Punnett (1917) and revisited by R. A. Fisher (1924). Let f be the purported allele for feeblemindedness, with frequency q. If 1% of the population has genotype ff, then, by the Hardy–Weinberg equilibrium principle, the initial frequency of f is

$$q = \sqrt{0.01} = 0.1$$

If all affected individuals are sterilized, then the fitness of genotype ff is zero (or, equivalently, the selection coefficient for genotype ff is -1). Using the equation developed in Box 5.7, we can calculate the value of q in successive generations, and from q we can calculate the frequency of genotype ff.

The result appears in Figure 5.21. Over 10 generations, about 250 years, the frequency of affected individuals declines from 0.01 to 0.0025.

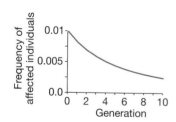

Figure 5.21 Predicted change in the frequency of homozygotes for a putative allele for feeblemindedness under a eugenic sterilization program that prevents homozygous recessive individuals from reproducing

Whether a geneticist saw this calculation as encouraging or discouraging depended on whether he or she saw the glass as partially empty or partially full. Some looked at the numbers, saw that it would take a very long time to completely eliminate feeblemindedness, and argued that compulsory sterilization was such a hopelessly slow solution that it was not worth the effort. Others, such as Fisher, dismissed this argument as "anti-eugenic propaganda." Fisher noted that after just one generation, the frequency of affected individuals would drop from 100 per ten thousand to 82.6 per ten thousand. "In a single generation," he wrote, "the load of public expenditure and personal misery caused by feeblemindedness...would be reduced by over 17 percent." Fisher also noted that most copies of the allele for feeblemindedness are present in heterozygous carriers rather than affected individuals. Along with East, Punnett, and others, Fisher called for research into methods for identifying carriers.

It is not entirely fair to use modern standards to criticize Goddard's research on the genetics of feeblemindedness. Mendelian genetics was in its infancy. Nonetheless, looking back after nearly a century, Goddard's evidence is deeply flawed.

First, the individuals whose case studies he reports are a highly diverse group. Some have Down syndrome; some have other forms of mental retardation. At least one is deaf and appears to be the victim of a woefully inadequate education. Some appear to have been deposited at Goddard's training school by widowed fathers who felt that children from a prior marriage were a liability in finding a new wife. Some may just have behaved differently than the directors of the school thought they should. Concluding the first case report in his book, Goddard writes of a 16-year-old who has been at the school for seven years:

> "Gertrude is a good example of that type of girl who, loose in the world, makes so much trouble. Her beauty and attractiveness and relatively high [intelligence] would enable her to pass almost anywhere as a normal child and yet she is entirely incapable of controlling herself and would be led astray most easily. It is fortunate for society that she is cared for as she is."

Second, Goddard's methods for collecting data were prone to distortion. He sent caseworkers to collect pedigrees from the families of the students at the training school. The caseworkers relied on hearsay and subjective judgements to assess the strength of mind of family members—many of whom were long since deceased.

Third, Goddard's method of analysis stacked the cards in favor of his conclusion. He first separated his 327 cases into a variety of categories: definitely hereditary cases; probably hereditary cases; cases caused by accidents; and cases with no assignable cause. He apparently placed cases in his "definitely hereditary" group only when they had siblings, recent ancestors, or other close kin also classified as feebleminded. When he later analyzed the data to determine whether feeblemindedness was a Mendelian trait, Goddard analyzed only the data from his "definitely hereditary" group. Given how he had filtered the data ahead of time, it is not too surprising that he concluded that feeblemindedness is Mendelian.

Although feeblemindedness is not among them, many genetic diseases are now known to be inherited as simple Mendelian traits. Yet eugenic sterilization has few advocates. One reason is that most serious genetic diseases are recessive and very rare; sterilization of affected individuals would have little impact on the frequency at which new affected individuals are born. A second reason is that mainstream attitudes about reproductive rights have changed to favor individual autonomy over societal mandates (Paul and Spencer 1995). A third reason is that, as we will discuss in the next section, there is a growing list of disease alleles that are suspected or known to be maintained in populations by heterozygote superiority. It would be futile and possibly ill-advised to try to reduce the frequency of such alleles by preventing reproduction by affected individuals.

5.4 Mutation

Second on the list of assumptions for the Hardy–Weinberg equilibrium principle was that there are no mutations. We now explore what happens to allele frequencies when this assumption is violated.

The last of the three questions posed at the outset of the chapter was how a highly deleterious allele, like the one that causes cystic fibrosis, could remain at relatively high frequency in a population. Our consideration of heterozygote superiority in the previous section hinted at one possible answer. Another potential answer is that new disease alleles are constantly introduced into populations by mutation. Before we can evaluate the merits of these two hypotheses for explaining the persistence of any particular disease allele, we need to discuss mutation in more detail.

In Chapter 4, we presented mutation as the source of all new alleles and genes. In its capacity as the ultimate source of all genetic variation, mutation provides the raw material for evolution. Here, we consider the importance of mutation as a force of evolution. How effective is mutation at changing allele frequencies over time? How strongly does mutation affect the conclusions of the Hardy–Weinberg analysis?

Adding Mutation to the Hardy–Weinberg Analysis: Mutation as an Evolutionary Force

Mutation by itself is generally not a potent force of evolution. To see why, return to our model population of mice. Imagine a locus with two alleles, *A* and *a*, with initial frequencies of 0.9 and 0.1. *A* is the wild-type allele, and *a* is a recessive loss-of-function mutation. Furthermore, imagine that copies of *A* are converted by mutation into new copies of *a* the rate of 1 copy per 10,000 per generation. This is a very high mutation rate, but it is within the range of mutation rates known (see Table 4.2 in Chapter 4). Back mutations that restore function are much less common than loss-of-function mutations, so we will ignore mutations that convert copies of *a* into new copies of *A*. Finally, imagine that all mutations happen while the gametes are in the gene pool.

Figure 5.22 follows the genotype and allele frequencies from one generation's adults through the gene pool to the next generation's zygotes. The adult genotypes are in the Hardy–Weinberg proportions:

AA	*Aa*	*aa*
0.81	0.18	0.01

When the adults produce gametes, the allele frequencies in the gene pool are as we specified:

A	*a*
0.9	0.1

Now, one of every ten thousand copies of allele *A* is converted into a new copy of allele *a*. The new frequency of *A* is given by the old frequency minus the fraction lost to mutation; the new frequency of *a* is given by the old frequency plus the fraction gained by mutation. That is,

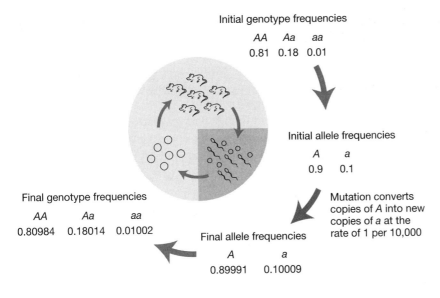

Initial genotype frequencies

AA	Aa	aa
0.81	0.18	0.01

Initial allele frequencies

A	a
0.9	0.1

Mutation converts copies of *A* into new copies of *a* at the rate of 1 per 10,000

Final allele frequencies

A	a
0.89991	0.10009

Final genotype frequencies

AA	Aa	aa
0.80984	0.18014	0.01002

Figure 5.22 Mutation is a weak force of evolution In a single generation in our model population, mutation produces virtually no change in allele and genotype frequencies.

$$A \qquad\qquad a$$
$$0.9 - (0.0001)(0.9) \qquad 0.1 + (0.0001)(0.9)$$
$$= 0.89991 \qquad\qquad = 0.10009$$

Finally, when the gametes combine at random to make zygotes, the zygote genotypes are in the new Hardy–Weinberg proportions:

AA	**Aa**	**aa**
0.80984	0.18014	0.01002

Note that the new allele and genotype frequencies are almost identical to the old allele and genotype frequencies. As a force of evolution, mutation has had virtually no effect.

But virtually no effect is not the same as exactly no effect. Could mutation of *A* into *a*, occurring at the rate of 1 copy per 10,000 every generation for many generations, eventually result in an appreciable change in allele frequencies? The graph in Figure 5.23 provides the answer (see Box 5.9 for a mathematical treatment). After one thousand generations, the frequency of allele *A* in our model population will be about 0.81. Mutation can cause substantial change in allele frequencies, but it does so slowly.

As mutation rates go, the value we used in our model, 1 per 10,000 per generation, is very high. For most genes, mutation is an even less efficient mechanism of allele frequency change.

Hardy–Weinberg analysis shows that mutation is a week force of evolution.

Mutation and Selection

Although mutation alone usually cannot cause appreciable changes in allele frequencies, this does not mean that mutation is unimportant in evolution. In combination with selection, mutation becomes a potent evolutionary force. This point is demonstrated by an experiment conducted in Richard Lenski's lab (Lenski and Travisano 1994; Elena et al. 1996). Lenski and co-workers studied the evolution of a strain of *Escherichia coli* that is incapable of recombination (here, recombination means conjugation and exchange of DNA among cells). For *E. coli* populations of this strain, mutation is the only source of genetic variation. The researchers

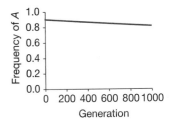

Figure 5.23 Over very long periods of time, mutation can eventually produce appreciable changes in allele frequency

BOX 5.9 A mathematical treatment of mutation as an evolutionary force

Imagine a single locus with two alleles: a wild-type allele, A, and a recessive loss-of-function mutation, a. Let μ be the rate of mutation from A to a. Assume that the rate of back mutation from a to A is negligible. If the frequency of A in this generation is p, then its frequency in the next generation is given by

$$p' = p - \mu p$$

If the frequency of a in this generation is q, then its frequency in the next generation is given by

$$q' = q + \mu p$$

The change in p from one generation to the next is

$$\Delta p = p' - p$$

which simplifies to

$$\Delta p = -\mu p$$

After n generations, the frequency of A is approximately

$$p_n = p_0 e^{-\mu n}$$

where p_n is the frequency of A in generation n, p_0 is the frequency of A in generation 0, and e is the base of the natural logarithms.

Readers familiar with calculus can derive the last equation as follows. First, assume that a single generation is an infinitesimal amount of time, so that we can rewrite the equation $\Delta p = -\mu p$ as

$$\frac{dp}{dg} = -\mu p$$

Now divide both sides by p, and multiply both sides by dg to get

$$\left(\frac{1}{p}\right) dp = -\mu\, dg$$

Finally, integrate the left side from frequency p_0 to p_n and the right side from generation 0 to n, then solve for p_n.

started 12 replicate populations with single cells placed in a glucose-limited, minimal salts medium—a demanding environment for these bacteria. After allowing each culture to grow to about 5×10^8 cells, Lenski and colleagues removed an aliquot (containing approximately 5 million cells) and transferred it to fresh medium. The researchers performed these transfers daily for 1500 days, or approximately 10,000 generations.

At intervals throughout the experiment, the researchers froze samples of the transferred cells for later analysis. Because *E. coli* are preserved but not killed by freezing, Lenski and colleagues could take ancestors out of the freezer and grow them up in a culture flask with an equivalent number of cells from descendant populations. These experiments allowed the team to directly measure the relative fitness of ancestral and descendant populations, as the growth rate of each under competition. In addition to monitoring changes in fitness over time in this way, the Lenski team measured cell size.

During the course of the study, both fitness and cell size increased dramatically in response to natural selection. The key point for our purposes is that these increases occurred in jumps (Figure 5.24). The step-like pattern resulted from a simple process: the occurrence of beneficial mutations that swept rapidly through the population. Each new mutation enabled the bacteria that carried it to divide at a faster rate. The frequency of the mutants quickly increased as they out-reproduced the other members of the population. Eventually, each new mutation became fixed in the population. The time from the appearance of each mutation to its fixation in the population was so short that we cannot see it in the figure. Most of the beneficial mutations caused larger cell size. Thus the plot of cell size over

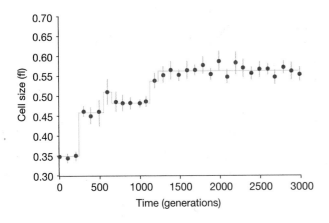

Figure 5.24 Changes over time in cell size of experimental *E. coli* populations. Each point on the plot represents the average cell size in the 12 replicate populations. The vertical lines are error bars; 95% of the observations fall within the range indicated by the bars. Reprinted with permission from Elena et al. (1996). Copyright © 1996, American Association for the Advancement of Science.

time also shows abrupt jumps. Between the appearance of one beneficial mutation and the next, all of the 12 replicate populations stood still. Why larger cells were beneficial in the nutrient-poor laboratory environment is a focus of ongoing research (Mongold and Lenski, 1996; Lenski et al. 1998).

The experiment by Lenski and colleagues reinforces one of the messages of Chapter 4. Without mutation, evolution would eventually grind to a halt. Mutation is the ultimate source of genetic variation.

Research with bacteria illustrates that while mutation itself is only a weak force of evolution, it nonetheless supplies the raw material on which natural selection acts.

Mutation-Selection Balance

Unlike the minority of mutations that led to increased cell size and higher fitness in Lenski et al.'s *E. coli* populations, most mutations are deleterious. Selection acts to eliminate such mutations from populations. Deleterious alleles persist, however, because they are continually created anew. When the rate at which copies of a deleterious allele are being eliminated by selection is exactly equal to the rate at which new copies are being created by mutation, the frequency of the allele is at equilibrium. This situation is called **mutation-selection balance**.

What is the frequency of the deleterious allele at equilibrium? If the allele is recessive, its equilibrium frequency, $\hat{q}$, is given by

$$\hat{q} = \sqrt{\frac{\mu}{s}}$$

where μ is the mutation rate, and s, the selection coefficient, is a number between 0 and 1 expressing the strength of selection against the allele (see Box 5.10 for a derivation). This equation captures with economy what intuition tells us about mutation-selection balance. If the selection coefficient is small (the allele is only mildly deleterious) and the mutation rate is high, then the equilibrium frequency of the allele will be relatively high. If the selection coefficient is large (the allele is highly deleterious) and the mutation rate is low, then the equilibrium frequency of the allele will be low.

Research by Brunhilde Wirth and colleagues (1997) on patients with spinal muscular atrophy provides an example. Spinal muscular atrophy is a neurodegenerative disease characterized by weakness and wasting of the muscles that control voluntary movement. It is caused by deletions in a locus on chromosome 5 called the telomeric survival motor neuron gene (*telSMN*). In some cases, the disease may be exacerbated by additional mutations in a nearby gene. Spinal muscular atrophy

At the same time selection removes deleterious alleles from a population, mutation constantly supplies new copies. In some cases, this balance between mutation and selection may explain the persistence of deleterious alleles in populations.

BOX 5.10   Allele frequencies under mutation-selection balance

Here we derive equations for predicting the equilibrium frequencies of deleterious alleles under mutation-selection balance. Imagine a single locus with two alleles, A_1 and A_2, with frequencies p and q. A_1 is the wild type; A_2 is deleterious. Let μ be the rate at which copies of A_1 are converted into copies of A_2 by mutation. Assume that the rate of back mutation is negligible.

Selection will continuously remove copies of A_2 from the population, while mutation will continuously create new copies. We want to calculate the frequency of A_2 at which these processes cancel each other. Following Felsenstein (1997), we will perform our calculation in a roundabout way. We will develop an equation in terms of p that describes mutation-selection balance for allele A_1. Then, we will solve the equation for q to get the equilibrium frequency of A_2. This approach may seem perverse, but it greatly simplifies the algebra.

Mutation-selection balance for a deleterious recessive allele

Imagine that A_2 is a deleterious recessive allele, such that the genotype fitnesses are given by

w_{11}	w_{12}	w_{22}
1	1	$1 - s$

where the selection coefficient s gives the strength of selection against A_2.

First, we will write an equation for p^*, the frequency of allele A_1 after selection has operated, but before mutations occur. From Box 5.3, this equation is

$$p^* = \frac{p^2 w_{11} + pq w_{12}}{p^2 w_{11} + 2pq w_{12} + q^2 w_{22}}$$

Substituting the fitnesses from the table above, and $(1 - p)$ for q, then simplifying gives

$$p^* = \frac{p}{1 - s(1 - p)^2}$$

Next we will write an expression for p', the frequency of allele A_1 after mutations occur. These mutations convert a fraction μ of the copies of A_1 into copies of A_2, leaving behind a fraction $(1 - \mu)$. Thus

$$p' = (1 - \mu)p^* = \frac{(1 - \mu)p}{1 - s(1 - p)^2}$$

Finally, when mutation and selection are in balance, p' is equal to p, the frequency of allele A_1 that we started with:

$$\frac{(1 - \mu)p}{1 - s(1 - p)^2} = p$$

This simplifies to

$$(1 - p)^2 = \frac{\mu}{s}$$

Substituting q for $(1 - p)$ and solving for q yields an equation for $\hat{q}$, the equilibrium frequency of allele A_2 under mutation-selection balance:

$$\hat{q} = \sqrt{\frac{\mu}{s}}$$

If A_2 is a lethal recessive, then $s = 1$, and the equilibrium frequency of A_2 is equal to the square root of the mutation rate.

Mutation-selection balance for a lethal dominant allele

Imagine that A_2 is a lethal dominant allele, such that the genotype fitnesses are given by

w_{11}	w_{12}	w_{22}
1	0	0

Now the expression for p^* simplifies to

$$p^* = 1$$

which makes sense because, by definition, selection removes all copies of the lethal dominant A_2 from the population. Now the expression for p' is

$$p' = 1 - \mu$$

and the equilibrium condition is

$$1 - \mu = p$$

Substituting $(1 - q)$ for p and simplifying gives

$$\hat{q} = \mu$$

In other words, the equilibrium frequency of A_2 is equal to the mutation rate.

is, after cystic fibrosis, the second most common lethal autosomal recessive disease in Caucasians (McKusick et al. 1999).

Collectively, the loss-of-function alleles of *telSMN* have a frequency of about 0.01 in the Caucasian population. Wirth and colleagues estimate that the selection coefficient is about 0.9. With such strong selection against them, we would expect that disease-causing alleles would slowly but inexorably disappear from the population. How, then, do they persist at a frequency of 1 in 100?

One possibility is that the disease alleles are being kept in the population by a balance between mutation and selection. If we substitute the allele frequency and selection coefficient for $\hat{q}$ and s in the equation on page 145, and then solve for μ, we find that this scenario requires a mutation rate of about 0.9×10^{-4} mutations per *telSMN* allele per generation. Wirth et al. analyzed the chromosomes of 340 individuals with spinal muscular atrophy, and the chromosomes of their parents and other family members. They found that 7 of the 340 affected individuals carried a new mutation not present in either parent. These numbers allowed the scientists to estimate directly the mutation rate at the *telSMN* locus (see Box 5.11). Their estimate is 1.1×10^{-4}. This directly measured mutation rate is in good agreement with the rate predicted under the hypothesis of a mutation-selection balance. Wirth et al. conclude that mutation-selection balance provides a sufficient explanation for the persistence of spinal muscular atrophy alleles.

Are the Alleles That Cause Cystic Fibrosis Maintained by a Balance Between Mutation and Selection?

Cystic fibrosis is caused by recessive loss-of-function mutations in a locus on chromosome 7 that encodes a protein called the cystic fibrosis transmembrane conductance regulator (CFTR). CFTR is a cell surface protein expressed in the mucus membrane lining the intestines and lungs. Gerald Pier and colleagues (1997) demonstrated that one of CFTR's key functions is to enable cells of the lung lining to ingest and destroy *Pseudomonas aeruginosa* bacteria. These bacteria cause chronic lung infections in individuals with cystic fibrosis, eventually leading to severe lung damage (Figure 5.25). Selection against the alleles that cause cystic fibrosis appears to be strong. Until recently, few affected individuals survived to reproductive age; those that do survive are often infertile. And yet the alleles that cause

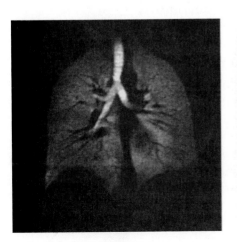
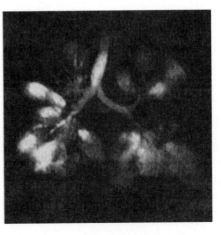

Figure 5.25 **A normal lung (left) versus a lung ravaged by the bacterial infections that accompany cystic fibrosis (right)** (Photos by G. Allan Johnson, Duke University Medical Center; *Scientific American* June 1999, page 34).

BOX 5.11 Estimating mutation rates for recessive alleles

Here, we present the method used by Brunhilde Wirth and colleagues (1997) to estimate mutation rates for recessive alleles. The key information required is the fraction of affected individuals that carry a brand-new mutant allele. With modern molecular techniques, this fraction can be obtained by direct examination of the chromosomes of affected individuals and their relatives.

Let q be the frequency of recessive loss-of-function allele a. Ignoring the extremely rare individuals with two new mutant copies, there are two ways to be born with genotype aa:

1. An individual can be the offspring of two carriers. The probablity of this outcome for a given birth is the product of: (a) the probability that an offspring of two carriers that will be affected; (b) the probability that the mother is a carrier; and (c) the probability that the father is a carrier. This probability is given by

$$\left[\frac{1}{4}\right] \times [2q(1-q)] \times [2q(1-q)]$$

2. An individual can be the offspring of one carrier and one homozygous dominant parent *and* can receive allele a from the affected parent and a new mutant copy of a from the unaffected parent. The probability of this outcome for a given birth is the product of (a) the probability that an offspring of one carrier will receive that carrier's mutant allele; (b) the probability that the mother is a carrier; (c) the probability that the father is a homozygous dominant; and (d) the mutation rate *plus* the same probability for the scenario in which the father is the carrier and the mother is the homozygous dominant:

$$\left\{\left[\frac{1}{2}\right] \times [2q(1-q)] \times [(1-q)^2] \times [\mu]\right\}$$

$$+ \left\{\left[\frac{1}{2}\right] \times [2q(1-q)] \times [(1-q)^2] \times [\mu]\right\}$$

$$= [2q(1-q)] \times [(1-q)^2] \times [\mu]$$

With these probabilities, we can write an expression for r, the fraction of affected individuals that carry one new mutant allele. This is the second probability divided by the sum of the second probability and the first. Simplified just a bit, we have

$$r = \frac{2q(1-q)(1-q)^2\mu}{2q(1-q)(1-q)^2\mu + q(1-q)q(1-q)}$$

Simplifying further yields

$$r = \frac{2(1-q)\mu}{2(1-q)\mu + q}$$

Finally, assume that q is small, so that $(1-q)$ is approximately equal to one. This assumption gives

$$r = \frac{2\mu}{2\mu + q}$$

which can be solved for μ:

$$\mu = \frac{rq}{2 - 2r}$$

The mutation rate for spinal muscular atrophy

In Caucasian populations, spinal muscular atrophy affects about 1 infant in 10,000, implying that the frequency of the mutant allele is

$$q = \sqrt{0.0001} = 0.01$$

Wirth and colleagues examined the chromosomes of 340 affected patients and their family members. The researchers discovered that 7 of their patients had a new mutant allele not present in either parent. Thus,

$$r = \frac{7}{340} = 0.021$$

Substituting these values for q and r into the equation for μ gives the estimate

$$\mu = \frac{(0.021)(0.01)}{2 - 2(0.021)} = 0.00011$$

The mutation rate for cystic fibrosis

In Caucasian populations, cystic fibrosis affects about 1 infant in 2500. Wirth and colleagues cite data from other authors to establish that only 2 of about 30,000 cystic fibrosis patients studied proved to have a new mutant allele not present in either parent. These figures give an estimated mutation rate of

$$\mu = 6.7 \times 10^{-7}$$

cystic fibrosis have a collective frequency of approximately 0.02 among people of European ancestry.

Could cystic fibrosis alleles be maintained at a frequency of 0.02 by mutation-selection balance? If we assume a selection coefficient of 1 and use the equation derived in Box 5.10, the mutation rate creating new disease alleles would have to be 4×10^{-4}. The actual mutation rate for cystic fibrosis alleles appears to be considerably lower than that: approximately 6.7×10^{-7} (see Box 5.11). We can conclude that a steady supply of new mutations cannot, by itself, explain the maintenance of cystic fibrosis alleles at a frequency of 0.02.

Our discussion of heterozygote superiority suggests an alternative explanation (Figure 5.16 and Box 5.8). Perhaps the the fitness cost suffered by cystic fibrosis alleles when they are in homozygotes is balanced by a fitness advantage they enjoy when they are in heterozygotes.

In other cases, the frequency of a deleterious allele may be too high to explain by mutation-selection balance. This may be a clue that heterozygotes have superior fitness.

Gerald Pier and colleagues (1998) hypothesized that cystic fibrosis heterozygotes might be resistant to typhoid fever and therefore have superior fitness. Typhoid fever is caused by *Salmonella typhi* bacteria. The bacteria initiate an infection by crossing the layer of epithelial cells that line the gut. Pier and colleagues suggested that *S. typhi* bacteria infiltrate the gut by exploiting the CFTR protein as a point of entry. If so, then heterozygotes, which have fewer copies of CFTR on the surface of their cells, should be less vulnerable to infiltration.

Pier and colleagues tested their hypothesis by constructing mouse cells with three different CFTR genotypes: homozygous wild-type cells; heterozygotes with one functional CFTR allele and one allele containing the most common human cystic fibrosis mutation, a single base-pair deletion called *ΔF508;* and homozygous *ΔF508* cells. The researchers exposed these cells to *Salmonella typhi*, then measured the number of bacteria that got inside cells of each genotype. The results were dramatic (Figure 5.26). As the researchers predicted, homozygous *ΔF508* cells were almost totally resistant to infiltration by *S. typhi,* while homozygous wild-type cells were highly vulnerable. Heterozygous cells were partially resistant; they accumulated 86% fewer bacteria than did the wild-type cells. These results are consistent with the hypothesis that cystic fibrosis disease alleles are maintained in human populations because heterozygotes have superior fitness during typhoid fever epidemics. Pier et al.'s research serves as another example in which an evolutionary analysis proved valuable in biomedical research.

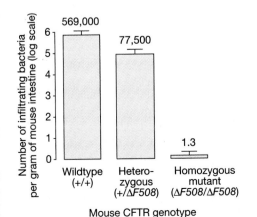

Figure 5.26   Cultured mouse cells heterozygous for cystic fibrosis show substantial resistance to infiltration by the bacteria that cause typhoid fever   Cells homozygous for the most common human disease allele are almost totally resistant. From Pier et al. (1998). Reprinted by permission from Nature 393: 79–82. © 1998, Macmillan Magazines Ltd.

Summary

Population genetics represents a synthesis of Mendelian genetics and Darwinian evolution, and is concerned with the mechanisms that cause allele frequencies to change from one generation to the next. The Hardy–Weinberg equilibrium principle is a null model that provides the conceptual framework for population genetics. It shows that under simple assumptions—no selection, no mutation, no migration, no genetic drift, and random mating—allele frequencies do not change. Furthermore, genotype frequencies can be calculated from allele frequencies.

When any one of the first four assumptions is violated, allele frequencies may change across generations. Selection, mutation, migration, and genetic drift are thus the four mechanisms of evolution. Nonrandom mating does not cause allele frequencies to change, and is thus not a mechanism of evolution. It can, however, alter genotype frequencies and thereby affect the course of evolution.

Population geneticists can measure allele and genotype frequencies in real populations. Thus, biologists can test whether allele frequencies are stable across generations and whether the genotype frequencies conform to Hardy–Weinberg expectations. If either of the conclusions of the Hardy–Weinberg analysis is violated, it means that one or more of the assumptions does not hold. The nature of the deviation from Hardy–Weinberg expectations does not, by itself, identify the faulty assumption. We can, however, often infer which mechanisms of evolution are at work based on other characteristics of the populations under study.

Selection occurs when individuals with different genotypes differ in their success at getting copies of their genes into future generations. It is a powerful force of evolution. Selection can cause allele frequencies to change from one generation to the next, and can take genotype frequencies away from Hardy–Weinberg equilibrium. Some patterns of selection tend to drive some alleles to fixation and others to loss; other patterns of selection serve to maintain allelic diversity in populations.

Alone, mutation is a weak evolutionary force. Mutation does, however, provide the genetic variation that is the raw material for evolution. In some cases a steady supply of new mutant alleles can balance selection against those same alleles, and thereby serve to hold allele frequencies at equilibrium.

Questions

1. Black color in horses is governed primarily by a recessive allele at the A locus. *AA* and *Aa* horses are nonblack colors such as bay, while *aa* horses are black all over. (Other loci can override the effect of the A locus, but we will ignore that complication.) A few years ago, a reader of the Usenet newsgroup "rec.equestrian" asked why there are relatively few black horses of the Arabian breed. One response was "Black is a rare color because it is recessive. More Arabians are bay or grey because those colors are dominant." What is wrong with this explanation? (Assume that the *A* and *a* alleles are in Hardy–Weinberg equilibrium, which was probably true at the time of this discussion.) Generally, what does the Hardy–Weinberg model show us about the impact that an allele's dominance or recessiveness has on its frequency? Should an allele become more common (or less common) simply because it is dominant (or recessive)?

2. In humans, the COL1A1 locus codes for a certain collagen protein found in bone. The normal allele at this locus is denoted with S. A recessive allele s is associated with reduced bone mineral density and increased risk of fractures in both *Ss* and *ss* women. A recent study of 1778 women showed that 1194 were *SS*, 526 were *Ss*, and 58 were *ss* (Uitterlinden et al. 1998).

   Are these two alleles in Hardy–Weinberg equilibrium in this population? How do you know? What information would you need to determine whether the alleles will be in Hardy–Weinberg equilibrium in the next generation?

3. We used Figure 5.11 as an example of how the frequency of an allele (*Adh*^{S} in fruit flies) does not change in unselected (control) populations, but does change in response to selection. However, look again at the unselected control lines in Figure 5.11. The frequency of the *Adh*^{S} allele in the two control populations did change a little, moving up and down over time. Which assumption of the Hardy–Weinberg model is most probably being violated? If this experiment were repeated, what change in experimental design would reduce this deviation from Hardy–Weinberg equilibrium?

4. Most animal populations have a 50:50 ratio of males to females. This does not have to be so; it is theoretically

possible for parents to produce predominantly male off-spring, or predominantly female offspring. Imagine a monogamous population with a male-biased sex ratio, say, 70% males and 30% females. Which sex will have an easier time finding a mate? As a result, which sex will probably have higher average fitness? Which parents will have higher fitness—those that produce mostly males, or those that produce mostly females? Now imagine the same population with a female-biased sex ratio, and answer the same questions. What sort of selection is probably maintaining the 50:50 sex ratio seen in most populations?

5. Discuss how each of the following recent developments may affect the frequency of alleles that cause cystic fibrosis (CF).
   a. Many women with CF now survive long enough to have children. (CF causes problems with reproductive ducts, but many CF women can bear children nonetheless. CF men are usually sterile.)
   b. Typhoid fever in developed nations has declined to very low levels since 1900.
   c. In some populations, couples planning to have children are now routinely screened for the most common CF alleles.
   d. Drug-resistant typhoid fever has recently appeared in several developing nations.

6. Consider what makes a new mutant allele dominant or recessive. To guide your thinking, imagine an enzyme that changes substance A to substance B. If B is a nutrient that is needed only in minimal amounts, will a loss-of-function mutation be dominant or recessive? If A is a toxin that must be entirely broken down, will a loss-of-function mutation be dominant or recessive? How about a new mutant allele that results in a form of the protein that can catalyze an entirely new reaction (say, from A to new substance C?) Can you think of other examples of protein function that will affect whether a new allele is dominant or recessive?

7. There are two common alleles for the human muscle enzyme ACE (angiotensin-converting enzyme)—a shorter "*D*" allele, and a longer "*I*" allele that has an insertion of 287 base pairs. The ACE coded by the *I* allele has lower activity, but it also associated with superior muscular performance after physical training. One study (Williams et al. 2000) of 35 *II* and 23 *DD* men found that though they didn't differ in muscular efficiency before training, after 11 weeks of aerobic training the *II* homozygotes had 8% greater muscular efficiency. The *I* allele is also associated with greater endurance and greater muscular growth after strength training. Speculate on why the *D* allele still remains at relatively high frequency in the human population. How could you test your ideas?

8. In our discussion of Jaeken syndrome in Section 5.2, we asserted that parents who are both carriers of the *R141H* allele can expect a different distribution of phenotypes among their children than parents who are carriers of two different disease alleles. Explain the logic behind this assertion. What genotypes and phenotypes, and in what ratios, should the following pairs of parents expect among their liveborn children? What would you tell these parents if you were a genetic counselor?

   Mother's genotype: +/*R141H*; Father's genotype: +/*R141H*

   Mother's genotype: +/*R141H*; Father's genotype: +/*Other*

   Mother's genotype: +/*Other*; Father's genotype: +/*Other*

Exploring the Literature

9. In the example of the scale-eating fish, we saw that frequency-dependent selection tends to maintain an even ratio of left-handed fish to right-handed fish. See the following references for some interesting cases of possible frequency-dependent selection in other species. How plausible do you find each scenario?

Raymond, M., D. Pontier, A. B. Dufour, and A. P. Møller. 1996. Frequency-dependent maintenance of left-handedness in humans. *Proceedings of the Royal Society of London,* Series B 263: 1627–1633.

Sinervo, B., and C. M. Lively. 1996. The rock-paper-scissors game and the evolution of alternative male strategies. *Nature* 380: 240–243.

Smithson, A., and M. R. MacNair. 1996. Frequency-dependent selection by pollinators: Mechanisms and consequences with regard to behaviour of bumblebees *Bombus terrestris* (L.) (Hymenoptera: Apidae). *Journal of Evolutionary Biology* 9: 571–588.

10. The version of the adaptive landscape presented in Box 5.7 and Box 5.8, in which the landscape is a plot of mean fitness as a function of allele frequency, is actually somewhat different from the original version of the concept that Sewall Wright presented in 1932. Furthermore, there is even a third common interpretation of the adaptive landscape idea. For a discussion of the differences among the three versions, see Chapter 9 in

Provine, W. B. 1986. *Sewall Wright and Evolutionary Biology.* Chicago: University of Chicago Press.

For Sewall Wright's response to Provine's history, see

Wright, S. 1988. Surfaces of selective value revisited. *The American Naturalist* 131: 115–123.

Wright's original 1932 paper is reprinted in Chapter 11 of

Wright, S. 1986. *Evolution: Selected Papers,* William B. Provine, ed. Chicago: University of Chicago Press.

11. If your library has the earliest volumes of the Journal of Heredity, read

Bell, Alexander Graham. 1914. How to improve the race. *Journal of Heredity* 5: 1–7.

Keep in mind that population genetics was in its infancy; Mendelism had yet to be integrated with natural se-

lection. What was accurate and inaccurate in Bell's understanding of the mechanisms of evolution? Would the policy Bell advocated actually have accomplished his aims? Why or why not? If so, would it have done so for the reasons Bell thought it would?

12. For an example in which strong natural selection caused rapid change in allele frequencies in a wild population, see

Johannesson, K., B. Johannesson, and U. Lundgren. 1995. Strong natural selection causes microscale allozyme variation in a marine snail. *Proceedings of the National Academy of Sciences, USA* 92: 2602–2606.

Citations

Much of the population genetics material in this chapter is modeled after presentations in the following:

Crow, J. F. 1983. *Genetics Notes.* Minneapolis, MN: Burgess Publishing.

Felsenstein, J. 1997. *Theoretical Evolutionary Genetics.* Seattle, WA: ASUW Publishing, University of Washington.

Griffiths, A. J. F., J. H. Miller, D. T. Suzuki, R. C. Lewontin, and W. M. Gelbert. 1993. *An Introduction to Genetic Analysis.* New York: W.H. Freeman.

Templeton, A. R. 1982. Adaptation and the integration of evolutionary forces. In R. Milkman, ed., *Perspectives on Evolution.* Sunderland, MA: Sinauer, 15–31.

Here is the list of all other citations in this chapter:

Castle, W. E. 1903. The laws of heredity of Galton and Mendel, and some laws governing race improvement by selection. *Proceedings of the American Academy of Arts and Sciences* 39: 223–242.

Cavener, D. R., and M. T. Clegg. 1981. Multigenic response to ethanol in *Drosophila melanogaster. Evolution* 35: 1–10.

Dawson, P. S. 1970. Linkage and the elimination of deleterious mutant genes from experimental populations. *Genetica* 41: 147–169.

Dean, M., M. Carrington, et al. 1996. Genetic restriction of HIV-1 infection and progression to AIDS by a deletion allele of the CKR5 structural gene. *Science* 273: 1856–1862.

East, E. M. 1917. Hidden feeblemindedness. *Journal of Heredity* 8: 215–217.

Elena, S. F., V. S. Cooper, and R. E. Lenski. 1996. Punctuated evolution caused by selection of rare beneficial mutations. *Science* 272: 1802–1804.

Elias, S., M. M. Kaback, et al. 1992. Statement of The American Society of Human Genetics on cystic fibrosis carrier screening. *American Journal of Human Genetics* 51: 1443–1444.

Fisher, R. A. 1924. The elimination of mental defect. *The Eugenics Review* 16: 114–116.

Foster, G. G., M. J. Whitten, T. Prout, and R. Gill. 1972. Chromosome rearrangements for the control of insect pests. *Science* 176: 875–880.

Goddard, H. H. 1914. *Feeblemindedness: Its Causes and Consequences.* New York: The Macmillan Company.

Hardy, G. H. 1908. Mendelian proportions in a mixed population. *Science* 28: 49–50.

Hori, M. 1993. Frequency-dependent natural selection in the handedness of scale-eating cichlid fish. *Science* 260: 216–219.

Kevles, D. J. 1995. *In the Name of Eugenics: Genetics and the Uses of Human Heredity.* Cambridge, MA: Harvard University Press.

Lane, H. 1992. *The Mask of Benevolence: Disabling the Deaf Community.* New York: Vintage Books.

Lenski, R. E., and M. Travisano. 1994. Dynamics of adaptation and diversification: A 10,000-generation experiment with bacterial populations. *Proceedings of the National Academy of Sciences, USA* 91: 6808–6814.

Lenski, R. E., J. A. Mongold, et al. 1998. Evolution of competitive fitness in experimental populations of *E. coli*: What makes one genotype a better competitor than another? *Antonie Van Leeuwenhoek International Journal of General and Molecular Microbiology* 73: 35–47.

Martinson, J. J., N. H. Chapman, et al. 1997. Global distribution of the CCR5 gene 32-base-pair deletion. *Nature Genetics* 16: 100–103.

Matthijs, G., E. Schollen, E. Van Schaftingen, J.-J. Cassiman, and J. Jaeken. 1998. Lack of homozygotes for the most frequent disease allele in carbohydrate-defcient-glycoprotein syndrome type 1A. *American Journal of Human Genetics* 62: 542–550.

McKusick, Victor A., et al. 1999. Spinal muscular atrophy I. Record #253300 in Online Mendelian Inheritance in Man. Center for Medical Genetics, Johns Hopkins University (Baltimore, MD) and National Center for Biotechnology Information, National Library of Medicine (Bethesda, MD). World Wide Web URL: http://www.ncbi.nlm.nih.gov/omim/

Mongold, J. A., and R. E. Lenski. 1996. Experimental rejection of a non-adaptive explanation for increased cell size in *Escherichia coli. Journal of Bacteriology* 178: 5333–5334.

Mukai, T., and A. B. Burdick. 1959. Single gene heterosis associated with a second chromosome recessive lethal in *Drosophila melanogaster. Genetics* 44: 211–232.

Paul, D. B., and H. G. Spencer. 1995. The hidden science of eugenics. *Nature* 374: 302–304.

Pier, G. B., M. Grout, and T. S. Zaidi. 1997. Cystic fibrosis transmembrane conductance regulator is an epithelial cell receptor for clearance of *Pseudomonas aeruginosa* from the lung. *Proceedings of the National Academy of Sciences, USA* 94: 12088–12093.

Pier, G. B., M. Grout, et al. 1998. *Salmonella typhi* uses CFTR to enter intestinal epithelial cells. *Nature* 393: 79–82.

Provine, W. B. 1971. *The Origins of Theoretical Population Genetics.* Chicago: The University of Chicago Press.

Punnett, R. C. 1917. Eliminating feeblemindedness. *Journal of Heredity* 8: 464–465.

Reilly, P. 1991. *The Surgical Solution: A History of Involuntary Sterilization in the United States.* Baltimore: Johns Hopkins University Press.

Stephens, J. C., D. E. Reich, et al. 1998. Dating the origin of the *CCR5-Δ32* AIDS-resistance allele by the coalescence of haplotypes. *American Journal of Human Genetics* 62: 1507–1515.

Uitterlinden A. G., H. Burger, et al. 1998. Relation of alleles of the collagen type IA1 gene to bone density and the risk of osteoporotic fractures in postmenopausal women. *New England Journal of Medicine* 338: 1016–21.

UNAIDS. 1998. AIDS epidemic update: December 1998. (Geneva, Switzerland). World Wide Web URL:http://www.unaids.org

United States Supreme Court. 1927. *Buck v. Bell,* 274 U.S. 200.

Weinberg, W. 1908. Ueber den nachweis der vererbung beim menschen. *Jahreshefte des Vereins für Vaterländische Naturkunde in Württemburg* 64: 368–382. English translation in Boyer, S. H. 1963. Papers on Human Genetics. Englewood Cliffs, NJ: Prentice Hall.

Williams, A. G., M. P. Rayson, et al. 2000. The ACE gene and muscle performance. *Nature* 403: 614.

Wirth, B., T. Schmidt, et al. 1997. De novo rearrangements found in 2% of index patients with spinal muscular atrophy: Mutational mechanisms, parental origin, mutation rate, and implications for genetic counseling. *American Journal of Human Genetics* 61: 1102–1111.

Yule, G. U. 1902. Mendel's laws and their probable relations to intra-racial heredity. *New Phytologist* 1: 193–207; 222–238.

Zar, J. H. 1996. *Biostatistical Analysis,* 3rd ed. Upper Saddle, NJ: Prentice Hall.

CHAPTER 6

Mendelian Genetics in Populations II: Migration, Genetic Drift, and Nonrandom Mating

Male greater prairie chickens advertising for mates. (Richard Day/Daybreak Imagery)

T HE GREATER PRAIRIE CHICKEN, *TYMPANUCHUS CUPIDO PINNATUS,* IS A two-pound bird with a ten-pound mating display (Figure 6.1). Each spring, the males congregate in communal breeding areas, called leks, where they stake out small territories and advertise for mates. They spread their tail feathers, stomp their feet, and inflate the bright orange air sacs on their throats. As the birds draw air into the sacs it makes a booming noise that is audible for miles—like the sound created when a person blows air across the mouth of a large empty bottle, but much louder (Thomas 1998). Females visit the lek, inspect the displaying males, and choose a mate.

Two hundred years ago, the state of Illinois was almost entirely covered with prairie (Figure 6.2a) and was home to millions of greater prairie chickens. In 1837, however, the steel plow was introduced (Thomas 1998). With the first blade that could break through the dense roots of prairie plants, the steel plow allowed the conversion of prairie into farmland. As the Illinois prairie shrank, the range of the Illinois greater prairie chicken contracted with it (Figure 6.2b–d). And as the bird's

Figure 6.1 **A greater prairie chicken**
This male has inflated his air sacs and fanned his feathers as part of his courtship display. (Richard Day/Daybreak Imagery)

range contracted, its numbers crashed: to 25,000 in 1933; 2000 in 1962; 500 in 1972; 76 in 1990 (Westemeier et al. 1991; Bouzat et al. 1998). By 1994, there were fewer than 50 greater prairie chickens left in Illinois (Westemeier et al. 1998). These remaining birds belonged to two remnant populations—one in Marion County and the other in Jasper County.

Efforts to save remnant populations of greater prairie chickens by restoring prairie habitat appeared at first to be succeeding. Soon, however, population sizes resumed their decline. Why?

Efforts to save the Illinois greater prairie chicken began with a ban on hunting in 1933 (Thomas 1998). In 1962 and 1967, respectively, the habitats occupied by the Jasper County and Marion County populations were established as sanctuaries, and as sites for the restoration and management of grasslands (Westemeier et al. 1998). Figure 6.3 tracks the number of males displaying on leks in Jasper County from 1963 to 1997. From the mid-1960s through the early 1970s, the number of birds increased steadily. The conservation measures appeared to be working. In the mid-1970s, however, the population began to crash again. The population hit its all-time low of five or six males in 1994, despite the fact that there was now more managed grassland available to the birds than there had been in 1963.

Why did the Jasper County prairie chicken population continue to decline from the mid-1970s to the mid-1990s, even though the amount of habitat available was increasing? And what did wildlife managers do to finally reverse the decline?

The answers to these questions involve three phenomena introduced in Chapter 5, but not discussed there: migration, genetic drift, and nonrandom mating. We identified these processes as potentially important factors in the evolution of populations when we developed the Hardy–Weinberg equilibrium principle. When an ideal population has no selection, no mutation, no migration, and an infinitely large size, and when individuals choose their mates at random, then (1) the al-

Figure 6.2 **Habitat destruction and the shrinking range of Illinois greater prairie chickens** Map (a) shows the extent of prairie in Illinois before the introduction of the steel plow. Maps (b), (c), and (d) show the distribution of the greater prairie chickens in 1940, 1962, and 1994. Source: From Fig. 1 in Westemeier et al. (1998). Derived from R. C. Anderson, *Transactions of the Illinois State Academy of Science* 63, 214 (1970). Reprinted by permission of the Illinois State Academy of Science.

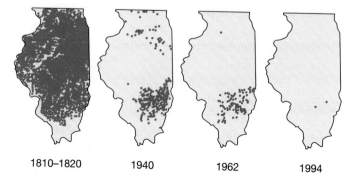

1810–1820   1940   1962   1994

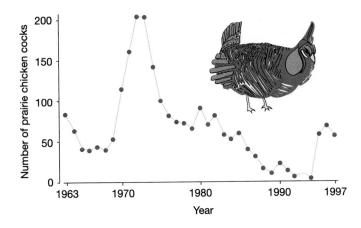

Figure 6.3 **A greater prairie chicken population in danger of extinction** This graph plots the number of male prairie chickens displaying each year on booming grounds in Jasper County, Illinois from 1963 to 1997. Redrawn with permission from Westemeier et al. (1998). Copyright © 1998, American Association for the Advancement of Science.

lele frequencies do not change from one generation to the next, and (2) the genotype frequencies can be calculated by multiplying the allele frequencies. In Chapter 5 we looked at what happens when we relax the assumptions of no selection and no mutation. In this chapter we will explore what happens when we relax the assumptions of no migration, infinite population size, and random mating. We will then return to the case of the Illinois greater prairie chicken, and address the questions it poses.

6.1 Migration

Migration, in an evolutionary sense, is the movement of alleles between populations. This use of the term migration is distinct from its more familiar meaning, which refers to the seasonal movement of individuals. To evolutionary biologists, migration means gene flow: The transfer of alleles from the gene pool of one population to the gene pool of another population. Migration can be caused by anything that moves alleles far enough to go from one population to another. Mechanisms of gene flow range from the occasional long-distance dispersal of juvenile animals to the transport of pollen, seeds, or spores by wind, water, or animals. The actual amount of migration among populations in different species varies enormously, depending on how mobile individuals or propagules are at various stages of the life cycle.

Adding Migration to the Hardy–Weinberg Analysis: Migration as an Evolutionary Force

To investigate the effects of migration on the two conclusions of the Hardy–Weinberg analysis, we consider a simple model of migration, called the one-island model. Imagine two populations: one on a continent, and the other on a small island offshore (Figure 6.4). Because the island population is so small relative to the continental population, any migration from the island to the continent will be inconsequential for allele and genotype frequencies on the continent. So migration, and the accompanying gene flow, is effectively one way, from the continent to the island. As usual, consider a single locus with two alleles, A_1 and A_2. Can migration from the continent to the island take the allele and genotype frequencies on the island away from Hardy–Weinberg equilibrium?

To see that the answer is yes, imagine that before migration, the frequency of A_1 on the island is 1.0 (that is, A_1 is fixed in the island population—see Figure 6.5).

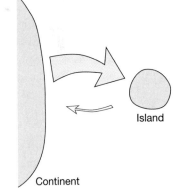

Figure 6.4 **The one-island model of migration** The arrows in the diagram show the relative amount of gene flow between the island and continental populations. Alleles arriving on the island from the continent represent a relatively large fraction of the island gene pool, whereas alleles arriving on the continent from the island represent a relatively small fraction of the continental gene pool.

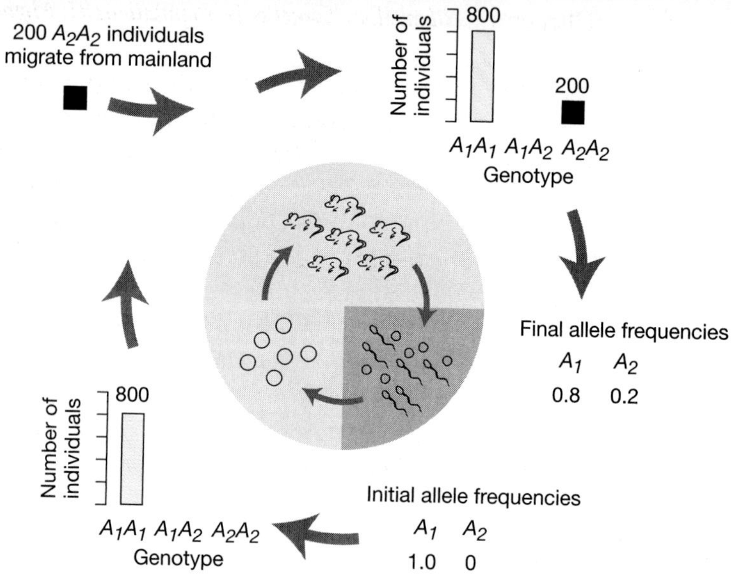

Figure 6.5 Migration can alter allele and genotype frequencies This diagram follows an imaginary island population of mice from one generation's gene pool (initial allele frequencies) to the next generation's gene pool (final allele frequencies). The bar graphs show the number of individuals of each genotype in the population at any given time. Migration, in the form of individuals arriving from a continental population fixed for allele A_2, increases the frequency of allele A_2 in the island population.

When gametes in a gene pool in which A_1 is fixed combine at random to make zygotes, the genotype frequencies among the zygotes are 1.0 for A_1A_1, 0 for A_1A_2, and 0 for A_2A_2. Our calculations will be simpler if we give our population a fixed size, so imagine that there are 800 zygotes, which we will let grow up to become adults.

Now suppose that the continental population is fixed for allele A_2, and that before the individuals on the island reach maturity, 200 individuals migrate from the

Box 6.1   An algebraic treatment of migration as an evolutionary force

Let p_I be the frequency of allele A_1 in an island population, and p_C be the frequency of A_1 in the mainland population. Imagine that every generation a group of individuals moves from the mainland to the island, where they constitute a fraction m of the island population. We want to know how the frequency of allele A_1 on the island changes as a result of migration, and whether there is an equilibrium frequency for A_1 at which there will be no further change even if migration continues.

We first write an expression for p_I', the frequency of A_1 on the island in the next generation. A fraction $(1 - m)$ of the individuals in the next generation were already on the island. Among these individuals, the frequency of A_1 is p_I. A fraction m of the individuals in the next generation came from the mainland. Among them, the frequency of A_1 is p_C. Thus the new frequency of A_1 in the island population is a weighted average of the frequency among the residents and the frequency among the immigrants:

$$p_I' = (1 - m)(p_I) + (m)(p_C)$$

We can now write an expression for Δp_I, the change in the allele frequency on the island from one generation to the next:

$$\Delta p_I = p_I' - p_I$$

Substituting our earlier expression for p_I' and simplifying gives

$$\Delta p_I = (1 - m)(p_I) + (m)(p_C) - p_I = m(p_C - p_I)$$

Finally, we can determine the equilibrium frequency of allele A_1 on the island. The equilibrium condition is no change in p_I. That is,

$$\Delta p_I = 0$$

If we set our expression for Δp_I equal to zero, we have

$$m(p_C - p_I) = 0$$

This expression shows that the frequency of A_1 will remain constant on the island if there is no migration ($m = 0$), or if the frequency of A_1 on the island is already identical to its frequency on the mainland ($p_I = p_C$). In other words, without any opposing force, migration will eventually equalize the frequencies of the island and mainland populations.

continent to the island. After migration, 80% of the island population is from the island, and 20% is from the continent. The new genotype frequencies are 0.8 for A_1A_1, 0 for A_1A_2, and 0.2 for A_2A_2. When individuals on the island reproduce, their gene pool will have allele frequencies of 0.8 for A_1 and 0.2 for A_2.

Migration has changed the allele frequencies in the island population, violating Hardy–Weinberg conclusion 1. Before migration, the island frequency of A_1 was 1.0; after migration, the frequency of A_1 is 0.8. The island population has evolved as a result of migration. (For an algebraic treatment of migration as a mechanism of allele frequency change, see Box 6.1).

Migration has also produced genotype frequencies among the adults on the island that are not consistent with Hardy–Weinberg conclusion 2. Under the Hardy–Weinberg equilibrium principle, a population with allele frequencies of 0.8 and 0.2 should have genotype frequencies of 0.64, 0.32, and 0.04. Compared to these expected values, the post-migration island population has an excess of homozygotes and a deficit of heterozygotes. A single bout of random mating will, of course, put the population back into Hardy–Weinberg equilibrium for genotype frequencies.

Migration is a potent force of evolution. In practice, migration is most important in preventing populations from diverging.

Empirical Research on Migration as a Mechanism of Evolution

The water snakes of Lake Erie (Figure 6.6) provide an empirical example of migration from a mainland population to an island population. These snakes (*Nerodia sipedon*) live on the mainland surrounding Lake Erie and on the islands in the lake.

(a)

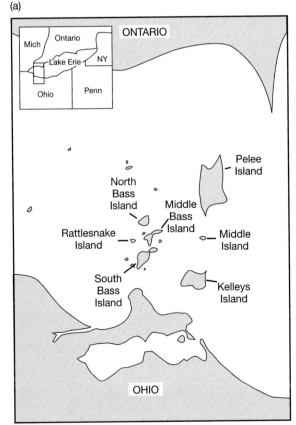

(b)

Figure 6.6   Water snakes and where they live   The map in (a) shows the island and mainland areas in and around Lake Erie where Richard King and colleagues studied migration as a force of evolution in water snakes. From King and Lawson (1995). Copyright © 1995 Evolution. Reprinted by permission. The photo in (b) shows unbanded, banded, and intermediate forms of the Lake Erie water snake (*Nerodia sipedon*). (Richard B. King)

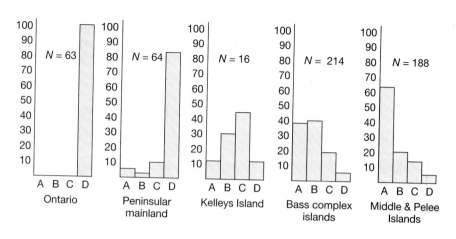

Figure 6.7 **Variation in color pattern within and between populations**   These histograms show frequency of different color patterns in various populations. Category A snakes are unbanded; category B and C snakes are intermediate; category D snakes are strongly banded. Snakes on the mainland tend to be banded; snakes on the islands tend to be unbanded or intermediate. From Camin and Ehrlich (1958). Copyright © 1958 Evolution. Reprinted by permission.

Individuals vary in appearance, ranging from strongly banded to unbanded. To a rough approximation, color pattern is determined by a single locus with two alleles, with the banded allele dominant over the unbanded allele (King 1993a).

On the mainland virtually all the water snakes are banded, whereas on the islands many snakes are unbanded (Figure 6.7). The difference in the composition of mainland versus island populations appears to be the result of natural selection caused by predators. On the islands, the snakes bask on limestone rocks at the water's edge. Following up on earlier work by Camin and Ehrlich (1958), Richard B. King (1993b) showed that among very young snakes unbanded individuals are more cryptic on island rocks than are banded individuals. The youngest and smallest snakes are presumably most vulnerable to predators. King (1993b) used mark-recapture studies, among other methods, to show that on the islands unbanded snakes indeed have higher rates of survival than banded snakes.

Migration of individuals from the mainland to islands appears to be preventing the divergence of island versus mainland populations of Lake Erie water snakes.

If selection favors unbanded snakes on the islands, then we would expect that the island populations would consist entirely of unbanded snakes. Why is this not the case? The answer, at least in part, is that every generation several banded snakes move from the mainland to the islands. The migrants bring with them alleles for banded coloration. When the migrant snakes interbreed with the island snakes, they contribute copies of the banded allele to the island gene pool. In this example, migration is acting as an evolutionary force in opposition to natural selection, preventing the island population from becoming fixed for the unbanded allele. (For an algebraic treatment of the influence of opposing forces of selection and migration on the Lake Erie water snakes, see Box 6.2.)

Migration as a Homogenizing Evolutionary Force Across Populations

Migration of water snakes from the mainland to the islands makes the island population more similar to the mainland population than it otherwise would be. This is the general effect of migration: It tends to homogenize allele frequencies across populations. In the water snakes, this homogenization is opposed by selection.

How far would the homogenization go if selection did not oppose it? The algebraic model developed in Box 6.1 shows that gene flow from a continent to an island will eventually drive the allele frequency on the island to a value exactly equal

Box 6.2   Selection and migration in Lake Erie water snakes

As described in the main text, the genetics of color pattern in Lake Erie water snakes can be roughly approximated by a single locus, with a dominant allele for the banded pattern and a recessive allele for the unbanded pattern (King 1993a). Selection by predators on the islands favors unbanded snakes. If the fitness of unbanded individuals is defined as 1, then the relative fitness of banded snakes is between 0.78 and 0.90 (King and Lawson 1995). So why has selection not eliminated banded snakes from the islands? Here we calculate the effect that migration has when it introduces new banded alleles into the island population every generation.

King and Lawson (1995) lumped all the island snakes into a single population, because snakes appear to move among islands much more often than they move from the mainland to the islands. King and Lawson used genetic techniques to estimate that 12.8 snakes move from the mainland to the island every generation. The scientists estimated that the total island snake population is between 523 and 4064 individuals, with a best estimate of 1262. This means that migrants represent a fraction of 0.003 to 0.024 of the population each generation, with a best estimate of 0.01.

With King and Lawson's estimates of selection and migration, we can calculate the equilibrium allele frequencies in the island population, at which the effects of selection and migration exactly balance each other. Let A_1 represent the dominant allele for the banded pattern, and A_2 the recessive allele for the unbanded pattern. Let p represent the frequency of A_1, and q the frequency of A_2. Following Box 5.3, we create individuals by random mating, then let selection act. After selection (but before migration), the new frequency of allele A_2 is

$$q^* = \frac{pqw_{12} + q^2w_{22}}{\bar{w}}$$

where w_{12} is the fitness of A_1A_2 heterozygotes, w_{22} is the fitness of A_2A_2 homozygotes, and $\bar{w}$ is the mean fitness of all the individuals in the population, given by $(p^2w_{11} + 2pqw_{12} + q^2w_{22})$.

For our first calculation, we will use $w_{11} = w_{12} = 0.84$, and $w_{22} = 1$. A relative fitness of 0.84 for banded snakes is the midpoint of the range within which King and Lawson (1995) estimated the true value to fall. This gives

$$q^* = \frac{pq(0.84) + q^2}{[p^2(0.84) + 2pq(0.84) + q^2]}$$

Substituting $(1 - q)$ for p gives

$$q^* = \frac{(1 - q)q(0.84) + q^2}{[(1 - q)^2(0.84) + 2(1 - q)q(0.84) + q^2]}$$

$$= \frac{0.84q + 0.16q^2}{0.84 + 0.16q^2}$$

Now we allow migration, with the new migrants representing, in this first calculation, a fraction 0.01 of the island's population (King and Lawson's best estimate). None of the new migrants carry allele A_2, so the new frequency of A_2 is

$$q' = (0.99)\frac{0.84q + 0.16q^2}{0.84 + 0.16q^2}$$

The change in q from one generation to the next is

$$\Delta q = q' - q = (0.99)\frac{0.84q + 0.16q^2}{0.84 + 0.16q^2} - q$$

Plots of Δq as a function of q appear in Figure 6.8. Look first at the green curve (b). This curve is for the function we just calculated. It shows that if q is greater than 0.05 and less than 0.94 in this generation, then q will be larger in the next generation (Δq is positive). If q is less than 0.05 or greater than 0.94 in this generation, then q will be smaller in the next generation (Δq is negative). The points where the curve crosses the horizontal axis, where $\Delta q = 0$, are the equilibrium points. The upper equilibrium point is stable: if q is less than 0.94, then q will rise in the next generation; if q is greater than 0.94, then it will fall in the next generation. Thus a middle-of-the-road prediction, given King and Lawson's estimates of selection and gene flow, is that the equilibrium frequency of the unbanded allele in the island population will be 0.94.

Curve (a) is a high-end estimate; it uses fitnesses of 0.78 for A_1A_1, 0.78 for A_1A_2, and 1 for A_2A_2, and a migration rate of 0.003 (0.3% of every generation's population are migrants). It predicts an equilibrium at $q = 0.99$. Curve (c) is a low-end estimate; it uses fitnesses of 0.90 for A_1A_1, 0.90 for A_1A_2, and 1 for A_2A_2, and a migration rate of 0.24 (2.4% of every generation's population are migrants). It predicts an equilibrium at $q = 0.64$.

Box 6.2 Continued

King and Lawson's best estimate of the actual frequency of A_2 is 0.73. This value is toward the low end of our range of predictions. Our calculation is a relatively simple one, and leaves out many factors, including recent changes in the population sizes of both the water snakes and their predators, as well as recent changes in the frequencies of banded versus unbanded snakes. For a detailed treatment of this example, see King and Lawson (1995).

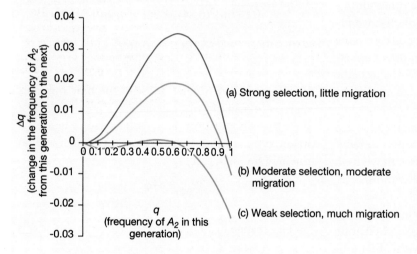

Figure 6.8 **The combined effects of selection and migration on allele frequencies in island water snakes** The curves show Δq as a function of q for different combinations of migration and selection. See text for details.

to what it is on the continent. In other words, if allowed to proceed unopposed by any other force of evolution, migration will eventually homogenize allele frequencies across populations completely.

Barbara Giles and Jérôme Goudet (1997) documented the homogenizing effect of gene flow on populations of red bladder campion, *Silene dioica*. Red bladder campion is an insect-pollinated perennial wildflower (Figure 6.9a). The populations that Giles and Goudet studied occupy islands in the Skeppsvik Archipelago, Sweden. These islands are mounds of material deposited by glaciers during the last ice age and left underwater when the ice melted. The area on which the islands sit is rising at a rate of 0.9 centimeters per year. As a result of this geological uplift, new islands are constantly rising out of the water. The Skeppsvik Archipelago thus contains dozens of islands of different ages.

Red bladder campion seeds are transported by wind and water, and the plant is among the first to colonize new islands. Campion populations grow to sizes of several thousand individuals. There is gene flow among islands as a result of both seed dispersal and the transport of pollen by insects. After a few hundred years, campion populations are invaded by other species of plants and by a pollinator-borne disease. Establishment of new seedlings ceases, and populations dwindle as individuals die.

Giles and Goudet predicted that young populations, having been founded by the chance transport of just a few seeds, would vary in their allele frequencies at a variety of loci. (We will consider why in more detail in Section 6.2.) Populations of intermediate age should be more homogeneous in their allele frequencies as a result of migration—that is, as a result of gene flow among populations via seed

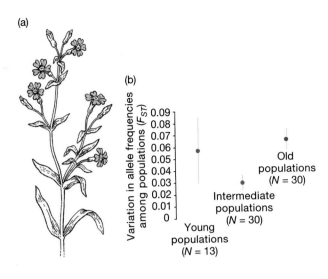

(a)

(b)

Figure 6.9   **Variation in allele frequencies among populations of red bladder campion, *Silene dioica***   (a) Red bladder campion, a perennial wildflower. (b) Giles and Goudet's (1997) measurements of variation in allele frequencies among populations. The red dots represent values of F_{ST} (see text); the vertical gray lines represent standard errors (larger standard errors represent less certain estimates of F_{ST}). There is less variation in allele frequencies among intermediate age populations than among young populations ($P = 0.05$). There is more variation in allele frequencies among old populations than among intermediate populations ($P = 0.04$). After Giles and Goudet (1997).

dispersal and pollen transport. Finally, the oldest populations, structured mainly by the fortuitous survival of a few remaining individuals, should again become more variable in their allele frequencies.

The researchers tested their predictions by collecting leaves from many individual red bladder campions on 52 islands of different ages. By analyzing proteins in the leaves, Giles and Goudet determined each individual's genotype at six enzyme loci. They divided their populations by age into three groups: young, intermediate, and old. For each of these groups, they calculated a test statistic called F_{ST}. A value for F_{ST} refers to a group of populations and reflects the variation in allele frequencies among the populations in the group. The value of F_{ST} can be anywhere from 0 to 1. Larger values represent more variation in allele frequency among populations.

The results confirm Giles and Goudet's predictions (Figure 6.9b). There is less variation in allele frequencies among populations of intermediate age than among young and old populations. The low diversity among intermediate populations probably reflects the homogenizing influence of gene flow. The higher diversity of young and old populations probably represents genetic drift, the subject of the next section.

In summary, migration is the movement of alleles from population to population. Within a single population, migration can cause allele frequencies to change from one generation to the next. For small populations receiving immigrants from large source populations, migration can be a potent mechanism of evolution. Across groups of populations, gene flow tends to homogenize allele frequencies. Thus migration tends to prevent the evolutionary divergence of populations.

6.2 Genetic Drift

In Chapter 2, we refuted the misconception that evolution by natural selection is a random process. To be sure, Darwin's mechanism of evolution depends on the generation of random variation by mutation. The variation generated by mutation is random in the sense that when mutation substitutes one amino acid for another in a protein, it does so without regard to whether the change will improve the protein's ability to function. But natural selection itself is anything but random. It is precisely the nonrandomness of selection in sorting among mutations that leads to adaptation.

We are now in a position to revisit the role of chance in evolution. Arguably, the most important insight from population genetics is that natural selection is not the only mechanism of evolution. Among the nonselective mechanisms of evolution, there is one that is absolutely random. That mechanism is genetic drift. Genetic drift does not lead to adaptation, but it does lead to changes in allele frequencies. In the Hardy–Weinberg model, genetic drift results from violation of the assumption of infinite population size.

A Model of Genetic Drift

To see how genetic drift works, imagine an ideal population similar to the ones we have worked with before, but finite—in fact, small—in size. As usual, we will focus on a single locus with two alleles, A_1 and A_2. Imagine that in the present generation's gene pool, allele A_1 is at frequency 0.6, and allele A_2 is at frequency 0.4 (Figure 6.10). We will let the gametes in this gene pool combine at random to make exactly ten zygotes. These ten zygotes will constitute the entire population for the next generation.

We can simulate the production of ten zygotes from our gene pool with a physical model. A bag containing 100 beans represents the gene pool. Sixty of the beans are black, representing allele A_1; forty of the beans are white, representing allele A_2. We make each zygote by shaking the bag, closing our eyes, and drawing out beans. First we draw a bean to represent the egg, note its genotype, and return it to the bag. Then we draw a bean to represent the sperm, note its genotype and return it to the bag. We are drawing beans from a bag as we write. The genotypes of the ten zygotes are

$$A_2A_1 \quad A_1A_1 \quad A_1A_1 \quad A_1A_1 \quad A_2A_2$$

$$A_1A_1 \quad A_2A_2 \quad A_1A_2 \quad A_1A_1 \quad A_1A_1$$

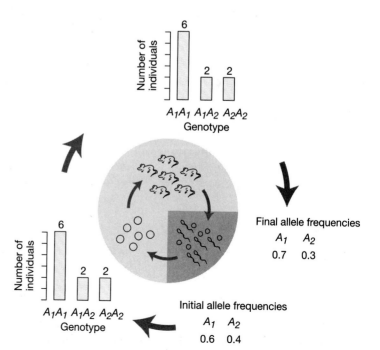

Figure 6.10 Chance events can alter allele and genotype frequencies This diagram follows an imaginary population of ten mice from one generation's gene pool (initial allele frequencies) to the next generation's gene pool (final allele frequencies). The bar graphs show the number of individuals of each genotype in the population at any given time. Genetic drift, in the form of sampling error in drawing gametes from the initial gene pool to make zygotes, increases the frequency of allele A_1. Note that many other outcomes are also possible.

Counting the genotypes, we have A_1A_1 at a frequency of 0.6, A_1A_2 at a frequency of 0.2, and A_2A_2 at a frequency of 0.2 (Figure 6.10). Counting the alleles, we see that when these zygotes grow up and reproduce, the frequency of allele A_1 in the new gene pool will be 0.7, and the frequency of allele A_2 will be 0.3 (Figure 6.10).

We have completed one turn of the life cycle of our model population. Nothing much seems to have happened, but note that both conclusions of the Hardy–Weinberg equilibrium principle have been violated. The allele frequencies have changed from one generation to the next, and we cannot calculate the genotype frequencies by multiplying the allele frequencies. The reason our population has failed to conform to the Hardy–Weinberg principle is simply that the population is small.

In populations of finite size, chance events—in the form of sampling error in drawing gametes from the gene pool—can cause evolution.

In a small population, chance events produce outcomes that differ from theoretical expectations. The chance events in our simulated population were the draws of beans from the bag to make zygotes. We picked black beans and white beans not in their exact predicted ratio of 0.6 and 0.4, but in a ratio that just happened to be a bit richer in black beans and a bit poorer in white beans. This kind of random discrepancy between theoretical expectations and actual results is called sampling error. Sampling error in the production of zygotes from a gene pool is **genetic drift**. Because it is nothing more than cumulative effect of random events, genetic drift cannot produce adaptation. But it can, as we have seen, cause allele frequencies to change. Blind luck is, by itself, a mechanism of evolution.

Sometimes it is difficult to see the difference between genetic drift and natural selection. In our model small population, copies of allele A_1 were more successful at getting into the next generation than copies of allele A_2. Differential reproductive success is selection, is it not? In this case, it is not. If it had been selection, the differential success of alleles in our model population would have been explicable in terms of the phenotypes the alleles confer on the individuals that carry them. Individuals with one or two copies of A_1 might have been better at surviving, finding food, or attracting mates. In fact, however, individuals carrying copies of allele A_1 were none of these things. They were just lucky; their alleles happened to get drawn from the gene pool more often. Selection is differential reproductive success that happens for a reason. Genetic drift is differential reproductive success that just happens.

Selection is differential reproductive success that happens for a reason; genetic drift is differential reproductive success that just happens.

Another way to see that genetic drift is different from selection is to recognize that the genotype and allele frequencies among our ten zygotes could easily have been different from what they turned out to be. To prove it, we can repeat the exercise drawing beans from our bag to make ten zygotes. This time, the genotypes of the zygotes are

$$A_1A_1 \quad A_1A_1 \quad A_1A_1 \quad A_2A_1 \quad A_1A_2$$
$$A_2A_2 \quad A_1A_2 \quad A_1A_1 \quad A_2A_1 \quad A_2A_2$$

Among this set of zygotes the genotype frequencies are 0.4 for A_1A_1, 0.4 for A_1A_2, and 0.2 for A_2A_2. The allele frequencies are 0.6 for A_1 and 0.4 for A_2.

Repeating the exercise a third time produces these zygotes:

$$A_1A_1 \quad A_1A_1 \quad A_1A_1 \quad A_1A_2 \quad A_1A_1$$
$$A_1A_2 \quad A_2A_1 \quad A_2A_2 \quad A_2A_2 \quad A_2A_2$$

Now the genotype frequencies are 0.4 for A_1A_1, 0.3 for A_1A_2, and 0.3 for A_2A_2, and the allele frequencies are 0.55 for A_1 and 0.45 for A_2.

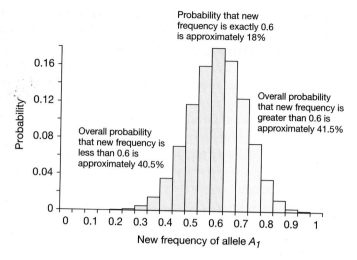

Figure 6.11 **The range of possible outcomes in our model population of ten mice** This graph shows the possible outcomes, and the probability of each, when we make 10 zygotes by drawing alleles from a gene pool in which alleles A_1 and A_2 have frequencies of 0.6 and 0.4. The single most probable outcome is that the allele frequencies will remain unchanged. However, the chance of this happening is only about 18%.

Here is a summary of the results from our model population:

	Frequency of A_1
In the gene pool	0.6
In the first set of 10 zygotes	0.7
In the second set of 10 zygotes	0.6
In the third set of 10 zygotes	0.55

The three sets of zygotes have shown us that if we start with a gene pool in which allele A_1 is at a frequency of 0.6 and make a population of just ten zygotes, the frequency of A_1 may rise, stay the same, or fall. In fact, the new frequency of A_1 among a set of ten zygotes drawn from our gene pool could turn out to be anywhere from 0 to 1.0, although outcomes at the extremes of this range are not likely. The graph in Figure 6.11 shows the theoretical probability of each possible outcome. Overall, there is about an 18% chance that the frequency of allele A_1 will stay at 0.6, about a 40.5% chance that it will drop to a lower value, and about a 41.5% chance that it will rise to a higher value. Readers should not just take our word for it; they should set up their own bag of beans and make a few batches of zygotes. Again, the point is that genetic drift is evolution that simply happens by chance.

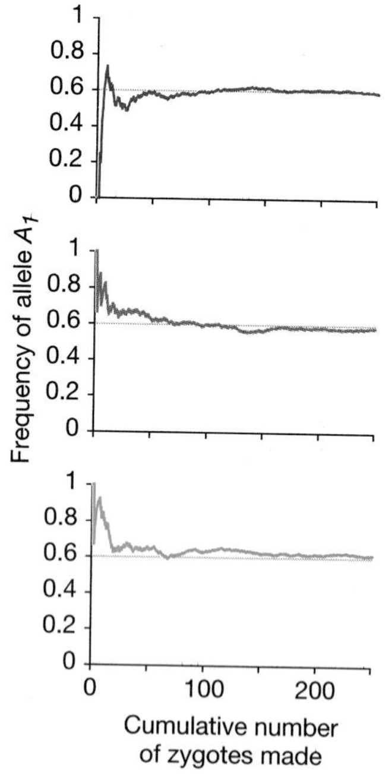

Genetic Drift and Population Size

Genetic drift is fundamentally the result of finite population size. If we draw beans from our bag to make a population of more than ten zygotes, the allele frequencies among the zygotes will get closer to the values predicted by the Hardy–Weinberg equilibrium principle. Drawing beans out of a bag quickly becomes tedious, so we used a computer to simulate drawing gametes to make not just 10, but 250 zygotes (Figure 6.12a). As the computer drew each gamete, it gave a running report of the frequency of A_1 among the zygotes it had made so far. At first this running allele frequency fluctuated wildly. For example, the first zygote turned out to have genotype A_2A_2, so the running frequency of allele A_1 started at zero. The next several zygotes were mostly A_1A_1 and A_1A_2, which sent the running frequency of allele A_1 skyrocketing to 0.75. As the cumulative number of zygotes made increased, the frequency of allele A_1 in the new generation bounced around

Figure 6.12 **A simulation of drawing alleles from a gene pool, run three times** At first the new frequency of allele A_1 fluctuates considerably, in a unique trajectory for each run. As the number of zygotes made increases, however, the new frequency of A_1 settles toward the expected value of 0.6.

less and less, gradually settling toward the expected value of 0.6. The deviations from expectation along the way to a large number of zygotes were random, as illustrated by the graphs in Figure 6.12b and (c). These graphs show two more sets of draws to make 250 zygotes. In each, the allele frequency in the new generation fluctuates wildly at first, but in a unique pattern. As in the first graph, however, the allele frequency in the new generation always eventually settles toward the theoretically predicted value of 0.6.

Our simulations demonstrate that sampling error diminishes as sample size increases. If we kept drawing gametes forever, to make an infinitely large population of zygotes, the frequency of allele A_1 among the zygotes would be exactly 0.6. Genetic drift is a powerful evolutionary mechanism in small populations, but its power declines in larger populations. We will return to this point in later sections.

Genetic drift is most important in small populations.

Empirical Research on Sampling Error as a Mechanism of Evolution: The Founder Effect

If we want to observe genetic drift in nature, the best place to look is in small populations. Populations are often small when they have just been founded by a group of individuals that have moved, or been moved, to a new location. The allele frequencies in the new population are likely, simply by chance, to be different than they are in the source population. This is called the **founder effect**.

The founder effect is a direct result of sampling error. For example, if 25 different alleles are present at a single locus in a continental population of insects, but just 10 individuals are on a log that rafts to a remote island, the probability is zero that the new island population will contain all of the alleles present on the continent. If, by chance, any of the founding individuals are homozygotes, allele frequencies in the new population will have shifted even more dramatically. In any founder event, some degree of random genetic differentiation is almost certain between old and new populations. In other words, the founding of a new population by a small group of individuals typically represents not only the establishment of a new population but also the instantaneous evolution of differences between the new population and the old population.

Peter Grant and Rosemary Grant (1995) watched the establishment of a new population of large ground finches (*Geospiza magnirostris*) in the Galápagos Islands. Grant and Grant had been working on the island of Daphne Major since 1973. Each year, large ground finches visited the island, with anywhere from 10 to 50 juveniles arriving after the breeding season and staying through the dry months. For the first several years that Grant and Grant were there, the visiting birds all left the island before the next breeding season began. The visiting finches were all members of some other island's population. Then in the fall of 1982, three males and two females, apparently enticed by early rains, stayed on Daphne Major to breed. These five birds formed pairs (one female bred with two different males), built eight nests over the course of the breeding season, and fledged 17 young during early 1983.

The five 1982–1983 breeders were the founders of a new population. Since 1983, large ground finches have bred on Daphne Major every year, with the exception of three drought years. By 1993, the Daphne Major breeding population included 23 males and 23 females. Through at least 1992, the majority of the Daphne Major breeders had been hatched on the island. They were natives of the new population.

Is the newly founded finch population genetically different from the source population? Although Grant and Grant do not have direct data on allele frequencies at specific loci, they do have extensive morphological measurements of the 238 ground finches that visited Daphne Major prior to the founding event, and of the five original Daphne Major breeders and 22 of their offspring. Grant and Grant assumed that the 238 nonbreeding visitors were representative of the source population, and compared them to the members of the newly founded population. In at least two morphological traits, bill width and bill shape in relation to body size, the members of the new population were significantly larger than the source population. Research on the new population of large ground finches, and on other Darwin's finches, suggests that these traits are heritable. Thus it appears that the founding event created a new population that is measurably different from the source population. Evolution occurred, not through selection but by random sampling error. This was genetic drift in the form of the founder effect.

When a new population is founded by a small number of individuals, it is likely that chance alone will cause the allele frequencies in the new population to be different from those in the source population. This is the founder effect.

Founder effects are often seen in genetically isolated human populations. For example, the Amish population of eastern Pennsylvania is descended from a group of about 200 European settlers who came to the United States in the 18th century. One of the founders—either the husband or wife (or both) in a couple named King—was a carrier for Ellis–van Creveld syndrome. Ellis–van Creveld syndrome is a rare form of dwarfism caused by a recessive allele on chromosome 4 (Bodmer and McKie 1995). The frequency of this allele is about 0.001 in most populations, but it is about 0.07 in the present-day Amish (Postlethwait and Hopson 1992). The high frequency of the allele in the Amish population is probably not due to any selective advantage conferred by the allele in either heterozygotes or homozygotes. Instead, the high frequency of the allele is simply due to chance. The allele was at a high frequency in the small population of founders and has continued to drift upward in subsequent generations. In the next section we will consider in detail the cumulative effect of genetic drift over the course of many generations.

Random Fixation of Alleles and Loss of Heterozygosity

We have seen that genetic drift can produce substantial change in allele frequencies in a single generation. Drift is even more powerful as a mechanism of evolution when its effects are compounded over many generations. We can investigate the cumulative effects of genetic drift with the same physical model we used before: black beans and white beans in a bag. We again set up a bag with 60 black beans and 40 white beans, representing a gene pool in which alleles A_1 and A_2 are at frequencies of 0.6 and 0.4. We will call the parents who produced this gene pool generation zero. As we did before, we now draw beans from the bag to simulate the production of ten zygotes by random mating. This time, the allele frequencies among the newly formed zygotes turn out to be 0.5 for A_1 and 0.5 for A_2. We will call these zygotes generation one.

To continue the simulation for another generation, we need to set up a new bag, with 50 black beans and 50 white beans, to represent generation one's gene pool. Drawing beans from this gene pool, we get the zygotes for generation two. Generation two's allele frequencies happen to be 0.4 for A_1 and 0.6 for A_2.

We now set up a bag with 40 black beans and 60 white beans and draw zygotes to make generation three. Generation three's allele frequencies are 0.45 for A_1 and 0.55 for A_2.

Now, we need a bag with 45 black beans and 55 white beans, and so on. The advantage of using a computer to simulate drawing beans from bags is rapidly becoming apparent.

Graphs (a), (b), and (c) in Figure 6.13 show the results of 100 successive generations of genetic drift in simulated populations of different sizes. Each graph

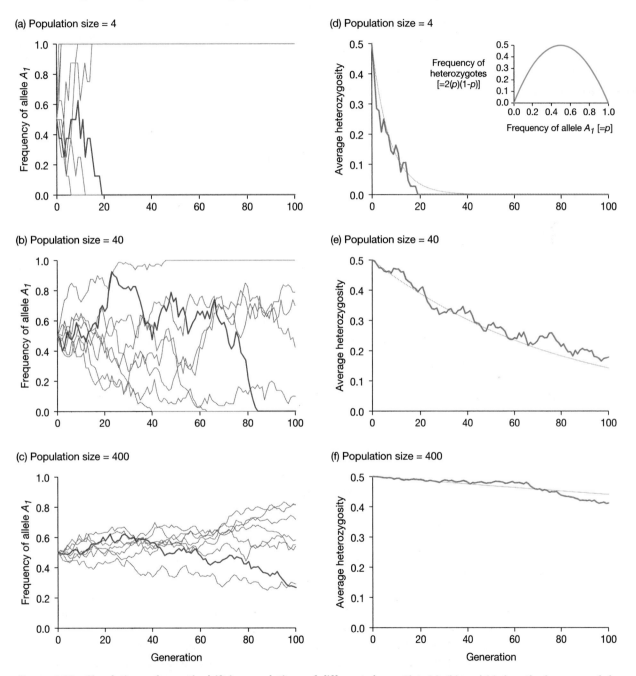

Figure 6.13 **Simulations of genetic drift in populations of different sizes** Plots (a), (b), and (c) show the frequency of allele A_1 over 100 generations. Eight populations are tracked in each plot, with one population highlighted in red. Plots (d), (e), and (f) show the average frequency of heterozygotes over 100 generations in the same sets of simulated populations. The gray curves represent the rate of decline predicted by theory. The inset in plot (d) shows the frequency of heterozygotes in a population, calculated as $2(p)(1 - p)$, as a function of p, the frequency of allele A_1. Collectively, the graphs in this figure show that genetic drift leads to random fixation of alleles and loss of heterozygosity, and that drift is a more powerful force of evolution in small populations.

tracks allele frequencies in eight populations. Every population starts with allele frequencies of 0.5 for A_1 and 0.5 for A_2. The populations tracked in graph (a) have just four individuals each, the populations tracked in graph (b) have 40 individuals each, and the populations tracked in graph (c) have 400 individuals each. Three patterns are evident:

Under genetic drift, every population follows a unique evolutionary path. Genetic drift is rapid in small populations and slow in large populations.

1. Because the fluctuations in allele frequency from one generation to the next are caused by random sampling error, every population follows a unique evolutionary path.

2. Genetic drift has a more rapid and dramatic effect on allele frequencies in small populations than in large populations.

3. Given sufficient time, genetic drift can produce substantial changes in allele frequencies, even in populations that are fairly large.

Note that if genetic drift is the only evolutionary force at work in a population—if there is no selection, no mutation, and no migration—then sampling error causes allele frequencies to wander between 0 and 1. This wandering is particularly apparent in the population whose evolution is highlighted in the graph in Figure 6.13b. During the first 25 generations allele A_1's frequency rose from 0.5 to over 0.9. Between generations 25 and 40 it dropped back to 0.5. Between generations 40 and 80 the frequency bounced between 0.5 and 0.8. Then the frequency of A_1 dropped precipitously, so that by generation 85 it hit zero and A_1 disappeared from the population altogether. The wandering of allele frequencies produces two important and related effects: (1) Eventually alleles drift to fixation or loss, and (2) the frequency of heterozygotes declines.

Random Fixation of Alleles

As any allele drifts between frequencies of 0 and 1.0, sooner or later the allele will meet an inevitable fate: Its frequency will hit one boundary or the other. If the allele's frequency hits 0, then the allele is lost forever (assuming that mutation or migration do not reintroduce it). If the allele's frequency hits 1, then the allele is said to be fixed, also forever. Among the eight populations tracked in Figure 6.13a, allele A_1 drifted to fixation in five and to loss in three. Among the eight populations tracked in Figure 6.13b, A_1 drifted to fixation in one and to loss in three. It is just a matter of time before A_1 will become fixed or lost in the other populations as well. As some alleles drift to fixation and others drift to loss, the allelic diversity present in a population declines.

If genetic drift is the only evolutionary force at work, eventually one allele will drift to a frequency of 1 (that is, to fixation) and all other alleles will be lost.

Now imagine a finite population in which there are several alleles present at a particular locus: A_1, A_2, A_3, A_4, and so on. If genetic drift is the only evolutionary mechanism at work, then eventually one of the alleles will drift to fixation. At the same moment one allele becomes fixed, the last of the other alleles will be lost.

We would like to be able to predict which alleles will meet which fate. We cannot do so with certainly, but we can give odds. Sewall Wright (1931) proved that the probability that any given allele in a population will be the one that drifts to fixation is equal to that allele's initial frequency (see Box 6.3). If, for example, we start with a finite population in which A_1 is at a frequency of 0.73, and A_2 is at a frequency of 0.27, there is a 73% chance that the allele that drifts to fixation will be A_1.

Box 6.3   The probability that a given allele will be the one that drifts to fixation

Sewall Wright (1931) developed a detailed theory of genetic drift. Among many other results, he showed that the probability that a given allele will be the one that drifts to fixation is equal to that allele's initial frequency. Wright's model of genetic drift is beyond the scope of this book, but we can provide an intuitive explanation of fixation probabilities.

Imagine a population of N individuals. This population contains a total of $2N$ alleles. Imagine that every one of these alleles is unique. Assume that genetic drift is the only mechanism of evolution at work.

At some point in the future, one of the $2N$ alleles will have drifted to fixation and all the others will have been lost. Each allele must have an equal chance of being the one that drifts to fixation; that is what we meant by our assumption that genetic drift is the only mechanism of evolution at work. So we have $2N$ alleles, each with an equal probability of becoming fixed. Each allele's chance of becoming fixed must therefore be $\frac{1}{2N}$.

Now imagine that instead of each allele being unique, there are x copies of allele A_1, y copies of allele A_2, and z copies of allele A_3. Each copy of allele A_1 has a $\frac{1}{2N}$ chance of being the one that drifts to fixation. Therefore, the overall probability that a copy of allele A_1 will be the allele that drifts to fixation is

$$x \times \frac{1}{2N} = \frac{x}{2N}$$

Likewise, the probability that a copy of allele A_2 will be the allele that drifts to fixation is $\frac{y}{2N}$, and the probability that a copy of allele A_3 will be the allele that drifts to fixation is $\frac{z}{2N}$.

Notice that, $\frac{x}{2N}$, $\frac{y}{2N}$, and $\frac{z}{2N}$ are also the initial frequencies of A_1, A_2, and A_3 in the population. We have shown that the probability that a given allele will be the one that drifts to fixation is equal to that allele's initial frequency.

Loss of Heterozygosity

As allele frequencies in a finite population drift toward fixation or loss, the frequency of heterozygotes in the population decreases. Graphs (d), (e), and (f) in Figure 6.13 show the decline in the frequency of heterozygotes in our simulated populations.

To see why the frequency of heterozygotes declines, look first at the inset in graph (d). The inset plots the frequency of heterozygotes, calculated as $2(p)(1 - p)$, in a random mating population as a function of p, the frequency of allele A_1. The frequency of heterozygotes has its highest value, 0.5, when A_1 is at frequency 0.5. As the frequency of A_1 drops toward 0 or rises toward 1, the frequency of heterozygotes falls. And, of course, if the frequency of A_1 reaches 0 or 1, the frequency of heterozygotes falls to 0.

Now look at graphs (a), (b), and (c). In any given generation, the frequency of A_1 may move toward or away from 0.5 in any particular population (so long as A_1 has not already been fixed or lost). Thus the frequency of heterozygotes in any particular population may rise or fall. However, the overall trend across all populations is for allele frequencies to drift away from intermediate values and toward 0 or 1. So the average frequency of heterozygotes, across populations, should tend to fall.

Now look at graphs (d), (e), and (f). The heavy blue line in each graph tracks the frequency of heterozygotes averaged across the eight populations in question. The frequency of heterozygotes does indeed tend to fall, rapidly in small populations and slowly in large populations. Eventually one allele or the other will become fixed in every population, and the average frequency of heterozygotes will fall to 0.

The frequency of heterozygotes in a population is sometimes called the population's **heterozygosity**. We would like to be able to predict just how fast the heterozygosity of finite populations can be expected to decline. Sewell Wright (1931) showed that, averaged across many populations, the frequency of heterozygotes obeys the relationship

As alleles drift to fixation or loss, the frequency of heterozygotes in the population declines.

$$H_{g+1} = H_g \left[1 - \frac{1}{2N} \right]$$

where H_{g+1} is the heterozygosity in the next generation, H_g is the heterozygosity in this generation, and N is the number of individuals in the population. The value of $\left[1 - \frac{1}{2N} \right]$ is always between $\frac{1}{2}$ and 1, so the expected frequency of heterozygotes in the next generation is always less than the frequency of heterozygotes in this generation. The gray curves in Figure 6.13d, (e), and (f) show the declines in heterozygosity predicted by Wright's equation.

To appreciate just one of the implications of the inevitable loss of heterozygosity in finite populations, imagine that you are responsible for managing a captive population of an endangered species. Suppose there are just 50 breeding adults in zoos around the world. Even if you could arrange the shipment of adults or semen to accomplish random mating, you would still see a loss in heterozygosity of 1% every generation due to genetic drift.

An Experimental Study on Random Fixation and Loss of Heterozygosity

Our discussion of random fixation and loss of heterozygosity has so far been based on simulated populations and mathematical equations. Peter Buri (1956) studied these phenomena empirically, in small laboratory populations of the fruit fly, *Drosophila melanogaster*. Adopting an approach that had been used by Kerr and Wright (1954), Buri established 107 populations of flies, each with eight females and eight males. All the founding flies were heterozygotes for alleles of an eye-color gene called *brown*. All the flies had the same genotype: bw^{75}/bw. Thus, in all 107 populations, the initial frequency of the bw^{75} allele was 0.5. Buri maintained these populations for 19 generations. For every population in every generation, Buri kept the population size at 16 by picking eight females and eight males at random to be the breeders for the next generation.

What results would we predict? If neither allele bw^{75} nor allele bw confers a selective advantage, then we expect the frequency of allele bw^{75} to wander at random by genetic drift in every population. Nineteen generations should be enough, in populations of 16 individuals, for many populations to become fixed for one allele or the other. Because allele bw^{75} has an initial frequency of 0.5, we expect this allele to be lost about as often as it becomes fixed. As the bw^{75} allele is drifting toward fixation or loss in each population, we expect the average heterozygosity across all populations to decline. The rate of decline in heterozygosity should follow Wright's equation, given in the previous section.

Buri's results confirm these predictions. Each small graph in Figure 6.14 is a histogram summarizing the allele frequencies in all 107 populations in a particular generation. The horizontal axis represents the frequency of the bw^{75} allele, and the vertical axis represents the number of populations showing each frequency. The frequency of bw^{75} was 0.5 in all populations in generation zero, which is not shown

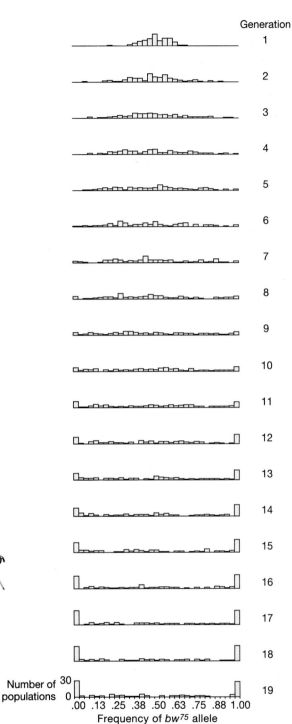

Generation: 1, 2, 3, 4, 5, 6, 7, 8, 9, 10, 11, 12, 13, 14, 15, 16, 17, 18, 19

Number of populations

.00 .13 .25 .38 .50 .63 .75 .88 1.00
Frequency of bw⁷⁵ allele

Figure 6.14 Nineteen generations of genetic drift in 107 populations of 16 fruit flies Each line is a histogram summarizing the allele frequencies in all 107 populations in a particular generation. The horizontal axis represents the frequency of the bw^{75} allele, and the vertical axis represents the number of populations showing each frequency. The frequency of bw^{75} was 0.5 in all populations in generation zero (not shown). By the end of the experiment, 30 populations had become fixed at a frequency of 0, and 28 had become fixed at a frequency of 1 (bottom line). Throughout the experiment, however, the distribution of allele frequencies remained symmetrical around 0.5. From data in Buri (1956), after Ayala and Kiger (1984).

in the figure. After one generation of genetic drift, most populations still had an allele frequency near 0.5, although one population had an allele frequency as low as 0.22 and another had an allele frequency as high as 0.69. As the frequency of the bw^{75} allele rose in some populations and fell in others, the distribution of allele frequencies rapidly spread out. In generation four, the frequency of bw^{75} hit 1 in a population for the first time. In generation six, the frequency of bw^{75} hit 0 in a population for the first time. As the allele frequency reached 0 or 1 in more and

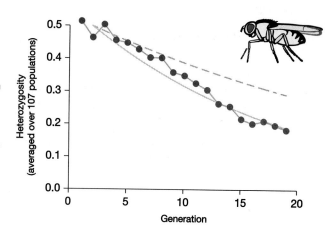

Figure 6.15 **The frequency of heterozygotes declined with time in Buri's experimental populations** The red dots show the frequency of heterozygotes in each generation, averaged across all 107 populations. The dashed gray curve shows the theoretical prediction for a population of 16 flies. The solid gray curve shows the theoretical prediction for a population of 9 flies. The graph demonstrates that (1) heterozygosity decreases across generations in small populations, and (2) although all the populations had an actual population of 16 flies, their effective population size was roughly 9. Replotted from data in Buri (1956), after Hartl (1981).

more populations, the distribution of frequencies became U-shaped. By the end of the experiment, bw^{75} had been lost in 30 populations and had become fixed in 28. The 30:28 ratio of losses to fixations is very close to the 1:1 ratio we would predict under genetic drift. During Buri's experiment there was dramatic evolution in nearly all 107 of the fruit fly populations, but natural selection had nothing to do with it.

The genetic properties of the *brown* locus were such that Buri could identify all three genotypes from their phenotypes. Thus Buri was able to directly assess the frequency of heterozygotes in each population. The frequency of heterozygotes in generation zero was 1, so the heterozygosity in generation one was 0.5. Every generation thereafter, Buri noted the frequency of heterozygotes in each population, then took the average heterozygosity across all 107 populations. Figure 6.15 tracks these values for average heterozygosity over the 19 generations of the experiment. Look first at the red dots, which represent the actual data. Consistent with our theoretical prediction, the average frequency of heterozygotes steadily declined.

Empirical studies confirm that under genetic drift alleles become fixed or lost and the frequency of heterozygotes declines. Indeed, these processes often happen faster than predicted.

The fit between theory and results is not perfect, however. The dashed gray curve in the figure shows the predicted decline in heterozygosity, using Wright's equation and a population size of 16. The actual decline in heterozygosity was more rapid than expected. The solid gray curve shows the predicted decline for a population size of 9; it fits the data well. Buri's populations lost heterozygosity as though they contained only 9 individuals instead of 16. In other words, the **effective population size** in Buri's experiment was 9 (see Box 6.4). Among the explanations are that some of the flies in each population may have died due to accidents before reproducing, or some males may have been rejected as mates by the females.

Buri's experiment with fruit flies shows that the theory of genetic drift allows us to make accurate qualitative predictions, and reasonably accurate quantitative predictions, about the behavior of alleles in finite populations—at least in the lab. In the next section we will consider evidence on random fixation of alleles and loss of heterozygosity in natural populations.

Random Fixation and Loss of Heterozygosity in Natural Populations

Alan Templeton and colleagues (1990) tested predictions about the random fixation of alleles by documenting the results of a natural experiment in Missouri's Ozark Mountains. Although now covered in oak-hickory forest, the Ozarks were

Box 6.4   Effective population size

The effective population size is the size of an ideal theoretical population that would lose heterozygosity at the same rate as an actual population of interest. The effective population size is virtually always smaller than the actual population size. In Buri's experiment, two possible reasons for the difference in effective versus actual population size are that (1) some of the flies in each bottle died (by accident) before reproducing and (2) fruit flies exhibit sexual selection by both male–male combat and female choice (see Chapter 9)—either of which could have prevented some males from reproducing.

The effective population size is particularly sensitive to differences in the number of reproductively active females versus males. When there are different numbers of each sex in a population, the effective population size N_e can be estimated as

$$N_e = \frac{4N_m N_f}{(N_m + N_f)}$$

where N_m is the number of males and N_f is the number of females.

To see how strongly an imbalanced sex ratio can reduce the effective population size, use the formula to show that: when there are 5 males and 5 females, $N_e = 10$; when there is 1 male and 9 females, $N_e = 3.6$; and when there is 1 male and 1000 females, $N_e = 4$. Consider the logistical problems involved in maintaining a captive breeding program for a species in which the males are extremely aggressive and will not tolerate each other's presence.

---

part of a desert during an extended period of hot, dry climate that lasted from 8000 to 4000 years ago. The desert that engulfed the Ozarks was contiguous with the desert of the American Southwest. Many southwestern desert species expanded their ranges eastward into the Ozarks. Among them was the collared lizard (*Crotaphytus collaris*). When the warm period ended, the collared lizard's range retracted westward again and the oak-hickory forest reinvaded the Ozarks. Within this forest, however, on exposed rocky outcrops, are small remnants of desert habitat called glades. Living in some of these glades are relict populations of collared lizards. Most populations are sufficiently isolated from each other that there is little or no gene flow among them. The relict populations are tiny; most harbor no more than a few dozen individuals.

Because of the small size of the glade populations, Templeton and colleagues predicted that the collard lizards of the Ozarks would bear a strong imprint of genetic drift. Within each population, most loci should be fixed for a single allele, and genetic variation should be very low. Which allele became fixed in any particular population should be a matter of chance, however, so there should be considerable genetic diversity among populations.

Templeton and colleagues assayed several glade populations for genetic variation. The researchers screened lizards for their genotypes at a variety of enzyme loci, for their ribosomal DNA genotypes, and for their mitochondrial DNA genotypes. The researchers identified among the lizards seven distinct multilocus genotypes. Confirming the predicted consequences of isolation and small population size, most glade populations are fixed for a single multilocus genotype, with different genotypes fixed in different populations (Figure 6.16).

Andrew Young and colleagues (1996) tested predictions about the effect of population size on heterozygosity with a comparative study of plants. The researchers compiled data from the literature and plotted two measures of overall genetic diversity against population size in three flowering herbs and a tree. The first measure of genetic diversity was genetic polymorphism, the fraction of loci within

Figure 6.16 **Genetic varia-tion in Ozark glade popula-tions of the collared lizard**
(a) The pie diagram gives a key to the seven distinct multilocus genotypes that Templeton et al. (1990) found in Ozark collared lizards. Each multilocus genotype is characterized by a malate de-hydrogenase (MDH) genotype (the two alleles are "slow" (S) and "fast" (F), a mitochondrial DNA haplotype (designated A–D), and a ribosomal DNA genotype (designated I–III). (b) This is a map of southern Mis-souri, showing the locations and genetic compositions of nine glade populations. The shading of each pie diagram represents the frequency in a single popula-tion of each multilocus genotype present. (c) This is an expanded map of a small piece of the map in (b). It gives the locations and genetic compositions of five more glade populations. From Temple-ton et al. (1990). Copyright © 1990 Alan R. Templeton. Reprint-ed by permission of the author.

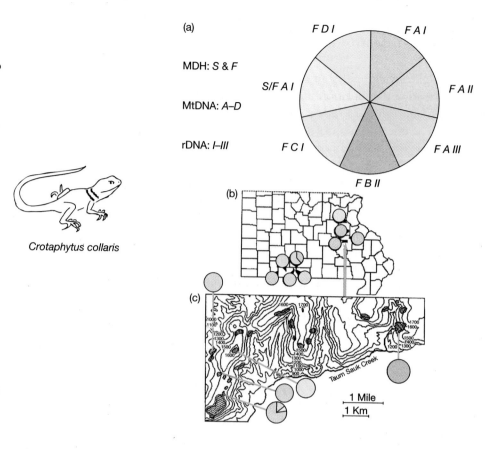

Crotaphytus collaris

the genome that have at least two alleles with frequencies higher than 0.01. The second was allelic richness, the average number of alleles per locus. Both of these measures are related to heterozygosity. If a given locus has more than one allele, and if a substantial number of individuals in the population are heterozygotes, then the locus contributes to high values of polymorphism and allelic richness. If, on the other hand, the locus is fixed for a single allele and no individual in the pop-ulation is a heterozygote, then the locus lowers the population's polymorphism and allelic richness. Because genetic drift is more pronounced in small populations than in large ones, and because genetic drift results in the loss of heterozygosity, Young and colleagues predicted that small populations would have lower levels of polymorphism and allelic richness. Young et al.'s plots appear in Figure 6.17. Con-sistent with their prediction, in almost every case smaller populations did indeed harbor less genetic diversity.

The studies by Templeton et al. and Young et al. show that in at least some nat-ural populations genetic drift leads, as predicted, to random fixation and reduced het-erozygosity. The loss of genetic diversity in small populations is of particular concern to conservation biologists, for two reasons. First, genetic diversity is the raw mater-ial for adaptive evolution. Imagine a species reduced to a few remnant populations by habitat destruction or some other environmental change. Genetic drift may rob the remnant populations of their potential to evolve in response to a changing en-vironment at precisely the moment the environment is changing most drastically. Sec-ond, a loss of heterozygosity also entails an increase in homozygosity. Increased homozygosity often leads to reduced fitness in experimental populations (see, for ex-ample, Polans and Allard 1989; Barrett and Charlesworth 1991). Presumably this in-

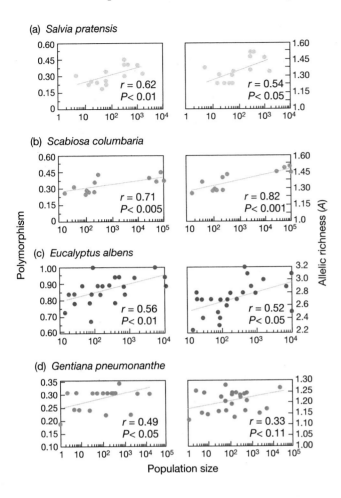

Figure 6.17 Population size and genetic diversity Each data point on these scatterplots represents a population of flowering plants. Polymorphism, plotted on the vertical axis of the graphs at left, is the proportion of allozyme loci at which the frequency of the most common allele in the population is less than 0.99. In other words, polymorphism is the fraction of alleles that are substantially polymorphic. Allelic richness, plotted on the vertical axis of the graphs at right, is the average number of alleles per locus. The statistic r is a measure of association, called the Pearson correlation coefficient, which varies from 0 (no association between variables) to 1 (perfect correlation). P specifies the probability that the correlation coefficient is significantly different from zero. *Salvia pratensis*, *Scabiosa columbaria*, and *Gentiana pneumonanthe* are all flowering herbs; *Eucalyptus albens* is a tree. Reprinted from Young et al. (1996). Copyright © 1996 Elsevier Science. Reprinted with permission of Elsevier Science.

volves the same mechanism as inbreeding depression: It exposes deleterious alleles to selection. We will consider inbreeding depression in Section 6.3.

The Rate of Evolution by Genetic Drift

The theory and experiments we have discussed in this section establish that sampling error can be an important mechanism of evolution. The final aspect of drift that we shall consider here is the rate of evolution when genetic drift is the only force at work.

First, we need to define what we mean by the rate of evolution at a single locus. We will take the rate of evolution to be the rate at which new alleles created by mutation are substituted for other alleles already present. Figure 6.18 illustrates the process of **substitution** and distinguishes substitution from mutation. The figure follows a gene pool of 10 alleles for 20 generations. Initially, all of the alleles are identical (white dots). In the fourth generation, a new allele appears (light orange dot), created by a mutation in one of the original alleles. Over several generations, this allele drifts to high frequency. In generation fifteen, a second new allele appears (blue dot), created by a mutation in a descendant of the first light orange allele. In generation nineteen, the last of the white alleles is lost. At this point, we can say that the light orange allele has been substituted for the white allele. Thus, by evolutionary substitution, we mean the fixation of a new mutation, with or without additional mutational change.

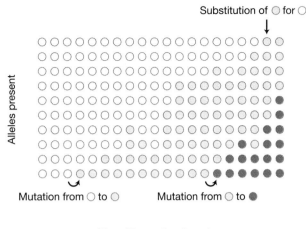

Figure 6.18 Mutation is the creation of a new allele; substitution is the fixation of the new allele, with or without additional mutational change This graph shows the 10 alleles present in each of 20 successive generations, in a hypothetical population of five individuals. During the time covered in the graph, the light orange allele was substituted for the white allele. The blue allele may ultimately be substituted for the light orange allele, or it may be lost.

When mutation, genetic drift, and selection interact, three processes occur: (1) Deleterious alleles appear and are eliminated by selection; (2) neutral mutations appear and are fixed or lost by chance; and (3) advantageous alleles appear and are swept to fixation by selection. The relative importance of (2) and (3) in determining the overall substitution rate is a matter of debate.

When genetic drift is the only mechanism of evolution at work, the rate of substitution is simply equal to the mutation rate (see Box 6.5). This is true regardless of the population size, because two effects associated with population size cancel each other out: More mutations occur in a larger population, but in a large population each new mutation has a smaller chance of drifting to fixation. Under genetic drift, large populations generate and maintain more genetic variation than small populations, but populations of all sizes accumulate substitutions at the same rate.

Of course, other mechanisms of evolution than drift are often at work. We can allow some natural selection into our model and still get a similar result. Imagine that some mutations are deleterious, while others are selectively neutral. The deleterious mutations will be eliminated by natural selection and will never become fixed. The rate of substitution will then be equal to the rate at which neutral mutations occur.

Evolutionary biologists are divided on the relevance of this calculation to real populations. All agree that one kind of mutation and one kind of selection have been left out (see Box 6.5). Some mutations are selectively advantageous, and are swept to fixation by natural selection more surely and much faster than drift would ever carry them. Evolutionists are of two minds, however, over how often this happens.

Proponents of the **neutral theory**, long championed by Motoo Kimura (1983), hold that advantageous mutations are exceedingly rare, and that most alleles of most genes are selectively neutral. Neutralists predict that for most genes in most populations, the rate of evolution will, indeed, be equal to the neutral mutation rate.

Proponents of the **selectionist theory**, most strongly championed by John Gillespie (1991), hold that advantageous mutations are common enough that they cannot be ignored. Selectionists predict that for many genes in most populations, the rate of substitution will reflect the action of natural selection on advantageous mutations.

The dispute between the neutralists and the selectionists is unresolved, and we will defer the presentation of empirical evidence until Chapter 18. The neutral theory is central, however, to many aspects of modern evolutionary biology. It provides a null model for the detection of selection at the level of DNA and protein sequences (see Chapters 18 and 19). And it provides the theoretical basis for the molecular clocks used to infer the ages of common ancestors from sequence data (see Chapter 13).

Box 6.5   **The rate of evolutionary substitution under genetic drift**

Here we show a calculation establishing that when genetic drift is the only mechanism of evolution at work, the rate of evolutionary substitution is equal to the mutation rate (Kimura 1968).

Imagine a diploid population of size N. Within this population are $2N$ alleles of the locus of interest, where by "alleles" we mean copies of the gene, regardless of whether they are identical or not. Let v be the rate of selectively neutral mutations per allele per generation, and assume that each mutation creates an allele that has not previously existed in the population. Then every generation, there will be

$$2Nv$$

new alleles created by mutation. Because by assumption all new alleles are selectively neutral, genetic drift is the only force at work. Each new allele has the same chance of drifting to fixation as any other allele in the population. That chance, equal to the frequency of the new allele, is

$$\frac{1}{2N}$$

Therefore, each generation, the number of new alleles that are created by mutation and are destined to drift to fixation, is

$$2Nv \times \frac{1}{2N} = v$$

The same argument applies to every generation. Therefore, the rate of evolution at the locus of interest is v substitutions per generation.

It will be useful for discussions in other chapters to explore in more detail what we mean by v, the rate of neutral mutations. Imagine that the locus of interest is a gene encoding a protein that is L amino acids long. Let u be the rate of mutations per codon per generation. The overall rate of mutation at our locus is given by

$$\mu = uL(d + a + f) = uLd + uLa + uLf$$

where d is the fraction of codon changes that are deleterious, a is the fraction that are selectively advantageous, f is the fraction that are selectively neutral, and $d + a + f = 1$. Note that the rightmost term, uLf, is equal to our earlier v.

In showing that the rate of substitution is equal to v, we assumed that d and a are both equal to zero. In any real population, of course, many mutations are deleterious and d is not zero. This does not change our calculation of the substitution rate. Deleterious alleles are eliminated by natural selection, and do not contribute to the rate of evolutionary substitution.

Proponents of the neutral theory hold that a is approximately equal to zero, and that f is much larger than a. Therefore they predict that evolutionary subsitution will be dominated by neutral mutations and drift, and will occur at the rate $v = uLf$, as we have calculated.

Proponents of the selectionist theory hold that a is too large to ignore, and that the rate of evolutionary substitution will be significantly influenced by the action of natural selection in favor of advantageous alleles.

In summary, genetic drift is a nonadaptive mechanism of evolution. Simply as a result of chance sampling error, allele frequencies can change from one generation to the next. Genetic drift is most powerful in small populations and when compounded over many generations. Ultimately, genetic drift leads to the fixation of some alleles and the loss of others, and to an overall decline in genetic diversity.

6.3 Nonrandom Mating

The final assumption of the Hardy–Weinberg analysis is that individuals in the population mate at random. In this section we relax that assumption and allow individuals to mate nonrandomly. Nonrandom mating does not, by itself, cause evolution. Nonrandom mating can nonetheless have profound indirect effects on evolution.

The most common type of nonrandom mating, and the kind we will focus on here, is inbreeding. Inbreeding is mating among genetic relatives. The effect of inbreeding on the genetics of a population is to increase the frequency of homozygotes compared to what is expected under Hardy–Weinberg assumptions.

Inbreeding decreases the frequency of heterozygotes and increases the frequency of homozygotes compared to expectations under Hardy–Weinberg assumptions.

To show how this happens, we will consider the most extreme example of inbreeding: self-fertilization, or selfing. Imagine a population in Hardy–Weinberg equilibrium with alleles A_1 and A_2 at initial frequencies of 0.5 each. The frequency of A_1A_1 individuals is 0.25, the frequency of A_1A_2 individuals is 0.5, and the frequency of A_2A_2 individuals is 0.25 (Figure 6.19a). Imagine that there are 1000 individuals in the population: 250 A_1A_1, 500 A_1A_2, and 250 A_2A_2. If all the individuals in the population reproduce by selfing, homozygous parents will produce all homozygous offspring, while heterozygous parents will produce half homozygous and half heterozygous offspring. Among 1000 offspring in our population, there will be 375 A_1A_1, 250 A_1A_2, and 375 A_2A_2. If the population continues to self for two more generations, then, among every 1000 individuals in the final generation, there will be 468.75 homozygotes of each type and 62.5 heterozygotes (Figure 6.19b). The frequency of heterozygotes has been halved every generation, and the frequency of homozgyotes has increased.

Conclusion 2 of the Hardy–Weinberg analysis is violated when individuals self. We cannot predict the genotype frequencies by multiplying the allele frequencies. Note that in generation three, in Figure 6.19b, the allele frequencies are still 0.5 for A_1 and 0.5 for A_2. Yet the frequency of heterozygotes is far less than $2(0.5)(0.5)$. Compared to Hardy–Weinberg expectations, there is a deficit of heterozygotes and an excess of homozygotes. The general case under selfing is shown algebraically in Table 6.1.

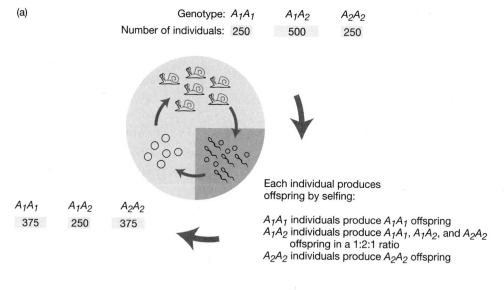

Figure 6.19 Inbreeding alters genotype frequencies (a) This figure follows the genotype frequencies in an imaginary population of 1000 snails from one generation's adults (top) to the next generation's zygotes (bottom left). The frequencies of both allele A_1 and A_2 are 0.5. The colored bar charts show the number of individuals with each genotype. Every individual reproduces by selfing. Homozygotes produce homozygous offspring and heterozygotes produce both heterozygous and homozygous offspring, so the frequency of homozygotes goes up, and the frequency of heterozygotes goes down. (b) These bar charts show what will happen to the genotype frequencies if this population continues to self for two more generations.

(a)

Genotype:	A_1A_1	A_1A_2	A_2A_2
Number of individuals:	250	500	250

A_1A_1	A_1A_2	A_2A_2
375	250	375

Each individual produces offspring by selfing:

A_1A_1 individuals produce A_1A_1 offspring
A_1A_2 individuals produce A_1A_1, A_1A_2, and A_2A_2 offspring in a 1:2:1 ratio
A_2A_2 individuals produce A_2A_2 offspring

(b)

Genotype:	A_1A_1	A_1A_2	A_2A_2	
Number of individuals:	250	500	250	Generation 0
	375	250	375	Generation 1
	437.5	125	437.5	Generation 2
	468.75	62.5	468.75	Generation 3

Table 6.1 **Changes in genotype frequencies with successive generations of selfing**

The frequency of allele A_1 is p and the frequency of allele A_2 is q. Note that allele frequencies do not change from generation to generation—only the genotype frequencies. After Crow (1983).

Generation	A_1A_1	Frequency of A_1A_2	A_2A_2
0	p^2	$2pq$	q^2
1	$p^2 + (pq/2)$	pq	$q^2 + (pq/2)$
2	$p^2 + (3\,pq/4)$	$pq/2$	$q^2 + (3\,pq/4)$
3	$p^2 + (7\,pq/8)$	$pq/4$	$q^2 + (7\,pq/8)$
4	$p^2 + (15\,pq/16)$	$pq/8$	$q^2 + (15\,pq/16)$

What about Hardy–Weinberg conclusion 1? Do the allele frequencies change from generation to generation under inbreeding? They did not in our numerical example. We can check the general case by calculating the frequency of allele A_1 in the gene pool produced by the population shown in the last row of Table 6.1. The frequency of allele A_1 in the gene pool is equal to the frequency of A_1A_1 adults in the population ($= p^2 + \frac{15pq}{16}$) plus half the frequency of A_1A_2 ($= \frac{1}{2}[\frac{pq}{8}]$). That gives

$$p^2 + \frac{15pq}{16} + \frac{1}{2}\left[\frac{pq}{8}\right] = p^2 + \frac{15pq}{16} + \frac{pq}{16} = p^2 + pq$$

Now substitute $(1 - p)$ for q to give $p^2 + p(1 - p) = p$. This is the same frequency for allele A_1 that we started out with at the top of Table 6.1. Although inbreeding does cause genotype frequencies to change from generation to generation, it does not cause allele frequencies to change. Inbreeding by itself, therefore, is not a mechanism of evolution. As we will see, however, inbreeding can have important evolutionary consequences.

Empirical Research on Inbreeding: The Malaria Parasite

Because inbreeding can produce a large excess of homozygotes, Hardy–Weinberg analysis can be used to detect inbreeding in nature. As an example, we consider research on a malaria parasite in New Guinea (Paul et al. 1995). The life cycle of this protozoan, *Plasmodium falciparum,* alternates between stages that live in mosquitoes and stages that live in humans (Figure 6.20). The only diploid part of the parasite's life cycle occurs in the mosquito; there, a stage called the oocyst resides in the midgut wall. The other stages, which infect the human liver and red blood cells and include the cells transmitted to mosquitoes, are haploid.

The biology of the *P. falciparum* malaria parasite suggests that inbreeding may be common in this species. Here is the logic: Years ago, W. D. Hamilton (1967) observed that unusual sex ratios are common when a single female parasite or parasitoid colonizes a new host. In the fig wasps Hamilton was studying, for example, females colonizing figs alone tended to produce many more female young than male young. Hamilton went on to develop the mathematics showing why this strategy evolved, and predicted that it would occur in any parasite where single foundresses are common (Hamilton 1967, 1979; see also Read et al. 1992). The

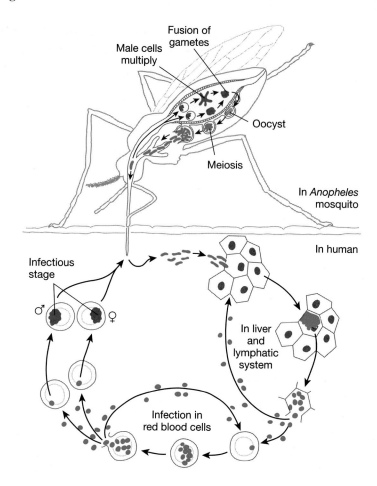

Figure 6.20 Life cycle of the malaria parasite *Plasmodium falciparum* The oocyst (orange) is diploid; all other stages of the parasite's life cycle (blue, red, and green) are haploid.

essence of the argument is this: In species in which brother–sister mating is the rule, females will have more grand-offspring if they produce only enough males to ensure that all their daughters will be fertilized.

What does this have to do with the malaria parasite? R. E. L. Paul and colleagues (1995), working in Karen Day's lab, observed a female-biased sex ratio (more females than males) in the infectious stages of *P. falciparum* . The researchers hypothesized that the phenomenon Hamilton discovered was at work in the parasite population they studied. Although malaria is common in New Guinea, the rate of transmission is relatively low. This means that every human infected tends to have only one to a few *P. falciparum* genotypes present. In addition, it appears that each cycle of infection in a human's red blood cells, which produces the type of *Plasmodium* cells picked up by mosquitoes, may be restricted to cells of a single genotype. The result is that each mosquito tends to become infected with one, or at most two, genotypes of *P. falciparum* cells. In effect, all the cells that the mosquito picks up are offspring of a single female. This infectious stage is where Paul et al. found the female-biased sex ratio. The few male cells that occur multiply inside the mosquito and then fuse with the female cells—often their own siblings—to form diploid oocysts. If this hypothesis is correct, then the oocysts should be strongly inbred, and should show a large excess of homozygotes.

Paul and colleagues estimated allele and genotype frequencies among oocysts for three *P. falciparum* protein-encoding genes: *MSP-1, MSP-2,* and *GLURP.* The

Table 6.2   **Allele frequencies for three polymorphic genes in the malaria parasite *Plasmodium falciparum***

	MSP-2		MSP-1		GLURP	
Allele	Observed Frequency	Allele	Observed Frequency	Allele	Observed Frequency	
A_1	0.02	A_1	0.02	A_1	0.07	
A_2	0.06	A_2	0.26	A_2	0.42	
A_3	0.18	A_3	0.19	A_3	0.28	
A_4	0.27	A_4	0.32	A_4	0.08	
A_5	0.12	A_5	0.12	A_5	0.15	
A_6	0.08	A_6	0.09			
A_7	0.05					
A_8	0.07					
A_9	0.09					
A_{10}	0.06					

Source: Calculated from Figure 1 in Paul et al. (1995).

scientists first dissected female mosquitoes and isolated the malaria oocysts encased in their stomach linings. The researchers then extracted DNA from the oocysts and directly analyzed it for allelic variation. All three protein-encoding loci were polymorphic, meaning that each had more than one allele. The data provide an estimate for the frequency of different alleles in the population (Table 6.2), and a count of the number of homozygotes and heterozygotes in the sample (Table 6.3).

Do the allele and genotype frequencies the researchers measured conform to those expected under Hardy–Weinberg conditions? The answer, resoundingly, is no (Table 6.3). Consistent with Paul and colleagues' prediction, there is an enormous excess of homozygotes in the parasite population and a corresponding deficit of heterozygotes.

Strictly speaking, the excess of homozygotes shows only that one or more of the Hardy–Weinberg assumptions is being violated in the malaria population. However, only nonrandom mating can easily produce homozygote excesses as large as the one Paul et al. found. In combination with the researchers' observations on the parasite's reproductive biology, the data in Tables 6.2 and 6.3 make a persuasive case that *P. falciparum* in New Guinea are indeed inbreeding.

Table 6.3   **The observed number of homozygotes and heterozygotes at three *P. falciparum* loci**

In each case, the observed number of individuals with a particular kind of genotype is compared to the number expected under Hardy–Weinberg conditions of random mating and no mutation, selection, migration, or genetic drift. In all three cases, the differences are statistically significant ($P < 0.01$; see Box 5.5).

	(a) MSP-2		(b) MSP-1		(c) GLURP	
	Observed	Expected	Observed	Expected	Observed	Expected
Homozygotes	55	10	38	9	40	12
Heterozygotes	9	54	1	30	1	29

Box 6.6   Genotype frequencies in an inbred population

Here we add inbreeding to the Hardy–Weinberg analysis. Imagine a population with two alleles at a single locus: A_1 and A_2, with frequencies p and q. We can calculate the genotype frequencies in the next generation by letting gametes find each other in the gene pool, as we would for a random mating population. The twist added by inbreeding is that the gene pool is not thoroughly mixed. Once we have picked an egg to watch, for example, we can think of the sperm in the gene pool as consisting of two fractions: a fraction $(1 - F)$ carrying alleles that are not identical by descent to the one in the egg; and the fraction F carrying alleles that are identical by descent to the one in the egg (because they were produced by relatives of the female that produced the egg). The calculations of genotype frequencies are as follows:

- **A_1A_1 homozygotes:** There are two ways we might witness the creation of an A_1A_1 homozygote. The first way is that we pick an egg that is A_1 (an event with probability p) and watch it get fertilized by a sperm that is A_1 by chance, rather than by common ancestry. The frequency of unrelated A_1 sperm in the gene pool is $p(1 - F)$, so the probability of getting a homozygote by chance is

$$p \times p(1 - F) = p^2(1 - F)$$

The second way to get a homozygote is to pick an egg that is A_1 (an event with probability p) and watch it get fertilized by a sperm that is A_1 because of common ancestry (an event with probability F). The probability of getting a homozygote this way is pF. The probability of getting an A_1A_1 homozygote by

either the first way or the second way is the sum of their individual probabilities:

$$p^2(1 - F) + pF$$

- **A_1A_2 heterozygotes:** There are two ways to get an A_1A_2 heterozygote. The first way is to pick an egg that is A_1 (an event with probability p) and watch it get fertilized by an unrelated sperm that is A_2. The frequency of A_2 unrelated sperm is $q(1 - F)$, so the probability of getting a heterozygote this first way is $pq(1 - F)$. The second way is to pick an egg that is A_2 (probability: q) and watch it get fertilized by an unrelated sperm that is A_1 [probability: $p(1 - F)$]. The probability of getting a heterozygote the second way is $qp(1 - F)$. The probability of getting a heterozygote by either the first way or the second way is the sum of their individual probabilities:

$$pq(1 - F) + qp(1 - F) = 2pq(1 - F)$$

- **A_1A_2 homozygotes:** We can get an A_2A_2 homozygote either by picking an A_2 egg (probability: q) and watching it get fertilized by an unrelated A_2 sperm [probability: $q(1 - F)$], or by picking an A_2 egg (probability: q) and watching it get fertilized by a sperm that is A_2 because of common ancestry (probability: F). The overall probability of getting an A_2A_2 homozygote is

$$q^2(1 - F) + qF$$

Readers may wish to verify that the genotype frequencies sum to 1.

General Analysis of Inbreeding

So far our treatment of inbreeding has been limited to self-fertilitization and sibling mating. But inbreeding can also occur as matings among more distant relatives, such as cousins. Inbreeding that is less extreme than selfing produces the same effect as selfing—it increases the proportion of homozygotes—but at a slower rate. For a general mathematical treatment of inbreeding, population geneticists use a conceptual tool called the **coefficient of inbreeding**. This quantity is symbolized by F, and is defined as the probability that the two alleles in an individual are identical by descent (meaning that both alleles came from the same ancestor allele in some previous generation). Box 6.6 shows that in an inbred population that otherwise obeys Hardy–Weinberg assumptions, the genotype frequencies are

$$\begin{array}{ccc} \mathbf{A_1A_1} & \mathbf{A_1A_2} & \mathbf{A_2A_2} \\ p^2(1-F)+pF & 2pq(1-F) & q^2(1-F)+qF \end{array}$$

Readers can verify these expressions by substituting the values $F = 0$, which gives the original Hardy–Weinberg genotype ratios, and $F = 0.5$, which represents selfing and gives the ratios shown for generation 1 in Table 6.1.

The same logic applies when many alleles are present in the gene pool. Then, the frequency of any homozygote A_iA_i is given by

$$p_i^2(1-F)+p_iF$$

and the frequency of any heterozygote A_iA_j is given by

$$2p_ip_j(1-F)$$

where p_i is the frequency of allele A_i and p_j is the frequency of allele A_j.

The last expression states that the fraction of individuals in a population that are heterozygotes (that is, the population's heterozygosity) is proportional to $(1 - F)$. If we compare the heterozygosity of an inbred population, H_F, with that of a random mating population, H_0, then the relationship will be

$$H_F = H_0(1-F)$$

Anytime F is greater than 0, the frequency of heterozygotes is lower in an inbred population than it is in a random mating population.

Computing F

To measure the degree of inbreeding in actual populations, we need a way to calculate F. Doing this directly requires a pedigree—a diagram showing the geneological relationships of individuals. Figure 6.21 shows a pedigree leading to a female who is the daughter of half-siblings. There are two ways this female could receive alleles that are identical by descent. One is that she could receive two copies of her

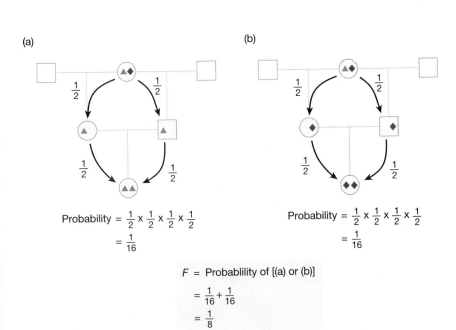

(a)

Probability $= \frac{1}{2} \times \frac{1}{2} \times \frac{1}{2} \times \frac{1}{2}$

$= \frac{1}{16}$

(b)

Probability $= \frac{1}{2} \times \frac{1}{2} \times \frac{1}{2} \times \frac{1}{2}$

$= \frac{1}{16}$

$F = $ Probablility of [(a) or (b)]

$= \frac{1}{16} + \frac{1}{16}$

$= \frac{1}{8}$

Figure 6.21 Calculating *F* from a pedigree In parts (a) and (b), squares represent males; circles represent females; arrows represent the movement of alleles from parents to offspring via gametes. The green triangles and blue diamonds represent alleles at a particular locus.

grandmother's "green triangle" allele (Figure 6.21a). This will happen if the grandmother passes the triangle allele to her daughter and to her son, and the daughter passes it to the granddaughter, and the son passes it to the granddaughter. The total probability of this scenario is $\frac{1}{16}$. The second way is that she could receive two copies of her grandmother's "blue diamond" allele (Figure 6.21b). The total probability of this scenario is $\frac{1}{16}$. The probability that the daughter of half-siblings will have two alleles identical by descent by either the first scenario or the second scenario is $\frac{1}{16} + \frac{1}{16} = \frac{1}{8}$. Thus, F for an offspring of half-siblings is $\frac{1}{8}$.

Inbreeding Depression

Inbreeding may lead to reduced mean fitness if it generates offspring homozygous for deleterious alleles.

Although inbreeding does not directly change allele frequencies, it can still affect the evolution of a population. Among the most important consequences of inbreeding for evolution is inbreeding depression.

Inbreeding depression usually results from the exposure of deleterious recessive alleles to selection. To see how this works, consider the extreme case illustrated by loss-of-function mutations. These alleles are often recessive, because a single wild-type allele can still generate enough functional protein, in most instances, to produce a normal phenotype. Even though they may have no fitness consequences at all in heterozygotes, loss-of-function mutations can be lethal in homozygotes. By increasing the proportion of individuals in a population that are homozygotes, inbreeding increases the frequency with which deleterious recessives affect phenotypes. Inbreeding depression refers to the effect these alleles have on the average fitness of offspring in the population.

Studies on humans have shown that inbreeding does, in fact, expose deleterious recessive alleles, and data from numerous studies consistently show that children of first cousins have higher mortality rates than children of unrelated parents (Figure 6.22). Strong inbreeding depression has also been frequently observed in captive populations of animals (for example, Hill 1974; Ralls et al. 1979).

Perhaps the most powerful studies of inbreeding depression in natural populations concern flowering plants, in which the inbreeding can be studied experimentally. In many angiosperms, selfed and outcrossed offspring can be produced

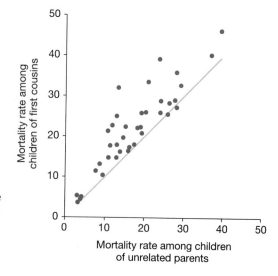

Figure 6.22 **Inbreeding depression in humans** Each dot on this graph represents childhood mortality rates for a human population. The horizontal axis represents mortality rates for children of unrelated parents; the vertical axis represents mortality rates for children of first cousins. The gray line shows where the points would fall if mortality rates for the two kinds of children were equal. Although childhood mortality rates vary widely among populations, the mortality rate for children of cousins is almost always higher than the rate for children of unrelated parents—usually by about four percentage points. Plotted from data in Bittles and Neel (1994).

from the same parent through hand pollination. In experiments like these, inbreeding depression can be defined as

$$\delta = 1 - \frac{w_s}{w_o}$$

where w_s and w_o are the fitnesses of selfed and outcrossed progeny, respectively. This definition makes levels of inbreeding depression comparable across species. Three patterns are starting to emerge from experimental studies.

First, inbreeding effects are often easiest to detect when plants undergo some sort of environmental stress. For example, when Michele Dudash (1990) compared the growth and reproduction of selfed and outcrossed rose pinks (*Sabatia angularis*), the plants showed some inbreeding depression when grown in the greenhouse or garden, but their performance diverged more strongly when they were planted in the field. Lorne Wolfe (1993) got a similar result with a waterleaf (*Hydrophyllum appendiculatum*): Selfed and outcrossed individuals had equal fitness when grown alone, but differed significantly when grown under competition. And in the common annual called jewelweed (*Impatiens capensis*), McCall et al. (1994) observed the strongest inbreeding effects on survival when an unplanned insect outbreak occurred during the course of their experiment.

Second, inbreeding effects are much more likely to show up later in the life cycle (not, for example, during the germination or seedling stage). This pattern is striking (Figure 6.23). Why does it exist? Wolfe (1993) suggests that maternal effects—specifically, the seed mother's influence on offspring phenotype through provisioning of seeds—can mask the influence of deleterious recessives until later in the life cycle.

Third, inbreeding depression varies among family lineages. Michele Dudash and colleagues (1997) compared the growth and reproductive performance of inbred versus outcrossed individuals from each of several families in two annual populations of the herb *Mimulus guttatus*. Some families showed inbreeding depression; others showed no discernable effect of type of mating; still others showed improved performance under inbreeding.

Inbreeding depression has been documented in natural populations of animals as well. Long-term studies in two separate populations of a bird called the great tit (*Parus major*) have shown that inbreeding depression can have strong effects on reproductive success. When Paul Greenwood and co-workers (1978) defined inbred matings as those between first cousins or more closely related individuals, they

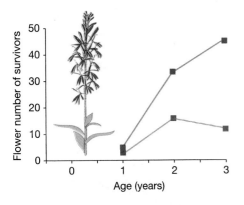

Figure 6.23 Inbreeding depression in flowering plants increases as individuals age   This graph compares the number of flowers produced (a measure of fitness) as a function of time for outcrossed (blue boxes) versus selfed (red boxes) individuals in *Lobelia cardinalis*, a perennial in the bluebell family. The disparity in performance increases with time, indicating that inbreeding depression becomes more pronounced with age. From Johnston (1992). Copyright © 1992 Evolution. Reprinted by permission.

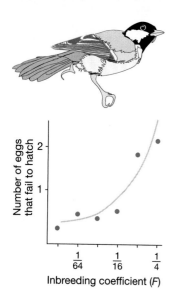

Number of eggs that fail to hatch

$\frac{1}{64}$ $\frac{1}{16}$ $\frac{1}{4}$

Inbreeding coefficient (*F*)

Figure 6.24 Inbreeding increases egg failure in great tits From van Noordwijk and Scharloo (1981). Copyright © 1992 Evolution. Reprinted by permission.

found that the survival of inbred nestlings was much lower than that of outbred individuals. Similarly, A. J. van Noordwijk and W. Scharloo (1981) showed that in an island population of tits, there is a strong relationship between the level of inbreeding in a pair and the number of eggs in a clutch that fail to hatch (Figure 6.24). More recently, Keller et al. (1994) found that outbred individuals in a population of song sparrows in British Columbia, Canada, were much more likely than inbred individuals to survive a severe winter.

Given the theory and data we have reviewed on inbreeding depression, it is not surprising that animals and plants have evolved mechanisms to avoid it. Mechanisms of inbreeding avoidance include mate choice, genetically controlled self-incompatibility, and dispersal. But under some circumstances, inbreeding may be unavoidable. In small populations, for example, the number of potential mates for any particular individual is limited. If a population is small and remains small for many generations, and if the population receives no migrants from other populations, then eventually all the individuals in the population will be related to each other even if mating is random. Thus, small populations eventually become inbred, and the individuals in them may suffer inbreeding depression. This can be a problem for rare and endangered species, and it creates a challenge for the managers of captive breeding programs, as we will see in Section 6.4.

In summary, nonrandom mating does not, by itself, alter allele frequencies. It is not, therefore, a mechanism of evolution. Nonrandom mating does, however, alter the frequencies of genotypes. It can thereby change the distribution of phenotypes in a population and alter the pattern of natural selection and the evolution of the population. For example, inbreeding increases the frequency of homozygotes and decreases the frequency of heterozygotes. This can expose deleterious recessive alleles to selection, leading to inbreeding depression.

6.4 Conservation Genetics of the Illinois Greater Prairie Chicken

We opened this chapter with the case of the Illinois greater prairie chicken (Figure 6.1), a once abundant bird that, in the mid-1990s, appeared to be destined for extinction. Like a great many other vulnerable and endangered species, the prairie chicken's worst enemy is habitat destruction (Figure 6.2). Before the introduction of the steel plow, prairie covered more than 60% of Illinois; today less than one hundredth of a percent of that prairie remains (Westemeier et al. 1998). Yet habitat destruction is not the prairie chicken's only problem. Beginning in the early 1960s, conservationists established prairie chicken reserves and worked to restore and maintain prairie habitats. From the late 1960s to the early 1970s, their efforts appeared to be working, as the prairie chicken's numbers began to rebound. But the apparent success was short-lived: By the mid-1970s, the prairie chicken population fell once again into a steady decline (Figure 6.3). Something else was now threatening the survival of the Illinois greater prairie chicken, but what? Our discussion of migration, genetic drift, and nonrandom mating have given us the tools to understand the likely answer.

Ronald Westemeier and colleagues (1998) developed a hypothesis that runs as follows: Destruction of the prairie did two things to the prairie chicken population. First, it directly reduced the size of the birds' population. Second, it fragmented the population that remained. By 1980, the few prairie chickens that survived in Illinois were trapped on small islands of prairie in a sea of farmland. Each island had its own small population of birds. These small populations were geographically isolated from each other and from populations in other states.

Small populations with little or no gene flow are precisely the setting in which genetic drift is most powerful. And genetic drift results in random fixation and declining heterozygosity. If some of the alleles that become fixed are deleterious recessives, then the average fitness of individuals will be reduced. A reduction in fitness due to genetic drift is reminiscent of inbreeding depression. In fact, it *is* inbreeding depression. Reduced heterozygosity due to drift and increased homozygosity due to inbreeding are two sides of the same coin. In a small population all individuals are related, and there is no choice but to mate with kin.

Michael Lynch and Wilfried Gabriel (1990) have proposed that an accumulation of deleterious recessives (a phenomenon known as genetic load) can lead to the extinction of small populations. They noted that when exposure of deleterious mutations produces a reduction in population size, the effectiveness of drift is increased. The speed and proportion of deleterious mutations going to fixation subsequently increases, which further decreases population size. Lynch and Gabriel termed this synergistic interaction between mutation, population size, and drift a "mutational meltdown."

Westemeier and colleagues suggested that the remnant populations of Illinois greater prairie chickens were trapped in just such a scenario. As the populations lost their genetic diversity, the birds began to suffer inbreeding depression. This inbreeding depression reduced individual reproductive success, and caused the remnant populations to continue their decline even as the amount of suitable habitat increased. The continued decline in population size led to even more drift, which led to worse inbreeding depression, and so on. The birds had fallen into an "extinction vortex" (see Soulé and Mills 1998).

To test their hypothesis, the researchers first used data from a long-term study of the Jasper County population to look for evidence of inbreeding depression. The researchers plotted the hatching success of prairie chicken eggs, a measure of individual fitness, as a function of time (Figure 6.25). Throughout the 1960s, over 90% of greater prairie chicken eggs in Jasper County hatched. This rate is comparable to what it was in the 1930s, and to what is today in larger prairie chicken populations in other states. By 1970, however, a steady decline in hatching

Early efforts to conserve remnant populations of greater prairie chickens apparently failed because the birds were suffering from inbreeding depression.

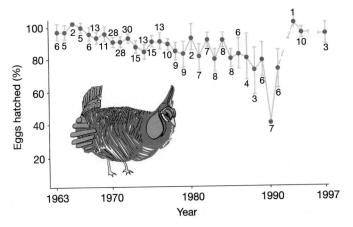

Figure 6.25   Declining hatching success in a greater prairie chicken population   This graph plots, for greater prairie chickens in Jasper County, Illinois, the fraction of eggs hatching each year from 1963 to 1997. The small number below each data point indicates the number of nests followed; the wiskers indicate ±1 standard error (a statistical measure of uncertainty in the estimated hatching rate). The decline in hatching success from the mid-1960s to the early 1990s appears to reflect inbreeding depression. Redrawn with permission from Westemeier et al (1998). Copyright © 1998, American Association for the Advancement of Science.

success had begun. By the late 1980s, the hatching rate dipped below 80%. The all-time low came in 1990, with fewer than 40% of the eggs hatching. The decline in hatching success is statistically significant, and represents a substantial reduction in individual fitness. In other words, it looks like inbreeding depression.

If the decline in hatching success in Jasper County greater prairie chickens was, in fact, due to inbreeding depression caused by genetic drift, then it should be accompanied by a genetic signature. The Jasper County population should show less genetic diversity than larger populations in other states, and less genetic diversity now than it had in the past. Juan Bouzat and colleagues (1998) analyzed the DNA of a number of greater prairie chickens from Illinois, Kansas, Minnesota, and Nebraska, and determined each bird's genotype at six selectively neutral loci (these were noncoding regions with variable numbers of short tandem repeats). As predicted, the Illinois birds had an average of just 3.67 alleles per locus, signficantly fewer than the 5.33 to 5.83 alleles per locus shown by the other populations (Table 6.4). The researchers were even able to extract DNA from 10 museum specimens that had been collected in Jasper County in the 1930s, plus 5 from the 1960s. As shown in the last column in Table 6.4, Bouzat and colleagues used the data from the museum specimens to estimate that the Jasper County population once had an average of at least 5.12 alleles per locus. Consistent with the extinction vortex hypothesis, the greater prairie chickens of Jasper County are genetically depauperate, compared to both their own ancestral population and other present-day populations.

The final test of the extinction vortex hypothesis was to use it to develop a practical conservation strategy. If the problem for the Jasper County prairie chicken population is reduced genetic diversity, then the solution is gene flow. Migrants from other populations should carry with them the alleles that have been lost in

Inbreeding depression in remnant populations of greater prairie chickens was caused by a loss of allelic diversity under genetic drift.

Table 6.4 **Number of alleles per locus found in each of the current populations of Illinois, Kansas, Minnesota, and Nebraska and estimated for the Illinois prebottleneck population**

Locus	Illinois	Kansas	Minnesota	Nebraska	Illinois prebottleneck*
ADL42	3	4	4	4	3
ADL23	4	5	4	5	5
ADL44	4	7	8	8	4
ADL146	3	5	4	4	4
ADL162	2	5	4	4	6
ADL230	6	9	8	10	9
Mean	3.67	5.83	5.33	5.83	5.12
SE	0.56	0.75	0.84	1.05	0.87
Sample size	32	37	38	20	15

Note: SE indicates standard error of mean number of alleles per locus. The Illinois population in column 1 shows signficantly less allelic diversity than the rest of the populations ($P < 0.05$).

*Number of alleles in the Illinois prebottleneck population include both extant alleles that are shared with the other populations and alleles detected in the museum collection.

Source: From Bouzat et al. (1998).

Jasper County. Reintroduction of these lost alleles should reverse the effects of drift and eliminate inbreeding depression. Natural migration of greater prairie chickens into Jasper County ceased long ago. But in 1992, conservation biologists began trapping greater prairie chickens in Minnesota, Kansas, and Nebraska, and moving them to Jasper County. The plan seems to be working. Westemeier and colleagues (1998) report that in 1993, 1994, and 1997, hatching rates in Jasper County were over 90%—higher than they had been in 25 years (Figure 6.25). And the Jasper County population is growing (Figure 6.3).

Migration, in the form of birds transported by biologists, appears to be restoring genetic diversity to remnant populations and alleviating inbreeding depression.

All of the data we have presented on Illinois greater prairie chickens come from observational studies, so it is always possible that some uncontrolled and unknown environmental variable is responsible for the variation in hatching success. On present evidence, however, Westemeier et al.'s extinction vortex hypothesis—involving migration, genetic drift, and nonrandom mating—appears to be the best explanation.

Summary

Among the important implications of the Hardy–Weinberg equilibrium principle is that natural selection is not the only mechanism of evolution. In this chapter, we examined violations of three assumptions of the Hardy–Weinberg analysis first introduced in Chapter 5, and considered their effects on allele and genotype frequencies.

Migration, in its evolutionary meaning, is the movement of alleles from one population to another. When allele frequencies are different in the source population than in the recipient population, migration causes the recipient population to evolve. As a mechanism of evolution, migration tends to homogenize allele frequencies across populations. In doing so, it may tend to eliminate adaptive differences between populations that have been produced by natural selection.

Genetic drift is evolution that occurs as a result of sampling error in the production of a finite number of zygotes from a gene pool. Just by chance, allele frequencies change from one generation to the next. Genetic drift is more dramatic in smaller populations than in large ones. Over many generations, drift results in an inexorable loss of genetic diversity. If some of the alleles that become fixed are deleterious recessives, genetic drift can result in a reduction in the fitness of individuals in the population.

Nonrandom mating does not directly change allele frequencies and is thus not strictly speaking a mechanism of evolution. However, nonrandom mating does influence genotype frequencies. For example, inbred populations have more homozygotes and fewer heterozygotes than otherwise comparable populations in which mating is random. An increase in homozygosity often exposes deleterious recessive alleles, and results in a reduction in fitness known as inbreeding depression.

As illustrated by the case of the Illinois greater prairie chicken, the phenomena discussed in this chapter find practical application in conservation efforts. Drift can rob small remnant populations of genetic diversity, resulting in inbreeding depression and greater risk of extinction. Migration can sometimes restore lost genetic diversity, improving a population's chances for long-term survival.

Questions

1. Conservation managers often try to purchase corridors of undeveloped habitat so that larger preserves are linked into networks. Why? What genetic goals do you think the conservation managers are aiming for?

2. The graph in Figure 6.26 shows F_{ST}, a measure of genetic differentiation between populations, as a function of geographic distance. The data are from human populations in Europe. Genetic differentiation has been calculated based on loci on the autosomes (inherited from both parents), the mitochondrial chromosome (inherited only from the mother), and the Y chromosome (inherited only from the father). Note that the patterns are different for

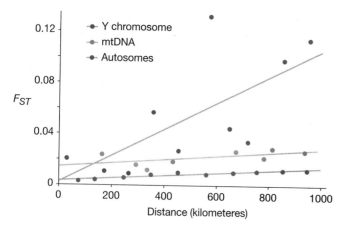

Figure 6.26 Genetic distance between human populations as a function of geographic distance Genetic distance (F_{ST}) is a measure of genetic differentiation among populations. Here it has been calculated based on autosomal loci (blue), mithochondrial loci (green), and Y-chromosome loci (red). From Seielstad et al. (1998). Copyright © 1998 Nature Genetics. Reprinted by permission of the Nature Publishing Group, New York, NY, and M. T. Seielstad, Ph.D.

the three different kinds of loci. Keep in mind that migration tends to homogenize allele frequencies across populations. Develop a hypothesis to explain why allele frequencies are more homogenized across populations for autosomal and mitochondrial loci than for Y-chromosome loci. Then go to the library and look up the following paper, to see if your hypothesis is similar to the one favored by the biologists who prepared the graph:

Seielstad, M. T., E. Minch, and L. L. Cavalli-Sforza. 1998. Genetic evidence for [....] in humans. *Nature Genetics* 20:278–280. [Part of title deleted to encourage readers to develop their own hypotheses.]

3. Loss of heterozygosity may be especially detrimental at MHC loci, because allelic variability at these loci increases disease resistance. Surveys of microsatellite loci show that the gray wolves on Isle Royale, Michigan are highly inbred (Wayne et al. 1991). This wolf population crashed during an outbreak of canine parvovirus during the 1980s. How might these disparate facts be linked? How could you test your ideas?

4. If you were a manager charged with conserving the collared lizards of the Ozarks, one of your tasks might be to reintroduce the lizards into glades in which they have gone extinct. When reintroducing lizards to a glade, you will have a choice between using only individuals from a single extant glade populations, or from several extant glade populations. What would be the evolutionary consequences of each choice, for both the donor and recipient populations? Which strategy will you follow, and why?

5. Recall Ellis–van Creveld syndrome, a genetic disease that is unusually common among the Amish. The Amish population in Pennsylvania now numbers well over 10,000.

a. What evolutionary forces are presently acting on the allele for Ellis–van Creveld syndrome in this population? Why do you think the allele has remained at relatively high frequency? How could you test your ideas?

b. Suppose hundreds of non–Amish people began marrying into the Amish population each year, and raised their children within the Amish community. What would happen to the frequency of Ellis–van Creveld syndrome, and why?

6. Bodmer and McKie (1995) review several cases, in addition to Ellis–van Creveld syndrome in the Amish, in which genetic diseases occur at unusually high frequency in populations that are, or once were, relatively isolated. An enzyme deficiency called hereditary tyrosinemia, for example, occurs at an unusually high rate in the Chicoutimi region north of Quebec City in Canada. A condition called porphyria is unusually common in South Africans of Dutch descent. Why are genetic diseases so common in isolated populations? What else do these populations all have in common?

7. Remote oceanic islands are famous for their endemic species—unique forms that occur nowhere else (see Quammen 1996 for a gripping and highly readable account). Consider the roles of migration and genetic drift in the establishment of new species on remote islands.

a. How do plant and animal species become established on remote islands? Do you think island endemics are more likely to evolve in some groups of plants and animals than others?

b. Consider a new population that has just arrived at a remote island. Is the population likely to be large or small? Will founder effects, genetic drift, and additional waves of migration from the mainland play a relatively large or a small role in the evolution of the new island population (compared to a similar population on an island closer to the mainland)? Do your answers help explain why unusual endemic species are more common on remote islands than on islands close to the mainland?

8. As we have seen, inbreeding can reduce offspring fitness by exposing deleterious recessive alleles. However, some

animal breeders practice generations of careful inbreeding within a family, or "line breeding," and surprisingly many of the line-bred animals, from champion dogs to prize cows, have normal health and fertility. How can it be possible to continue inbreeding for many generations without experiencing inbreeding depression due to recessive alleles? (*Hint:* Responsible animal breeders do not breed animals known to carry deleterious traits.) Generally, if a small population continues to inbreed for many generations, what will happen to the frequency of the deleterious recessive alleles over time?

9. In the mid-1980s, conservation biologists reluctantly recommended that zoos should not try to preserve captive populations of all the endangered species of large cats. For example, some biologists recommended ceasing efforts to breed the extremely rare Asian lion, the beautiful species seen in Chinese artwork. In place of the Asian lion, the biologists recommended increasing the captive populations of other endangered cats, such as the Siber-

ian tiger and Amur leopard. By reducing the number of species kept in captivity, the biologists hoped to increase the captive population size of each species to several hundred, preferably at least 500. Why did the conservation biologists think that this was so important as to be worth the risk of losing the Asian lion forever?

10. In this chapter we saw that in many cases, gene frequencies in small populations change at different rates than in large populations. As a review, state whether the following processes will typically have greater, smaller, or similar effects on evolution in small vs. large populations:

   Selection
   Migration
   Genetic drift
   Inbreeding
   New mutations per individual
   New mutations per generation in the whole population
   Substitution of a new mutation for an old allele
   Fixation of a new mutation

Exploring the Literature

11. For a paper that explores migration as a homogenizer of allele frequencies among human populations, see

   Parra, E. J., Marcini, A., et al. 1998. Estimating African-American admixture proportions by use of population-specific alleles. *American Journal of Human Genetics* 63: 1839–1851.

12. For another example like the research on collared lizards by Templeton and colleagues (1990) in which biologists took advantage of a natural experiment to make test predictions about the effect of genetic drift on genetic diversity, see

   Eldridge, M. D. B., King, J. M., et al. 1999. Unprecedented low levels of genetic variation and inbreeding depression in an island population of the black-footed rock-wallaby. *Conservation Biology* 13: 531–541.

13. We mentioned in Section 6.3 that inbreeding depression is a concern for biologists trying to conserve endangered organisms with small population sizes. Geneticists have recently discovered that inbreeding depression varies among environments and among families. For papers that explore the implications of this discovery for conservation efforts, see

   Pray, L. A., J. M. Schwartz, C. J. Goodnight, and L. Stevens. 1994. Environmental dependency of inbreeding depression: Implications for conservation biology. *Conservation Biology* 8: 562–568.

   Pray, L. A., and C. J. Goodnight. 1995. Genetic variation

in inbreeding depression in the red flour beetle *Tribolium castaneum*. *Evolution* 49: 176–188.

14. Determining the minimum population size necessary to make the extinction of a species unlikely over the long term is an active area of research in conservation genetics. The following papers explore this question:

   Lande, R. 1995. Mutation and conservation. *Conservation Biology* 9: 782–791.

   Lynch, M. 1996. A quantitative genetic perspective on conservation issues. In J. C. Avise and J. Hamrick, eds. *Conservation Genetics: Case Histories from Nature.* New York: Chapman and Hall, 471–501.

15. Cheetahs have long been used as a classic example of a species whose low genetic diversity put it at increased risk of extinction. Other researchers have debated the validity of this view. For a start on the literature, see

   Menotti-Raymond, M., and S. J. O'Brien. 1993. Dating the genetic bottleneck of the African cheetah. *Proceedings of the National Academy of Sciences, USA* 90: 3172–3176.

   Merola, M. 1994. A reassessment of homozygosity and the case for inbreeding depression in the cheetah, *Acinonyx jubatus:* Implications for conservation. *Conservation Biology* 8: 961–971.

16. For other attempts to determine whether low genetic diversity threatens the survival of populations, see

Ledberg, P. L. 1993. Strategies for population reintroduction: Effects of genetic variability on population growth and size. *Conservation Biology* 7: 194–199.

Jimenez, J. A., K. A. Hughes, G. Alaks, L. Graham, and R. C. Lacy. 1994. An experimental study of inbreeding depression in a natural habitat. *Science* 266: 271–273.

Sanjayan, M. A., K. Crooks, G. Zegers, and D. Foran. 1996. Genetic variation and the immune response in natural populations of pocket gophers. *Conservation Biology* 10: 1519–1527.

Literature Cited

Much of the population genetics material in this chapter is modeled after presentations in the following:

Crow, J. F. 1983. *Genetics Notes.* Minneapolis, MN: Burgess Publishing.

Felsenstein, J. 1997. *Theoretical Evolutionary Genetics.* Seattle, WA: ASUW Publishing, University of Washington.

Griffiths, A. J. F., J. H. Miller, D. T. Suzuki, R. C. Lewontin, and W. M. Gelbert. 1993. *An Introduction to Genetic Analysis.* New York: W. H. Freeman.

Maynard Smith, J. 1998. *Evolutionary Genetics.* Oxford University Press, Oxford.

Roughgarden, J. 1979. *Theory of Population Genetics and Evolutionary Ecology: An Introduction.* MacMillan Publishing, New York.

Templeton, A. R. 1982. Adaptation and the integration of evolutionary forces. In R. Milkman, ed., *Perspectives on Evolution.* Sunderland, MA: Sinauer, 15–31.

Here is the list of all other citations in this chapter:

Ayala, F. J., and J. A. Kiger, Jr. 1984. *Modern Genetics.* Menlo Park, CA: Benjamin/Cummings.

Barrett, S. C. H., and D. Charlesworth. 1991. Effects of a change in the level of inbreeding on the genetic load. *Nature* 352: 522–524.

Bittles, A. H., and J. V. Neel. 1994. The costs of human inbreeding and their implications for variations at the DNA level. *Nature Genetics* 8: 117–121.

Bodmer, W., and R. McKie. 1995. *The Book of Man.* New York: Scribner.

Bouzat, J. L., H. A. Lewin, and K. N. Paige. 1998. The ghost of genetic diversity past: Historical DNA analysis of the greater prairie chicken. *American Naturalist* 152: 1–6.

Buri, P. 1956. Gene frequency in small populations of mutant *Drosophila. Evolution* 10: 367–402.

Camin, J. H., and P. R. Ehrlich. 1958. Natural selection in water snakes (*Natrix sipedon* L.) on islands in Lake Erie. *Evolution* 12: 504–511.

Dudash, M. R. 1990. Relative fitness of selfed and outcrossed progeny in a self-compatible, protandrous species, *Sabatia angularis* L. (Gentianaceae): A comparison in three environments. *Evolution* 44: 1129–1139.

Dudash, M. R., D. E. Carr, and C. B. Fenster. 1997. Five generations of enforced selfing and outcrossing in *Mimulus guttatus:* Inbreeding depression variation at the population and family level. *Evolution* 51: 54–65.

Giles, B. E., and J. Goudet. 1997. Genetic differentiation in *Silene dioica* metapopulations: Estimation of spatiotemporal effects in a successional plant species. *American Naturalist* 149: 507–526.

Gillespie, J. H. 1991. *The Causes of Molecular Evolution.* New York: Oxford University Press.

Grant, P. R., and B. R. Grant. 1995. The founding of a new population of Darwin's finches. *Evolution* 49: 229–240.

Greenwood, P. J., P. H. Harvey, and C. M. Perrins. 1978. Inbreeding and dispersal in the great tit. *Nature* 271: 52–54.

Hamilton, W. D. 1967. Extraordinary sex ratios. *Science* 156: 477–488.

Hamilton, W. D. 1979. Wingless and fighting males in fig wasps and other insects. In M. S. Blum and N. A. Blum, eds., *Sexual Selection and Reproductive Competition in Insects.* New York: Academic Press, 167–220.

Hartl, D. L. 1981. *A Primer of Population Genetics.* Sunderland, MA: Sinauer.

Hill, J. L. 1974. *Peromyscus:* Effect of early pairing on reproduction. *Science* 186: 1042–1044.

Johnston, M. 1992. Effects of cross and self-fertilization on progeny fitness in *Lobelia cardinalis* and *L. siphilitica. Evolution* 46: 688–702.

Keller, L., P. Arcese, J. N. M. Smith, W. M. Hochachka, and S. C. Stearns. 1994. Selection against inbred song sparrows during a natural population bottleneck. *Nature* 372: 356–357.

Kerr, W. E., and S. Wright. 1954. Experimental studies of the distribution of gene frequencies in very small populations of *Drosophila melanogaster.* I. Forked. *Evolution* 8: 172–177.

Kimura, M. 1968. Evolutionary rate at the molecular level. *Nature* 217: 624–626.

Kimura, M. 1983. *The Neutral Theory of Molecular Evolution.* New York: Cambridge University Press.

King, R. B. 1987. Color pattern polymorphism in the Lake Erie water snake, *Nerodia sipedon insularum. Evolution* 41: 241–255.

King, R. B. 1993a. Color pattern variation in Lake Erie water snakes: Inheritance. *Canadian Journal of Zoology* 71: 1985–1990.

King, R. B. 1993b. Color-pattern variation in Lake Erie water snakes: Prediction and measurement of natural selection. *Evolution* 47: 1819–1833.

King, R. B., and R. Lawson. 1995. Color-pattern variation in Lake Erie water snakes: The role of gene flow. *Evolution* 49: 885–896.

King, R. B., and R. Lawson. 1997. Microevolution in island water snakes. *BioScience* 47: 279–286.

Lynch, M., and W. Gabriel. 1990. Mutation load and the survival of small populations. *Evolution* 44: 1725–1737.

McCall, C., D. M. Waller, and T. Mitchell-Olds. 1994. Effects of serial inbreeding on fitness components in *Impatiens capensis. Evolution* 48: 818–827.

Paul, R. E. L., M. J. Packer, M. Walmsley, M. Lagog, L. C. Ranford-Cartwright, R. Paru, and K. P. Day. 1995. Mating patterns in malaria parasite populations of Papua, New Guinea. *Science* 269: 1709–1711.

Polans, N. O., and R. W. Allard. 1989. An experimental evaluation of the recovery potential of ryegrass populations from genetic stress resulting from restriction of population size. *Evolution* 43: 1320–1324.

Postlethwait, J. H., and J. L. Hopson. 1992. *The Nature of Life,* 2nd ed. New York: McGraw-Hill.

Quammen, D. 1996. *The Song of the Dodo.* New York: Touchstone.

Ralls, K., K. Brugger, and J. Ballou. 1979. Inbreeding and juvenile mortality in small populations of ungulates. *Science* 206: 1101–1103.

Read, A. F., A. Narara, S. Nee, A. E. Keymer, and K. P. Day. 1992. Gametocyte sex ratios as indirect measures of outcrossing rates in malaria. *Parasitology* 104: 387–395.

Seielstad, M. T., E. Minch, and L. L. Cavalli-Sforza. 1998. Genetic evidence for a higher female migration rate in humans. *Nature Genetics* 20: 278–280.

Soulé, M. E., and L. S. Mills. 1998. No need to isolate genetics. *Science* 282: 1658–1659.

Templeton, A. R., K. Shaw, E. Routman, and S. K. Davis. 1990. The genetic consequences of habitat fragmentation. *Annals of the Missouri Botanical Garden* 77: 13–27.

Thomas, J. 1998. A bird's race toward extinction is halted. *The New York Times* 29 December: D3.

van Noordwijk, A. J., and W. Scharloo. 1981. Inbreeding in an island population of the great tit. *Evolution* 35: 674–688.

Wayne, R. K., N. Lehman, D. Girman, P. J. P. Gogan, D. A. Gilbert, K. Hansen, R. O. Peterson, U. S. Seal, A. Eisenhawer, L. D. Mech, and R. J. Krumenaker. 1991. Conservation genetics of the endangered Isle Royale gray wolf. *Conservation Biology* 5: 41–51.

Wright, S. 1931. Evolution in Mendelian populations. *Genetics* 16: 97–159.

Westemeier, R. L., S. A. Simpson, and D. A. Cooper. 1991. Successful exchange of prairie-chicken eggs between nests in two remnant populations. *Wilson Bulletin* 103:717–720.

Westemeier, R. L., J. D. Brawn, et al. 1998. Tracking the long-term decline and recovery of an isolated population. *Science* 282: 1695-1698.

Wolfe, L. M. 1993. Inbreeding depression in *Hydrophyllum appendiculatum:* Role of maternal effects, crowding, and parental mating history. *Evolution* 47: 374–386.

Young, A., T. Boyle, and T. Brown. 1996. The population genetic consequences of habitat fragmentation for plants. *Trends in Ecology and Evolution* 11: 413–418.

CHAPTER 9

Sexual Selection

Marine iguanas of the Galápagos. The red iguana is a large adult male. He is surrounded by smaller males and females. (Martin Wikelski, University of Illinois at Urbana-Champaign)

MALES AND FEMALES ARE OFTEN STRIKINGLY DIFFERENT IN SIZE, APPEARANCE, and behavior. In marine iguanas, for example, the sexes differ in body mass by a factor of two. The males are larger, and become intensely territorial during the breeding season. The females are smaller, and remain gregarious throughout the year. In long-tailed widow birds, adults of opposite sex have plumages so distinct that it would be easy to mistake them for different species. The males are jet black, carry tailfeathers several times the length of their own bodies, and have red and yellow shoulder patches. The females are colored a cryptic brown, with short tail feathers and no shoulder patches. In gray tree frogs, the males have dark throats and produce a melodious call. The females have white throats and are silent. In stalk-eyed flies, both sexes wear their eyes on the ends of long thin stalks, but males have longer eyestalks than females. In some species of pipefish, the females have blue stripes and skin folds on their bellies, which the males lack. The photos of males and females in Figure 9.1 provide additional examples.

In humans, too, females and males are conspicuously different. The differences include not just the obvious and essential ones like our genitalia and reproductive organs, but also facial structure, vocal tone, distribution of body fat and body hair, and body size. The difference in body size between women and men is documented in Figure 9.2.

(b) Guppies

(a) Red deer

(c) Golden toads

Figure 9.1 **The differences between males and females (the sexual dimorphism) in red deer (*Cervus elaphus*), guppies (*Poecilia reticulata*), and golden toads (*Bufo periglenes*)** In (a), the male is on the left; in (b) and (c), the male on the top. ([a] M. Hamblin/Animals Animals/Earth Scenes; [b] Michael Gunther/PA; [c] M. Fogden/Animals Animals/Earth Scenes)

A difference between the sexes is called a sexual dimorphism.

A difference between the males and females of a species is called a **sexual dimorphism**. In this chapter, we ask why sexual dimorphism occurs in such a great variety of organisms. It is a question Charles Darwin (1871) wrote half a book about, and it has captivated evolutionary biologists ever since.

In previous chapters, we have explained many features of organisms with the theory of evolution by natural selection. The goal has been to discover whether the features in question are adaptive, and if so, then how they improve the survival or fecundity of the individuals that possess them. But differences between the

Figure 9.2 **Women and men differ in height** For each of more than 200 human societies, the average height of the men is plotted against the average height of the women. The diagonal line shows where the points would fall if men and women were of equal height. People vary widely in height from society to society: In the shortest society, the average man is about 143 cm tall (about 4 feet, 8 inches) and the average woman about 135 cm (~4'5"); in the tallest society, the average man is about 180 cm tall (~5'11") and the average woman about 165 cm (~5'5"). But in every society the average man is taller than the average woman, usually by about 10%. From Rogers and Mukherjee (1992).

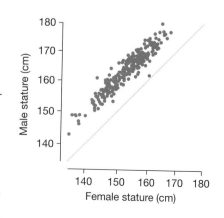

sexes of a species are often hard to explain with the theory of evolution by natural selection.

For example, compare the evolution of beak size in Darwin's finches (Chapter 3) to the evolution of long tail feathers in male long-tailed widow birds (Figure 9.3). Two problems arise. First, when the finches get hit by a drought and small soft seeds become rare, big beaks are as useful to the females as to the males. But if long tail feathers can improve the survival or fecundity of a widow bird, then why do only the males have them? Second, big beaks help the finches survive droughts by allowing the finches to open large hard seeds and get more to eat. But how could those enormously long tail feathers improve the survival, or the fecundity, of widow birds? Long tail feathers probably make male widow birds easier for predators to find and catch. Furthermore, growing long tail feathers requires considerable energy. Any energy spent on feathers is energy that cannot be spent on making offspring. It appears that the theory of evolution by natural selection can explain neither why male and female widow birds are different, nor why the unusual trait, long tail feathers, exists at all.

As Darwin himself was the first to recognize, sex provides a solution to the puzzle of sexual dimorphism. To see why, consider life without sex. For organisms that reproduce without sex (see Chapter 7), getting genes into the next generation is fairly straightforward. The two main challenges are surviving long enough to reproduce, and then reproducing. Sex complicates life by adding a third major challenge: finding a member of the opposite sex and persuading him or her to cooperate.

Charles Darwin recognized that individuals vary not only in their success at surviving and reproducing, but also in their success at persuading members of the opposite sex to mate. About birds, for example, Darwin wrote, "Inasmuch as the act of courtship appears to be with many birds a prolonged and tedious affair, so it occasionally happens that certain males and females do not succeed during the proper season, in exciting each other's love, and consequently do not pair" (1871, page 107). In its evolutionary consequences, failing to mate is equivalent to dying young: The victim makes no genetic contribution to future generations. Darwin had already applied the label natural selection to differences among individuals in survival and reproduction. Differences among individuals in success at getting mates he called **sexual selection**. We can develop a theory of evolution by sexual selection that is logically equivalent to the theory of evolution by natural selection. If there is heritable variation in a trait that affects the ability to obtain mates, then variants conducive to success will become more common over time.

Our goal in this chapter is to explore how the theory of evolution by sexual selection explains the frequent existence of conspicuous differences between females and males, particularly when those differences involve traits that seem likely to impair survival. We first review classical work that elucidated the precise mechanism through which sexual reproduction creates different selection pressures

Sexual dimorphism is a puzzle, because natural selection cannot explain it.

Figure 9.3 The sexual dimorphism in long-tailed widow birds (*Euplectes progne*) The male is black with long tail feathers and red and yellow shoulder patches; the female is brown and cryptic.

for females versus males. Then we consider recent research on the evolutionary consequences of these differing selection pressures in different species.

9.1 Asymmetries in Sexual Reproduction

In this section we argue that sexual reproduction creates different selection pressures for females versus males. The logic we develop to support this conclusion was clearly articulated by A. J. Bateman (1948) and refined by Robert Trivers (1972). It hinges on a crucial fact: Eggs (or pregnancies) are more expensive than ejaculates. In more general terms, females typically make a larger parental investment in each offspring than males. By parental investment we mean energy and time expended both in constructing an offspring and in caring for it. Ultimately, parental investment is measured in fitness. Parental investment increases the reproductive success of the offspring receiving it. At the same time, it decreases the remaining reproductive success that the investing parent may achieve in the future by way of additional offspring.

Consider the parental investments made by male and female orangutans. Adult orangutans of opposite sex tolerate each other's company only for the purpose of mating (Nowak 1991). After a brief tryst, including a copulation that lasts about 15 minutes, the male and female go their separate ways. If a pregnancy results, then the mother, who weighs about 40 kilograms, will carry the fetus for 8 months, give birth to a 1-kilogram baby, nurse it for about 3 years, and continue to protect it until it reaches the age of 7 or 8. For the father, who weighs about 70 kilograms, the beginning and end of parental investment is a few grams of semen, which he can replace in a matter of hours or days. In their pattern of parental investment, orangutans are typical mammals. Females provide substantial parental care and males provide none whatsoever in more than 90% of mammal species (Woodroffe and Vincent 1994).

Because female mammals provide such intensive parental care, mammals present a somewhat extreme example of disparity in parental investment. In most animal species, neither parent cares for the young: Mated pairs just make eggs, fertilize them, and leave them. But in these species, too, females usually make a larger investment in each offspring than males. Eggs are typically large and yolky, with a big supply of stored energy and nutrients. Think of a sea turtle's eggs, some of which are as large as a hen's eggs. Most sperm, on the other hand, are little more than DNA with a propeller. Even when a single ejaculate delivers hundreds of millions of sperm, the ejaculate seldom represents more than a fraction of the investment contained in a clutch of eggs.

The key to explaining sexual dimorphism is in recognizing that sexual reproduction imposes different selection pressures on females versus males.

Recognizing that eggs are more expensive than ejaculates allows us to predict that there will be a profound difference in the factors that limit the lifetime reproductive success of females versus males. A female's potential reproductive success is relatively small, and her realized reproductive success is likely to be limited more by the number of eggs she can make (or pregnancies she can carry) than by the number of males she can convince to mate with her. In contrast, a male's potential reproductive success is relatively large, and his realized reproductive success is likely to be limited more by the number of females he can convince to mate with him than by the number of ejaculates he can make. In other words, we predict this fundamental asymmetry: Access to females will be a limiting resource for males, but access to males will not be a limiting resource for females.

Asymmetric Limits on Reproductive Success in Fruit Flies

A. J. Bateman (1948) tested this prediction in laboratory populations of the fruit fly, *Drosophila melanogaster*. Bateman set up small populations of flies in bottles. Each population consisted of three virgin males and three virgin females. Each fly was heterozygous for a unique dominant genetic mutation: one that gave the fly curly wings, for example, or hairless patches on parts of its body. Bateman let the flies mate with each other, then raised their offspring to adulthood. He was able to identify about half of the offspring of each parent by looking at the mutations the offspring inherited. In this way, Bateman could figure out which females had mated with which males, and vice versa. He could also calculate the relative number of offspring each parent produced. Note that the males and females living together in a bottle all had exactly three potential mates. Their number of actual mates varied from zero to three. If the factors that limit reproductive success are different for the two sexes, then the data for the two sexes should show different relationships between reproductive success and number of actual mates.

The combined results from two dozen experiments appear in Figure 9.4. These results confirm the prediction that the two sexes differ in the factors that limit reproductive success:

Because females typically invest more in each offspring than males, a female's reproductive success is limited by the number of eggs she can make. In contrast, a male's reproductive success is limited by the number of females he can mate with.

- For males, reproductive success increased in direct proportion with number of mates (Figure 9.4a). Males also showed considerable variation in number of mates, with many males in the extreme groups with zero mates and three mates (Figure 9.4b). These two patterns combined to produce considerable variation

(a) Reproductive success versus number of mates:

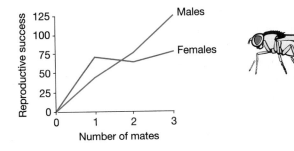

(b) Variation in number of mates:

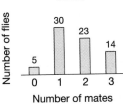
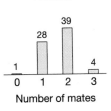

(c) Variance in reproductive success in four groups of experiments:

	Male Variance	Female Variance	Male Variance / Female Variance
Group 1	1604	985	1.63
Group 2	1700	209	8.14
Group 3	2798	993	2.82
Group 4	1098	277	3.97

Figure 9.4   The combined results from Bateman's experiments   In (c), variation in reproductive success is characterized by the variance among individuals in number of offspring. To calculate the variance of a list of numbers, first calculate the mean. Then take the difference between each number and the mean. These differences are called the deviations from the mean. Now take each deviation and square it. The mean of the squared deviations is the variance. The larger the variation among the numbers in a list, the larger the variance. After Bateman (1948).

among males in reproductive success (Figure 9.4c): Males with three mates were big winners; males with no mates were big losers.

- For females, reproductive success did not substantially increase with more than one mate (Figure 9.4a). Further, females showed less variation in number of mates, with most females having one or two (Figure 9.4b). These two patterns combined to produce relatively little variation among females in reproductive success (Figure 9.4c): There were few big winners and few big losers.

In Bateman's experimental fly populations, access to mates indeed proved to be a limiting resource for males, but not for females. Sexual selection, or variation in fitness due to variation in success at getting mates, was much stronger in males than in females. Evolutionary biologists believe that this pattern is quite general (although not universal). And it has important consequences for how members of each sex approach mating.

Behavioral Consequences of Asymmetric Limits on Fitness

The asymmetry in the factors that limit reproductive success for females versus males allows us to predict differences in the mating behavior of the two sexes:

Sexual selection theory predicts that males will compete with each other over access to mates, and that females will be choosy.

- Males should be competitive. If the fitness of males is limited by access to females, then we predict that males will compete among themselves over opportunities to mate.
- Females should be choosy. If the fitness of females is not limited by opportunities to mate, but any given mating may involve the commitment by the female to a large investment in offspring, then we predict that females will be selective about whom they mate with.

Male–male competition for mates and female choosiness can play out in two ways. First, in species in which males can directly monopolize access to females, males typically fight with each other over such monopolies. The females then mate with the winners. This form of sexual selection is called **intrasexual selection**, because the key event that determines reproductive success involves interactions among the members of a single sex (the males fight). Second, in species in which males cannot directly control access to females, the males advertise for mates. The females then choose among the advertisers. This form of sexual selection is called **intersexual selection**, because the key event that determines reproductive success involves an interaction between members of the two sexes (females choose males).

Many readers will have noticed that our treatment of asymmetries in sexual reproduction has been full of crass generalizations. We want to emphasize that expectations of male–male competition and female choosiness are not based on anything inherent to maleness or femaleness per se, but on the observation that females commonly invest much more per offspring than males. This investment pattern is broken in a great variety of species. When fathers care for young, for example, male parental investment per offspring may be comparable to, or even greater than, female parental investment. Species with male parental care include humans, many fish, about 5% of frogs, and over 90% of birds. When males actually do invest more per offspring than females, access to mates will be a limiting resource for females. When access to mates is limiting for females instead of males, we predict that *females* will compete with each other over access to males, and that *males* will be choosy. Toward the end of this chapter, we will return to "sex-role re-

versed" species to see if they are exceptions that can prove the rules of sexual selection. For now, however, we will focus on sexual selection by male–male competition and female choice.

9.2 Male–Male Competition: Intrasexual Selection

Sexual selection by male–male competition occurs when individual males can
monopolize access to females. Males may monopolize females through direct control of the females themselves, or through control of some resource important to
females. In this section, we consider examples of research into three forms of
male–male competition: outright combat, sperm competition, and infanticide.

Combat

Outright combat is the most obvious form of male–male competition for mates.
Intrasexual selection involving male–male combat over access to mates can favor
morphological traits including large body size, weaponry, and armor. Male–male
combat also selects for effective tactics.

Male–male competition can take the form of combat over access to females.

Our example comes from the marine iguanas (*Amblyrhynchus cristatus*) of the
Galápagos Islands (Figure 9.5). Marine iguanas have a life-style unique among the
lizards. They make their living grazing on algae in the intertidal zone. Between
bouts of grazing, they bask on rocks at the water's edge. Basking warms the iguanas, which aids digestion and prepares them for their next foray into the cold water.
Marine iguanas grow to different sizes on different islands, but, as we mentioned
earlier, on any given island the males get larger than the females (Figure 9.6a).

The sexual size dimorphism in marine iguanas is an excellent example for the
study of sexual selection, because we know a great deal about how marine iguana size is affected by natural selection (Wikelski et al. 1997; Wikelski and Trillmich
1997). Martin Wikelski and Fritz Trillmich documented natural selection on iguana body size by monitoring the survival of marked individuals on two islands over
one to two years. Natural selection was much harsher on Genovesa than on Santa
Fé, but it was clearly at work on both islands. Moreover, selection was stabilizing.
Medium-sized iguanas survived at higher rates than either small iguanas or large
iguanas (Figure 9.6b).

Potential agents of this natural selection on body size are few. Marine iguanas
do not compete with other species for food and have virtually no predators. Other

Figure 9.5 **A Galápagos marine iguana foraging on algae
in the intertidal zone** (Martin
Wikelski, University of
Illinois at Urbana-Champaign)

Figure 9.6 **Natural selection on body size in marine iguanas** (a) Histograms showing the size distributions of male and female marine iguanas on two different Galápagos Islands, Genovesa and Santa Fé. The asterisks mark the maximum sizes at which iguanas were able to maintain their weight in two different years (1991–1992 and 1992–1993). From Wikelski et al. (1997). (b) Survival rates of marked individuals of different sizes (snout–vent length, mm) from March 1991 to March 1992 on Genovesa, and from February 1990 to February 1992 on Santa Fé. The sample sizes, or number of individuals in each group, are given by *n*. From Wikelski and Trillmich (1997).

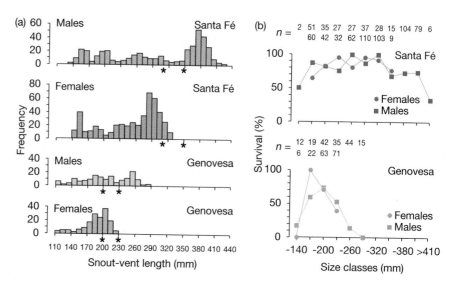

than reproduction, about all the iguanas have to contend with is competition for food among themselves.

Larger iguanas can harvest more algae, and thus gather more energy, but they also expend more energy on metabolism. Wikelski and colleagues (1997) found during two different years that small iguanas ran a net energy surplus, but large iguanas ran a net energy deficit. Consistent with the hypothesis that the availability of food limits body size, the largest iguanas on Santa Fé and Genovesa lost weight during both 1991–1992, a bad year for algae, and 1992–1993, a fairly good year (see also Wikelski and Thom 2000). The largest sizes at which iguanas were able to maintain their weight are indicated by the asterisks in Figure 9.6a.

Now compare Figure 9.6a with Figure 9.6b. The maximum sizes at which iguanas could sustain their weight are close to the optimal sizes for survival. Furthermore, the largest females in each population are near the optimal size for survival, but the largest males are much larger than the optimal size. The large body size of male marine iguanas is thus an evolutionary puzzle: We cannot explain it by natural selection, because Wikelski and Trillmich have shown that natural selection acts against it. It is exactly the kind of puzzle for which Darwin invoked sexual selection.

As we discussed earlier, a crucial issue in sexual selection is the relative parental investment per offspring made by females versus males. In marine iguanas, the parental investment by females is much larger. Each female digs a nest on a beach away from the basking and feeding areas, buries her eggs, guards the nest for a few days, and then abandons it (Rauch 1988). Males provide no parental care at all. So parental investment by females consists mostly of producing eggs, and parental investment by males consists entirely of producing ejaculates. Females lay a single clutch of one to six eggs each year, into which they put about 20% of their body mass (Rauch 1985; Rauch 1988; Wikelski and Trillmich 1997). Compared to the female investment, the cost of the single ejaculate needed to fertilize all the eggs in a clutch is paltry. This difference in investment suggests that the maximum potential reproductive success of males is much higher than that of females. Number of mates will limit the lifetime reproductive success of males, but not females.

The iguanas' mating behavior is consistent with these inferences. Females copulate only once each reproductive season. Martin Wikelski, Silke Bäurle, and their

Figure 9.7   **Male marine iguanas in combat**   (Martin Wikelski, University of Illinois at Urbana-Champaign)

field assistants followed several dozen marked females on Genovesa. The researchers watched the females from dawn to dusk every day during the entire month-long mating season in 1992–1993 and 1993–1994 (Wikelski and Bäurle 1996). They also watched the marked females from dawn to dusk every day during the subsequent nesting seasons. Every marked female that dug a nest and laid eggs had been seen copulating, but no marked female had been seen copulating more than once. Male iguanas, in contrast, attempt to copulate many times with many different females. But the opportunity to copulate with females is a privilege a male iguana has to fight for (Figure 9.7).

Prior to the mating season each year, male iguanas stake out territories on the rocks where females bask between feeding bouts. In these small, densely packed territories (Figure 9.8a), males attempt to claim and hold ground by ousting male interlopers. Confrontations begin with head-bobbing threats, and escalate to chases and head pushing. If neither male backs down, fights can end with bites leav-

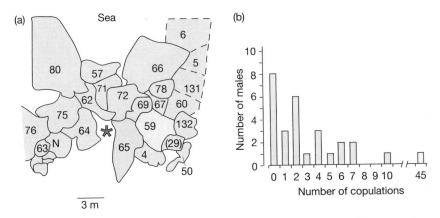

Figure 9.8   **Mating success in male marine iguanas**   (a) A cluster of iguana mating territories on Camaaño Islet, Galápagos. Lines show boundaries of mating territories on 16 January 1978; numbers identify territory owners. As the scale bar for this map shows, mating territories are only a few square meters in size. The dark blue asterisk indicates where Krisztina Trillmich sat to watch the iguanas. (Camaaño Islet has only 880m of shoreline and supports a population of nearly 2000 iguanas.) From Trillmich (1983). (b) Histogram showing variation in number of copulations obtained by male iguanas on mating territories shown in (a). Note the break in the horizontal scale; the most successful male, iguana 59, got more than four times as many copulations as any of his rivals. The histogram includes only males that claimed a territory for at least a short time during the mating season. From Trillmich (1983).

ing serious injuries on the head, neck, flanks, and legs (Trillmich 1983). While a male holds a territory, he has a more or less exclusive right to mate with any receptive females that happen to be there, typically females that use the territory as their basking site (Rauch 1985). Because only some males manage to claim territories, and some males manage to maintain their claims for a longer period than others, there is extreme variation among males in the number of copulations obtained (Figure 9.8b).

Because claiming and holding a territory involves combat with other males, bigger males tend to win. In the iguana colony that Krisztina Trillmich (1983) studied on Camaaño Islet, the male that got 45 copulations (Figure 9.8b), far more than any other male, was iguana 59 (his territory is shown in Figure 9.8a). His neighbor, iguana 65, was the second most successful with 10 copulations. Both of their territories were females' favorite early-morning and late-afternoon basking places. Trillmich reported that iguana 59 was the largest male in the colony; that to claim his territory, he had to eject four other males who tried to take it; and that during his tenure, he lost parts of it to four neighboring males who were pushing their territories in from the sides. Wikelski and co-workers studied iguana colonies on Genovesa and Santa Fé (Wikelski et al. 1996; Wikelski and Trillmich 1997). Consistent with Krisztina Trillmich's observations, these researchers found that the mean size of males that got to copulate was significantly larger than the mean size of all males that tried to copulate (Table 9.1).

If we assume that body size is heritable in marine iguanas, then we have variation, heritability, and differential mating success. These are the elements of evolution by sexual selection. We thus have an explanation for why male marine iguanas get so much bigger than the optimal size for survival. Male iguanas get big because bigger males get more mates and pass on more of their big-male genes.

Male–male combat, analogous to that in marine iguanas, happens in a great variety of species, including the red deer shown in Figure 9.1. When mating opportunities are a limiting resource for males, and when males can monopolize either the females themselves, or some resource that is vital to the females and

Male marine iguanas fight over territories where females congregate. Large iguanas win more fights, claim better territories, and thus get to copulate with more females. This pattern of sexual selection has led to the evolution of large body size in males.

Table 9.1 Sexual selection differentials for male body size in marine iguana colonies on Santa Fé and Genovesa

Body size is given as snout–vent length (SVL). The standardized selection differential (see Chapter 7) is the difference between the average body size of all males that copulated at least once and the average body size of all males that tried to copulate, expressed in standard deviations of the distribution of body sizes of all males that tried to copulate. (The standard deviation is the square root of the variance.) Both standardized selection differentials are positive ($P < 0.05$), indicating that males that got to copulate were larger on average than males that tried to copulate. From Wikelski and Trillmich (1997).

	N	Average size (SVL)	Standard deviation	Standardized selection differential
Santa Fé				
Males that copulated	253	401	13	0.42
All males that tried to	343	390	26	
Genovesa				
Males that copulated	25	243	26	0.77
All males that tried to	147	227	21	

thus sure to attract them, males fight among themselves for access to the females or the resource. In addition to large body size, this kind of sexual selection leads to the evolution of other traits that are assets in combat, such as weaponry and armor. Male–male combat can also lead to the evolution of alternative male mating strategies (see Box 9.1).

Sperm Competition

Male–male competition does not necessarily stop when copulation is over. The real determinant of a male's mating success is not whether he copulates, but whether his sperm fertilize eggs. If an animal has internal fertilization, and if a female mates with two or more different males within a short period, then the sperm from the males will be in a race to the eggs. Indeed, females may produce litters or clutches in which different offspring are fathered by different males. Batches of offspring with multiple fathers have been documented in a variety of animals, including squirrels (Boellstorff et al. 1994), bears (Schenk and Kovacs 1995), birds (Gibbs et al. 1990), lizards (Olsson et al. 1994), and spiders (Watson 1991). It happens in humans too; Smith (1984) reviews reports of twins with different fathers.

Given sperm competition, what traits contribute to victory? One useful trait might simply be the production of large ejaculates containing many sperm. If sperm competition is something of a lottery, then the more tickets a male buys, the better his chances of winning. This hypothesis has been tested by Matthew Gage (1991) with the Mediterranean fruit fly, *Ceratitis capitata*. Gage's experiment was based on the observation that, although ejaculates are cheaper than eggs, they are not free (see, for example, Nakatsuru and Kramer 1982). Gage reasoned that if male Mediterranean fruit flies are subject to any constraints on sperm production, they might benefit from conserving their sperm, using during each copulation only the minimum number necessary to ensure complete fertilization of the female's eggs. But if larger ejaculates contribute to victory in sperm competition, males whose sperm are at risk of competition should release more sperm during copulation than males whose sperm are not at risk. If the number of sperm released is unimportant to the outcome of competition, then males should release the same number of sperm regardless of the risk of competition.

Gage raised and mated male medflies under two sets of conditions. One group of 20 he raised by themselves and allowed to mate in private; the other group of 20 he raised in the company of another male and allowed to mate in the presence of that second male. Immediately after each mating, Gage dissected the females and counted the number of sperm the males had released. Males raised and mated in the presence of a potential rival ejaculated more than $2\frac{1}{2}$ times as many sperm (average $\pm$ standard error = 3520 ± 417) as males raised and mated in isolation (1379 ± 241), a highly significant difference ($P < 0.0001$). Gage's interpretation was that large ejaculates do contribute to victory in sperm competition, and that male medflies dispense their sperm to balance the twin priorities of ensuring successful fertilization and conserving sperm.

In addition to large ejaculates, sperm competition has apparently led to various other adaptations. Males may prolong copulation, deposit a copulatory plug, or apply pheromones that reduce the female's attractiveness (Gilbert 1976; Sillén-Tullberg 1981; Thornhill and Alcock 1983). During copulation in many species of damselflies, the male uses special structures on his penis to scoop out sperm left by the female's previous mates (Figure 9.9; Waage 1984, 1986). R. E. Hooper and

Male–male competition can take the form of sperm competition.

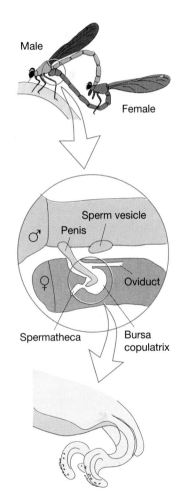

Figure 9.9 Sperm competition in damselflies During copulation (top), the male uses the barbed horns on his penis (bottom) to remove sperm left by the female's previous mates. Redrawn from Waage (1984).

Box 9.1 Alternative male mating strategies

Victory in male–male combat typically goes to the large, strong, and well armed. But what about the smaller males? Is their only chance at fitness to survive until they are large enough to win fights? Often small males attempt to mate by employing alternative strategies. Sometimes they succeed.

In marine iguanas, small adult males are ousted from the mating territories on the basking grounds. But many do not give up; they continue trying to get females to copulate with them. The small males are not terribly successful, but they do get about 5% of the matings in the colony (Wikelski et al. 1996). Needless to say, small males attempting to mate with females are often harassed by other males. This happens to large territorial males too, but it happens more often to small males. Furthermore, copulations by small males are more likely to be disrupted before the male has time to ejaculate (Figure 9.10).

The small males solve the problem of disrupted copulations by ejaculating ahead of time (Wikelski and Bäurle 1996). They use the stimulation of an attempted copulation, or even of seeing a female pass by, to induce ejaculation. The males then store the ejaculate in their cloacal pouches. If he gets a chance to mate, a small male transfers his stored ejaculate to the female at the beginning of copulation. Wikelski and Bäurle examined the cloacae of a dozen females caught immediately after copulations that had lasted less than three minutes. None of these females had copulated earlier that mating season, but 10 of the 12 females had old ejaculates in their cloacae that must have been transferred during the short copulation.

The sperm in these old ejaculates were viable. From dawn to dusk every day for about a month, Wikelski and Bäurle watched five of the females until they laid their eggs. None of the five copulated again, but all laid fertilized eggs.

Prior ejaculation appears to be a strategy practiced more often by small nonterritorial males than by large territorial males. Wikelski and Bäurle caught 13 nonterritorial and 13 territorial males at random; 85% of the nonterritorial males had stored ejaculates in their cloacal pouches, versus only 38% of the territorial males ($P < 0.05$). This difference is unlikely to result from more frequent copulation by territorial males, because even territorial males copulate only about once every six days (Wikelski et al. 1996).

Alternative, or sneaky male, mating strategies have also evolved in a variety of other species. In coho salmon, *Oncorhynchus kisutch*, for example, males return from the sea to spawn at two different ages (Gross 1984; Gross 1985; Gross 1991). One group, called hooknoses, returns at 18 months. They are large, armed with enlarged hooked jaws, and armored with cartilaginous deposits along their backs. The other group, called jacks, returns at 6 months. They are small, poorly armed, and poorly armored.

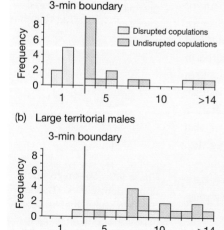

(a) Small nonterritorial males

(b) Large territorial males

Figure 9.10 Duration of copulations by male marine iguanas Histograms showing the distribution of copulation durations for (a) 24 small nonterritorial males, and (b) 20 large territorial males. Orange areas indicate copulations that were disrupted by other males. The red vertical line at 3 minutes marks the approximate amount of time a male must copulate before he can ejaculate. Large territorial males had copulations that were significantly longer and less likely to be disrupted before the 3-minute boundary. From Wikelski and Bäurle (1996). Copyright © 1996, The Royal Society. Reprinted by permission of The Royal Society and the author.

Box 9.1 **Continued**

When a female coho is ready to mate, she digs a nest and then lays her eggs in it. As she prepares the nest, males congregate. The males use one of two strategies in trying to fertilize the female's eggs (Figure 9.11). Some males fight for a position close to the female. These fighters quickly sort themselves out by size. When the female lays her eggs, the males spawn over them in order. The first male to spawn fertilizes the most eggs. Other males do not fight for position, but instead look for a hiding place near the female. When the female lays her eggs, these sneakers attempt to dart out and spawn over the eggs.

Among hooknoses, those that adopt the fighting strategy are more successful. Among jacks, those that adopt the sneaky strategy are more successful. The relative fitness of hooknoses versus jacks depends, in part, on the frequency of each type of male in the breeding population.

There is an important distinction between the iguana example and the coho example. In marine iguanas, the small nonterritorial males appear to be making the best of a bad situation while they grow to a large enough size to successfully fight for a territory. In coho, a male irreversibly becomes either a hooknose or a jack. Which strategy a male coho pursues depends on a mixture of environmental and genetic factors.

Figure 9.11 Alternative mating strategies in coho salmon This figure shows a coho mating group. The large fish at the right (upstream) is a female that has built a nest and is ready to lay her eggs. Downstream from the female are five males that have opted for the fighting strategy. These males, four hooknoses and a jack, have sorted themselves out by size. Two other jacks have opted for the sneaky strategy. They have found hiding places near the female, one behind a rock, the other in a shallow. After Gross (1991). Copyright © 1991, Ecological Society of America. Reprinted by permission.

M. T. Siva-Jothy (1996) used genetic paternity tests to show that this strategy is highly effective. In the damselfly species they studied, the second male to mate with a female fertilized nearly all of the eggs produced during her first postcopulatory bout of oviposition.

Infanticide

In some species of mammals, competition between males continues even beyond conception. One example, discovered by B. C. R. Bertram (1975) and also studied by Craig Packer and Anne Pusey (reviewed in Packer et al. 1988), happens in lions. The basic social unit of lions is the pride. The core of a pride is a group of closely related females—mothers, daughters, sisters, nieces, aunts, and so on—and their cubs. Also in the pride is a small group of adult males; two or three is a typical number. The males are usually related to each other, but not to the adult females. This system is maintained because females reaching sexual maturity stay in the pride they were born into, whereas newly mature males move to another pride.

Male–male competition can take the form of infanticide.

The move for young adult males from one pride to another is no stroll in the park. The adult males already resident in the new pride resist the invaders. That is why males stay with their other male kin: Each group, the residents and the newcomers, forms a coalition. The residents fight the newcomers, sometimes violently, over the right to live in the pride. If the residents win, they stay in the pride and the newcomers search for a different pride to take over. If the residents lose, they are evicted, and the newcomers have exclusive access to the pride's females—

Figure 9.12 Lion infanticide In this photo by George B. Schaller, a male lion has just killed another male's cub, which it now carries in its mouth.

exclusive, that is, until another coalition of younger, stronger, or more numerous males comes along and kicks them out. Pusey and Packer found that the average time a coalition of males holds a pride is a little over two years. Because residence in a pride is the key to reproductive success in lions, males in a victorious coalition quickly begin trying to father cubs. One impediment to quick fatherhood, however, is the presence of still-nursing cubs fathered by males of the previous coalition. That is because females do not return to breeding condition until after their cubs are weaned.

By killing other males' cubs, male lions gain more opportunities to mate.

How can the males overcome this problem? They frequently employ the obvious, if grisly, solution: They kill any cubs in the pride that are not weaned (Figure 9.12). Packer and Pusey have shown that this strategy causes the cubs' mothers to return to breeding condition an average of eight months earlier than they otherwise would. Infanticide by males is the cause of about 25% of all cub deaths in the first year of life, and over 10% of all lion mortality.

Infanticide improves the males' reproductive prospects, but is obviously detrimental to the reproductive success of the females. The females have two options for making the best of their own interests in this bad situation (Packer and Pusey 1983). One is to defend their cubs from infanticidal males, which females often do, occasionally at the cost of their own lives. Nonetheless, Packer and Pusey report that young cubs rarely survive more than two months in the presence of a new coalition of males. The females' other tactic is to spontaneously abort any pregnancies in progress when a new coalition gains residence in the pride. This cuts the females' losses: They do not waste energy and time on cubs that would be killed anyway shortly after birth. With this shift in focus to female reproductive strategy, we leave the subject of male–male conflict and move to the other side of sexual selection: female choice.

9.3 Female Choice

There is a great variety of species in which male reproductive success is limited by opportunities to mate, but in which males are unable to monopolize either females themselves or any resource vital to females. In many such species, the males advertise for mates. Females typically inspect advertisements of several males before they choose a mate. Sexual selection by female choice leads to the evolution of elaborate courtship displays by males.

Charles Darwin first asserted that female choice is an important mechanism of selection in 1871, in *The Descent of Man, and Selection in Relation to Sex*. Although widely accepted today, the notion that females actively discriminate among individual males was controversial for several decades. Most evolutionary biologists thought that female discrimination was limited to choosing a male of the right species (see Trivers 1985). Beyond allowing females to identify a mate of the right species, male courtship displays were thought to function primarily in overcoming a general female reluctance to mate. Once ready to mate, a female would accept any male at hand.

We begin this section by describing two experiments that demonstrate that females are in fact highly selective, actively choosing particular males from among the many available. We then consider the functions of female choosiness. Potential benefits to a choosy female include the acquisition of good genes for her offspring, and the aquisition of resources offered by males. Alternatively, females may prefer male displays that exploit preexisting sensory biases built into the females' nervous systems.

When males cannot monopolize access to females, they often compete by advertising for mates. Although biologists were long skeptical that females discriminate among the advertising males, female choice is now well established.

Female Choice in Barn Swallows

Our first experiment demonstrating active female choice comes from the work of Anders Møller on barn swallows. Barn swallows, *Hirundo rustica*, are small insect-eating birds that breed in colonies of up to 80 individuals. The swallows Møller (1988) studied breed in Denmark during spring and summer, after spending the European winter in Africa. Upon arriving in a Danish breeding colony, each male swallow sets up a territory a few square meters in size. He then tries to attract a mate by displaying his tail while perching and flying. Each female visits several males, then chooses one to pair with. Once paired, the male and female together build a mud nest in the male's territory. In this nest the pair raises one or, if they have time before summer's end, two clutches of young. The female incubates the eggs by herself, but both parents feed the chicks.

At first glance, barn swallows may not seem promising subjects for a study of sexual selection. The fact that the males help care for the young should tend to equalize parental investment by the two sexes, and the fact that the swallows appear to mate monogamously suggests that neither sex should be in short supply for the other. Barn swallows are, however, sexually dimorphic. The males are more brightly colored than the females, and they tend to be slightly larger (Figure 9.13a). The biggest difference is that the outermost tail feathers, which are elongated in both sexes, are about 15% longer in males than in females (Figure 9.13b).

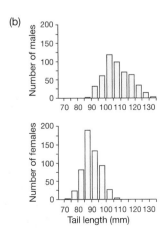

(a)

(b)

Number of males

200
150
100
50
0
70 80 90 100 110 120 130

Number of females

200
150
100
50
0
70 80 90 100 110 120 130
Tail length (mm)

Figure 9.13 **Sexual dimorphism in barn swallows** (a) A female (left) and a male (right). Note that the male has richer colors, and longer outer tailfeathers. (Leonard Lee Rue III/Visuals Unlimited) (b) The distribution of tail streamer length in male and female barn swallows. The distributions overlap, but the average male has longer tail feathers than the average female. From Møller (1991).

Three additional factors suggest that sexual selection may be at work in barn swallows. First, even in a monogamous species in which both sexes care for the young, males and females may vary in quality, both as parents and as donors of genes to offspring. The members of both sexes should thus benefit, in higher reproductive success, by trying to identify and attract the best mate possible. Second, although barn swallows appear to be monogamous, many, in fact, are not. Males sometimes solicit copulations with females other than their pair-mates. When these offers of extra-pair copulation are accepted by the females, as occasionally they are, the successful male may benefit by fathering offspring that some other male will help to raise. Third, the trait that differs most prominently between the sexes—the length of the long outer tail feathers—is precisely the trait that males show off when advertising for mates. Møller hypothesized that sexual selection does indeed occur in barn swallows, through the mechanism of female choice, and that females prefer to mate with males displaying longer tail feathers.

Møller captured and color-banded 44 males that had established territories, but not yet attracted mates. He divided them at random into four groups of 11, and altered the tail feathers of each group as follows:

- **Shortened tail feathers.** Møller clipped about 2 centimeters out of the middle of each outer tail feather, then reattached the feather tips to the bases with superglue.
- **Mock-altered (control I).** Møller clipped the tail feathers, then glued them back together. This did not change the length of the feathers, but it otherwise subjected the birds to the same handling, clipping, and gluing as the shortened and lengthened groups.
- **Unaltered (control II).** Møller captured and banded these birds, but did nothing to their tail feathers.
- **Elongated tail feathers.** Møller added, by clipping and gluing, the 2 cm of feather removed from the shortened group into the middles of the tail feathers of these birds.

Møller then released the birds back into their colony. He predicted that if females prefer males with longer tail feathers, then the males with elongated tails would attract mates sooner, and fledge more young, than either control I males or control II males. The control males should, in turn, be more successful than the shortened males. If, on the other hand, the females have no preferences based on tail feathers, then there should be no differences in success among the groups.

Female barn swallows prefer to mate with males whose tail feathers are longest.

The results appear in Figure 9.14. The elongated males, on average, attracted mates more quickly than the control males, and control males attracted mates more quickly than shortened males (Figure 9.14a). Among the advantages of attracting a mate quickly is that the male and his partner can get an earlier start on rearing a clutch of chicks. An earlier start means that the parents are more likely to have time to raise a second clutch before the summer ends (Figure 9.14b). Finally, the advantage of raising two clutches is that the parents fledge more chicks over the course of the summer (Figure 9.14c).

The female barn swallows had additional opportunities to be choosy whenever they were solicited by males for extra-pair copulations. Møller was able to watch the birds closely enough to estimate the rates at which the male swallows at-

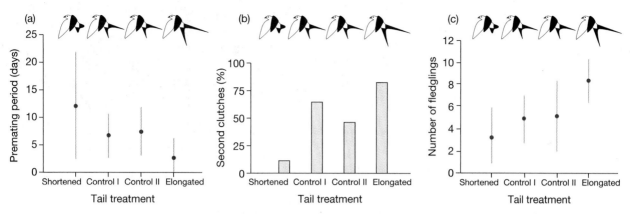

Figure 9.14   Anders Møller's data on reproductive success and tail length in male barn swallows   (a) Length of time required by males to attract a mate. Red dots represent the average for each group; the vertical lines represent the standard deviation (a statistical measure of the amount of variation within each group). There were significant differences among groups ($P < 0.01$). (b) Differences in time required to attract a mate carried over into which males had time to raise a second clutch of chicks. Bar height indicates the percentage of males in each group who, with their mates, raised two clutches. Again, there was significant variation among groups ($P < 0.02$). (c) Differences in second-clutch success carried over into reproductive success—the number of chicks each male had fledged by summer's end. The meanings of dots and lines are the same as in (a). There was significant variation among groups ($P < 0.001$). Elongated males fledged more chicks than control males, who in turn fledged more chicks than shortened males. From Møller (1988).

tempted to copulate with females other than their pair-mates, the rates at which the females they solicited accepted these copulations, and the rates at which the study males' pair-mates copulated with other males. The males in the four study groups showed no differences in the rates at which they attempted to gain extra-pair copulations. Nor did their pair-mates differ in the rates at which they were solicited. The males in the groups did differ, however, in the rates at which the extra-pair females they propositioned actually accepted them for copulation (Table 9.2). Furthermore, the males' pair-mates differed in the rates at which they accepted extra-pair copulations with other males (Table 9.2). Apparently, females who had to settle for less desirable short-tailed males attempted to compensate by copulating out-of-pair with more desirable long-tailed males. Thanks to these females, the long-tailed males won again, at the expense of the short-tails. (For more on extra-pair copulations in birds, see Box 9.2.)

Table 9.2   **Extra-pair copulations in Møller's barn swallow experiment**

The numbers reported are rates, measured as extra-pair copulations per hour. P values give statistical significance of variation among groups. From Møller (1988).

	Male Tail Treatment				
Extra-pair copulations	**Shortened tails**	**Control I**	**Control II**	**Lengthened tails**	***P***
By males	0	0	0	0.040	< 0.001
By their social pair-mates	0.036	0.014	0.017	0	< 0.01

x 9.2 **Extra-pair copulations**

Barn swallows are somewhat unusual in that a careful observer can see enough copulations to estimate the rate of extra-pair copulations directly. In recent years, however, biologists have developed methods of genetic analysis that enable them to indirectly estimate the rate of extra-pair copulations. Figure 9.15 shows two such tests performed on red-winged blackbirds.

Figure 9.15a shows paternity analysis using a restriction-fragment length polymorphism. The photo in the figure depicts an electrophoresis gel (see Box 4.1). Each lane in this electrophoresis gel contains DNA that has been extracted from an individual bird, cut with a restriction enzyme, and labeled with a probe that recognizes a sequence of DNA that occurs at a single locus. Bands on the gel are inherited as simple Mendelian alleles. Individual M_1 (center lane) is an adult male red-wing who had two mates on his territory, F_1 and F_2. M_2 and M_3 are adult male neighbors of M_1, F_1, and F_2. The numbers 1, 2, and 3 rep-

resent chicks in the nest shared by M_1 and F_1. Chick 1 has a band in its lane (arrow) that is present in neither its mother (F_1) nor its social father (M_1). This band is present, however, in M_2. We can infer that F_1 had an extra-pair copulation with M_2 (or with an unknown male with the same genotype). The numbers 4, 5, and 6 represent chicks in the nest shared by M_1 and F_2. Chick 6 has a band in its lane (arrow) that is present in neither its mother (F_2) nor its social father (M_1). This band is present, however, in M_3. We can infer that F_2 had an extra-pair copulation with M_3.

Figure 9.15b shows a paternity analysis of the same families using DNA fingerprints. Each lane contains DNA that has been extracted from an individual bird, cut with a restriction enzyme, and labeled with a probe that recognizes a sequence of DNA that occurs at many loci. Bands on the gel are inherited as simple Mendelian alleles, although we do not know which band corresponds to an allele at which locus. The

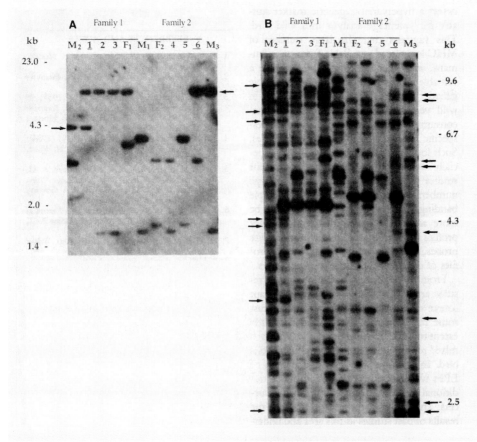

Figure 9.15 Genetic analyses demonstrating extra-pair copulations in red-winged blackbirds (a) A paternity analysis using a traditional restriction-fragment length polymorphism. (b) A paternity analysis of the same families using DNA fingerprints. Reprinted with permission from H. L. Gibbs et al., 1990. Realized reproductive success of polygynous red-winged blackbirds revealed by DNA markers. *Science* 250: 1394–96, Dec. 7, 1990, p. 1395, Fig. 1. Copyright © 1990. American Association for the Advancement of Science.

Box 9.2 Continued

DNA fingerprints confirm the same cases of extra-pair copulation we inferred from the gel in Figure 9.15a.

How common is extra-pair copulation in birds? Elizabeth Gray (1997) used DNA fingerprints to assess the frequency of extra-pair copulation in a population of red-winged blackbirds. She estimated that in a given breeding season between 50 and 64% of all nests contained at least one chick sired by a male other than its social parent. Red-winged black birds are not unusual. By using genetic paternity tests, biologists have discovered that many socially monogamous birds engage in frequent extra-pair copulations.

Møller's experiment demonstrates that female barn swallows are choosy. As Møller predicted, females prefer pair-mates with longer tail feathers. And for males, being one of the more desirable mates results in higher reproductive success.

Female Choice in Gray Tree Frogs

Our second experiment demonstrating active female choice comes from the work of H. Carl Gerhardt and colleagues (1996) on gray tree frogs. Gray tree frogs, *Hyla versicolor*, live in woodlands in the eastern United States. During the breeding season, males produce a melodious mating call attractive to females. Each call consists of a series of pulses, or trills. Some males give long calls, consisting of many pulses, while other males give short calls. In addition, some males are fast callers, giving many calls per minute, while other males are slow callers. Gerhardt and colleagues suspected, for at least two reasons, that female gray tree frogs discriminate among potential mates on the basis of their calls. First, when an individual male hears that many other males are calling too, he sometimes increases both the length and speed of his calls. Second, several times in the field the researchers had seen females approach and mate with the more distant of two calling males. The researchers hypothesized that females prefer to mate with longer- and faster-calling males.

Gerhardt and colleagues captured female gray tree frogs in nature and tested their preferences in the laboratory. In one series of experiments, the researchers released females between a pair of loudspeakers (Figure 9.16a). Each speaker played a computer-synthesized mating call. To make their experiment conservative, the researchers made the call they expected to be less attractive louder, either by increasing the volume on that speaker, or by releasing the female closer to it. Then they waited to see which speaker the female would approach. They found that 30 of 40 females (75%) preferred long calls to short calls, even when the short calls were louder, and that 35 of 51 females (69%) preferred fast calls to slow calls, even when the slow calls were louder.

Female gray tree frogs prefer to mate with males that give longer calls, and males that repeat their calls more rapidly.

In another experiment, Gerhardt and colleagues released female frogs facing two loudspeakers (Figure 9.16b). The closer speaker played short calls, while the more distant speaker played long calls. The researchers found that 38 of 53 females (72%) went past the short-calling speaker to approach the long-calling speaker.

The experiments of Gerhardt et al. show that female gray tree frogs are choosy. As the researchers predicted, females prefer males giving longer and faster calls.

Female choice, as illustrated by barn swallows and gray tree frogs, is thought to be the selective force responsible for the evolution of a great variety of male advertisement displays—from the gaudy tail feathers of the peacock, to the chirping

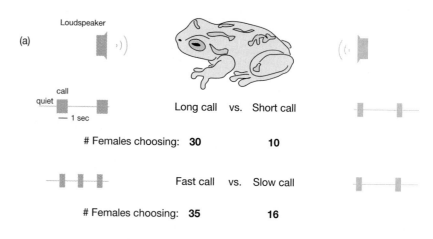

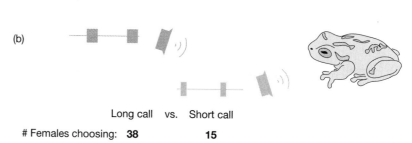

Figure 9.16 Gerhardt et al.'s data on the preferences of female gray tree frogs (a) Most females prefer long calls to short calls, even when the short calls are initially louder ($P < 0.001$), and fast calls to slow calls, even when the slow calls are initially louder ($P < 0.005$). (b) Most females will pass a loudspeaker playing short calls to approach a loudspeaker playing long calls ($P < 0.001$). After Gerhardt el al. (1996).

of crickets, to the chemical attractant of silk moths. Some male displays, like those of peacocks, are loud and clear; others, like those of barn swallows, are more subtle. It is curious that an extra two centimeters added to two tail feathers should make a male barn swallow so much more attractive to females as to dramatically improve his reproductive success. Why should the females care about such a small difference? And for that matter, why should females care about any of the advertisements, even the loud ones, that males use to attract mates? We will consider three explanations.

Choosy Females May Get Better Genes for Their Offspring

A variety of factors have been suggested to explain female preferences.

One possibility is that the displays given by males are indicators of genetic quality. If males giving more attractive displays are genetically superior to males giving less attractive displays, then choosy females will secure better genes for their offspring (Fisher 1915, Williams 1966, Zahavi 1975).

Allison Welch and colleagues (1998) used an elegant experiment to investigate whether male gray tree frogs giving long calls are genetically superior to males giving short calls (Figure 9.17). During two breeding seasons, the researchers collected unfertilized eggs from wild females. They divided each female's clutch into separate batches of eggs, then fertilized one batch of eggs with sperm from a long-calling male, and the other batch of eggs with sperm from a short-calling male. They reared some of the tadpoles from each batch of eggs on a generous diet, and the others on a restricted diet.

This experimental design allowed Welch and colleagues to compare the fitness of tadpoles that were maternal half-siblings—that is, tadpoles with the same mother, but different fathers. When comparing tadpoles fathered by long-calling males versus short-calling males, the researchers did not have to worry about uncontrolled differences in the genetic contribution of the mothers, because the mothers were the same.

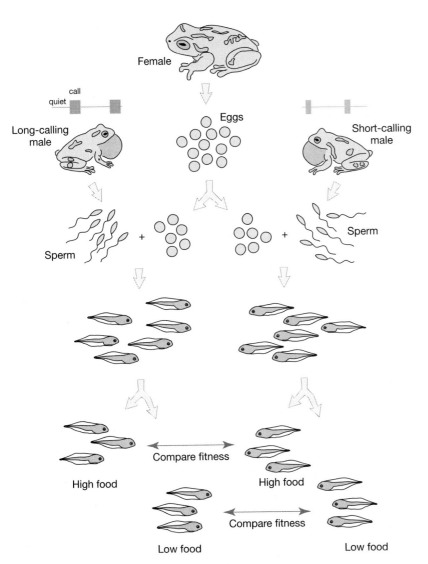

Figure 9.17   Welch et al.'s experiment to determine whether male gray tree frogs that give long calls are genetically superior to males that give short calls   Overall, the experiment included batches of eggs from 20 different females fertilized with sperm from 25 different pairs of males.

Welch and colleagues measured five aspects of offspring performance related to fitness: larval growth rate (faster is better); time to metamorphosis (shorter is better); mass at metamorphosis (bigger is better); larval survival; and post-metamorphic growth (faster is better). The results of their comparisons appear in Table 9.3. In 18 comparisons between the offspring of long-calling males versus short-calling males, there was either no significant difference, or better performance by the offspring of long callers. The offspring of short callers never did better. Overall, the data indicate that the offspring of long-calling males have significantly higher fitness. This result is consistent with the good genes hypothesis. The exact nature of the genetic difference between long-calling frogs versus short-calling frogs is a subject for future research.

Choosy female gray tree frogs get better genes for their offspring.

Choosy Females May Benefit Directly Through the Acquisition of Resources

In many species the males provide food, parental care, or some other resource that is beneficial to the female and her young. If it is possible to distinguish good providers from poor ones, then choosy females reap a direct benefit in the form

Table 9.3 **Fitness of the offspring of long-calling male frogs vs. short-calling male frogs**

NSD = no significant difference; LC better = offspring of long-calling males performed better than offspring of short-calling males; − = no data taken. The overall result: Offspring fathered by long-calling males had significantly higher fitness than their maternal half-sibs fathered by short-calling males ($P < 0.0008$).

	1995		1996	
Fitness measure	High food	Low food	High food	Low food
Larval growth	NSD	LC better	LC better	LC better
Time to metamorphosis	LC better	NSD	LC better	NSD
Mass at metamorphosis	NSD	LC better	NSD	NSD
Larval survival	LC better	NSD	NSD	NSD
Postmetamorphic growth	—	—	NSD	LC better

of the resource provided. Such is the case in the hangingfly (*Bittacus apicalis*), studied by Randy Thornhill (1976). Hangingflies live in the woods of eastern North America, where they hunt for other insects. After a male catches an insect, he hangs from a twig and releases a pheromone to attract females. When a female approaches, the male presents his prey. If she accepts it, the pair copulates while she eats (Figure 9.18a). The larger the prey, the longer it takes her to eat it, and the longer the pair copulates (Figure 9.18b). The longer the pair copulates, the more

(a)

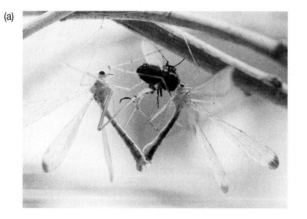

Figure 9.18 Courtship and mating in hangingflies (a) A female (right) copulates with a male while eating a blowfly he has captured and presented to her. (Randy Thornhill, University of New Mexico). (b) The larger the gift the male presents to the female, the longer the pair copulates. Copulation ends after about 20 minutes, even if the female is still eating. A lady beetle presented by one male is an exception to the general pattern. Even though the beetle was fairly large, the female hangingfly rejected it and broke off copulation almost immediately. (c) The longer a pair copulates, the more sperm the female allows the male to transfer. The male must present a gift that takes at least five minutes to eat, or the female accepts no sperm. From Thornhill (1976). Copyright © 1997, American Naturalist. Reprinted by permission of The University of Chicago Press.

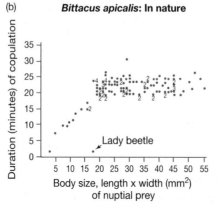

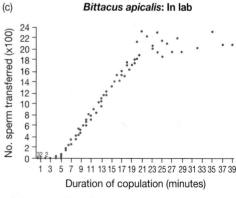

sperm the female accepts from the male (Figure 9.18c). If she finishes her meal in less than 20 minutes, the female breaks off the copulation and flies away looking for another male and another meal. The female's preference for males bearing large gifts benefits her in two ways: (1) It provides her with more nutrients, allowing her to lay more eggs; and (2) it saves her from the need to hunt for herself. Hunting is dangerous, and males die in spider webs at more than twice the rate of females. The males behave in accord with the same kind of economic analysis: If the female is still eating after accepting all the sperm she can, the male grabs his gift back and flies off to look for a second female to share it with.

Choosy female hanging flies get food from their mates.

Choosy Females May Have Preexisting Sensory Biases

Females use their sensory organs and nervous systems for many other purposes than just discriminating among potential mates. It is possible that selection for such abilities as avoiding predators, finding food, and identifying members of the same species may result in sensory biases that make females particularly responsive to certain cues (see Enquist and Arak 1993). This may in turn select on males to display those cues, even if the cues would otherwise have no relation to mating or fitness. In other words, the preexisting bias, or sensory exploitation, hypothesis holds that female preferences evolve first and that male mating displays follow.

Research by Heather Proctor on the water mite *Neumania papillator* illustrates sensory exploitation (1991; 1992). Members of this species are small freshwater animals that live amid aquatic plants, and make their living by ambushing copepods. Water mites have simple eyes that can detect light, but cannot form images. Instead of vision, water mites rely heavily on smell and touch. Both males and females hunt copepods by adopting a posture Proctor calls *net-stance*. The hunting mite stands on an aquatic plant with its four hind legs, rears up, and spreads its four front legs to form a sort of net. The mite waits until it detects vibrations in the water that might be produced by a swimming copepod, then turns toward the source of the vibrations and clutches at it.

Mating in *Neumania papillator* does not involve copulation. Instead, the male attaches sperm-bearing structures called spermatophores to an aquatic plant, then attempts to induce the female to accept them. He does this by fanning water across the spermatophores toward the female. The moving water carries to the female pheromones released by the spermatophores. When the female smells the pheromones, she may pick up the spermatophores.

Male water mites search for females by moving about on aquatic vegetation. When a male smells a female, he walks in a circle while lifting and trembling his front legs (Figure 9.19a). If the male has detected a female that is still there, not just the scent of one that has recently left, the female typically turns toward the trembling male. Often she also clutches at him. At this point, the male deposits his spermatophores and begins to fan (Figure 9.19b).

Proctor suspected that male leg-trembling during courtship evolved in *N. papillator* because it mimics the vibrations produced by copepods, and thereby elicits predatory behavior from the female. She tested this hypothesis with a series of experiments in which she observed the behavior of water mites under a microscope. First, Proctor measured the frequency of vibrations produced by trembling males, and compared it to the frequency of vibrations produced by copepods. Water mites tremble their legs at frequencies of 10 to 23 cycles per second, well within the

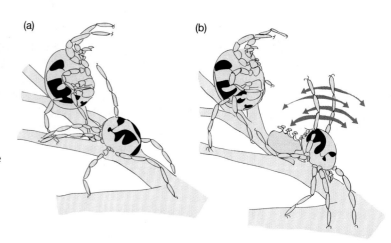

(a) **(b)**

Figure 9.19 **Courtship in the water mite,** *Neumania papillator* (a) The female (on the left) is in net-stance, waiting to ambush a copepod; the male has found her and is now trembling his legs. (b) The female has turned toward the male in response to the trembling. The male has deposited spermatophores and is now fanning water across them. The sausage-shaped objects on top of the spermatophores are sperm packets. Redrawn from Proctor (1991) by permission of Academic Press.

Choosy female water mites may simply be responding to courting males as though the males were prey.

copepod range of 8 to 45 cycles per second. Second, Proctor observed the behavior during net-stance of female water mites when they were alone, when they were with copepods, and when they were with males. Females in net-stance rarely turned and never clutched unless copepods or males were present, and the behavior of females toward males was similar to their behavior toward copepods. Third, Proctor observed the responses to male mites of hungry females versus well-fed females. Hungry females turned toward males, and clutched them, significantly more often than well-fed females. All of these results are consistent with the hypothesis that male courtship trembling evolved to exploit the predatory behavior of females.

Males employing leg trembling during courtship probably benefit in several ways. First, males appear to use the female response to trembling to determine whether a female is actually present. Proctor observed that a male that has initiated courtship by trembling is much more likely to deposit spermatophores if the female clutches him than if she does not. Second, trembling appears to allow males to distinguish between receptive females versus unreceptive ones. Proctor observed that a male has a strong tendency to deposit spermatophores for the first female he encounters that remains in place after he initiates courtship, but that virgin females are more likely to remain in place than are nonvirgins. Third, males appear to use the female response to trembling to determine which direction the female is facing. Proctor observed that males deposit their spermatophores in front of the female more often than would be expected by chance. These benefits mean that a male that trembles should get more of his spermatophores picked up by females than would a hypothetical male that does not tremble. In other words, a male that trembles would enjoy higher mating success. This is consistent with the hypothesis that trembling evolved by sexual selection.

A key prediction of the sensory exploitation hypothesis is that net-stance evolved before male trembling. Proctor tested this hypothesis by using a suite of morphological characters to estimate the phylogeny of *Neumania papillator* and several related water mites. (Methods for estimating phylogenies will be covered in Chapter 13.) She noted which species have net stance, and which species have male courtship trembling. She then inferred the places on the phylogeny at which net-stance and courtship trembling are most likely to have evolved, based on the assumption that simpler evolutionary scenarios are more probable. Proctor concluded that one of two evolutionary scenarios is most likely to be correct (Figure 9.20).

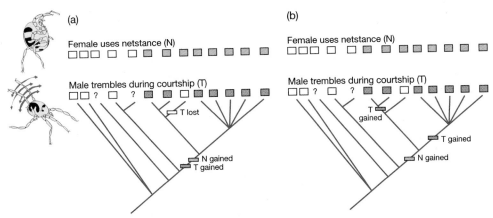

Figure 9.20   A phylogeny of the water mite *Neumania papillator* and several related species
The boxes above the tips of the branches indicate which species have net-stance, and which species have male courtship trembling. A colored box indicates the trait is present; an open box indicates the trait is absent. The two versions of the phylogeny show the two most likely scenarios for the evolution of these two traits. Redrawn from Proctor (1992) by permission of Academic Press.

In the first scenario, net-stance and courtship trembling both evolved at the base of the branch that includes all species with either or both of these traits, and trembling was subsequently lost once (Figure 9.20a). In the second scenario, net-stance evolved at the base of the branch, and courtship trembling subsequently evolved twice. The first scenario supplies insufficient evidence to test the prediction that net-stance evolved before trembling. We simply cannot tell, under this scenario, whether one trait evolved before the other, or the two traits evolved simultaneously. The second scenario is consistent with the prediction that net-stance evolved first. Which scenario is closest to the truth remains unkown. However, given the phylogenetic evidence in combination with the data from her obervations of water mite behavior, Proctor concludes that sensory exploitation is the best explanation for the evolution of courtship trembling.

Other Explanations for Female Choice

We have considered three explanations for female choice that provide good reasons why females might prefer some male displays over others. It is also possible, however, that female preferences are essentially arbitrary. One version of this idea is the sexy-son hypothesis. According to this hypothesis, once a particular male advertisement display is favored by a majority of females, selection on females will automatically reinforce a preference for the fashionable trait. The reason is that females choosing fashionable mates will have more fashionable sons, and therefore more grandchildren, than females choosing unfashionable mates. A more technically detailed version of the idea that selection may reinforce arbitrary preferences, called the runaway selection hypothesis, is discussed in Box 9.3.

We should note that all the explanations for female choice that we have discussed are mutually compatible. It is possible, at least in principle, for a single courtship display to indicate genetic quality, to predict direct benefits the female is likely to receive, to exploit biases in the female's sensory system, and to be reinforced by selection in favor of sexy sons. Much contemporary research on sexual selection is focussed on determining the relative importance of these different factors in the evolution of female preferences. One approach is to test several alternative hypotheses in a single

Theory also suggests that female preferences can be completely arbitrary.

Box 9.3   Runaway sexual selection in stalk-eyed flies?

Runaway selection is an idea first elaborated by Ronald Fisher in 1915, and perhaps traceable to a remark made by T.H. Morgan in 1903 (reviewed in Anderson 1994). The idea is worth explaining in some detail, because it illustrates useful concepts in evolutionary genetics. We will discuss runaway selection in the context of research by Gerald Wilkinson and colleagues on the stalk-eyed flies of Southeast Asia.

Stalk-eyed flies carry their eyes on the ends of long thin appendages. In both sexes bigger flies have longer eyestalks, but males have longer stalks for their size than females. By day the flies are solitary and forage for rotting plants. In the evening, the flies congregate beneath overhanging stream banks, where they cling in small groups to exposed root hairs and spend the night (Figure 9.21). At dawn and dusk, the flies roosting together on a root hair often mate with each other. Neither sex cares for the young, so a female's investment in each offspring is larger than a male's. Not surprisingly, males attempt to evict each other from the root-hair roosts in order to be the only male in the group at mating time. In male–male confrontations, the male with longer eyestalks typically wins, so male–male competition may partially explain the evolution of eyestalks (Burkhardt and de la Motte 1983; Burkhardt and de la Motte 1987; Panhuis and Wilkinson 1999). As we will see, however, there is evidence that female choice has also played a role.

To see how the runaway selection hypothesis works, imagine a population of stalk-eyed flies in which both males and females are variable, males in the lengths of their eyestalks and females in their mat-

ing preferences for stalk length. These two patterns of variation should combine to produce assortative mating; that is, the females that prefer the longest stalks will mate with the longest-stalked males, and the females that prefer the shortest stalks will mate with the shortest-stalked males (Figure 9.22a). Assume, furthermore, that in both sexes the variation is heritable—that is, that at least part of the variation in stalk length, and part of the variation in preference, is due to variation in genes (see Chapter 7). Under these assumptions, offspring that receive from their fathers genes for long eyestalks tend to also receive from their mothers genes for a preference for long-stalked males. In other words, if the assortative mating persists for some generations, then it will establish a genetic correlation (linkage disequilibrium) between the stalk-length genes and the preference genes (see Chapter 7). If we were to take a group of males, mate each with a number of randomly chosen females, and then examine their sons and daughters, we would find that sons with long eyestalks tend to have sisters with a preference for long-stalked-males (Figure 9.22b). This association means that if we conduct artificial selection on the stalk lengths of the males (and only on the males), we should get a correlated evolutionary response in the preferences of the females (Figure 9.22c).

Wilkinson and Paul Reillo (1994) tested the prediction that selection on male stalk length will produce a correlated response in female preferences. Wilkinson and Reillo collected stalk-eyed flies (*Cyrtodiopsis dalmanni*) in Malaysia and used them to establish three laboratory populations. In each population, the researchers separated the males and females immediately after the adult flies emerged from their pupae, and kept them apart for two to three months. Wilkinson and Reillo then chose breeders for the next generation of each population as follows. For the control line, they used 10 males and 25 females picked at random. For the long-selected line, they used the 10 males with longest eyestalks from a pool of 50 males picked at random, and 25 females picked at random. For the short-selected line, they used the 10 males with shortest eyestalks from a pool of 50 males picked at random, and 25 females picked at random. After 13 genera-

Figure 9.21   A group of Malaysian stalk-eyed flies (*Cyrtodiopsis whitei*) gathered on a root hair to spend the night   The largest fly is a male; the others are females (Gerald Wilkinson, University of Maryland).

Box 9.3 Continued

tions the populations had diverged substantially in eyestalk length. Wilkinson and Reillo then performed paired-choice tests to assay female preferences in each population.

In each test, Wilkinson and Reillo placed two males in a cage with five females. The males had the same body size, but one was from the long-selected line, and thus had eyestalks that were long, and the other was from the short-selected line, and thus had eyestalks that were short (but still longer than the eyestalks of females from any line). The two males were separated by a clear plastic barrier, and each had his own artificial root hair on which to roost. In the center of the plastic barrier was a hole, just large enough to allow the females to pass back and forth, but too small for the males, with their longer eyestalks, to fit through. Wilkinson and Reillo then watched to see

which male attracted more females. The scientists performed 15 to 25 tests for each of the three lines. In both the control and the long-selected lines, more females chose to roost for the night with the long-stalked male. In the short-selected line, however, more females chose to roost for the night with the short-stalked male (Figure 9.23). Artificial selection for short eyestalks in males had changed the mating preferences of females.

This result neatly accomplishes several things at once:

- It demonstrates that female stalk-eyed flies are choosy.
- It demonstrates that both male eyestalk length and female preference are heritable.
- It illustrates that selection on one trait can produce an evolutionary response in another trait (see Chapter 7).

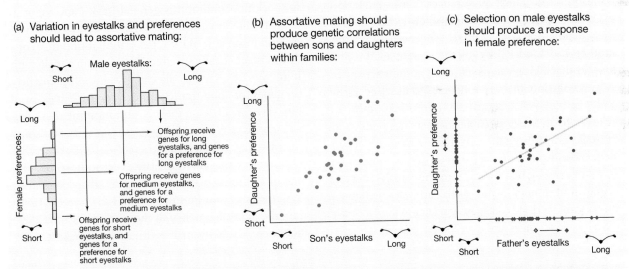

Figure 9.22 Runaway selection illustrated with stalk-eyed flies   (a) Assortative mating. Females with different tastes choose among males with different eyestalk lengths. If both traits are heritable, then offspring receiving genes for long eyestalks also tend to receive genes for "long" tastes. (b) A genetic correlation between male stalk length and female preference. Each point represents the average value of the offspring of a male mated with each of a number of randomly chosen females. Males whose sons have long eyestalks also tend to have daughters that seek long eyestalks in their mates. After Figure 4.6 in Arnold (1983). (c) Female preference evolves as a correlated response to selection on male stalk length. Each circle represents the stalklength and preference, respectively, of a father-daughter pair. The fathers are also represented by diamonds on the horizontal axis, and the daughters by diamonds on the vertical axis. If we select the longest-stalked males as breeders (red diamonds on the horizontal axis and red circles), we should see a response in the daughters. The arrows indicate the selection differential and predicted response (see Chapter 7). The gray diamond below the horizontal axis marks the average of all fathers in the population, and the red diamond marks the average of selected fathers. The gray diamond to the left of the vertical axis marks the average of all daughters, and the red diamond marks the average of daughters of selected males. After Falconer (1989).

Box 9.3   Continued

- It is consistent with Fisher's 80-year-old prediction that sexual selection by female choice produces genetic correlations between male traits and female preferences.

The scenario for the evolution of long eyestalks by runaway selection is as follows. At some time in the past, eyestalks were much shorter than they are now. At some point, a situation arose in which a majority of the females preferred longer-than-average eyestalks. Perhaps a preference for long stalks was favorable for females, because males with longer stalks were genetically superior, or perhaps the female preference was the result of genetic drift. Whatever the cause of the initial female preference, the consequence was that the males with long eyestalks left more offspring. As Fisher first noted, this can create a positive feedback loop, because as Wilkinson and Reillo's experiment showed, selection on males for longer eyestalks produces a correlated response in female preferences. Each generation's males have longer eyestalks than their fathers had, but each generation's females prefer longer stalks than their mothers did. Under the right circumstances, this positive-feedback loop can result in the automatic, or runaway, evolution of ever-longer eyestalks (see Fisher 1958; Lande 1981; Arnold 1983). In other words, it is at least theoretically possible that females prefer long eyestalks not because this preference carries any intrinsic fitness advantage for females or their young, or because of sensory biases built into the females' nervous systems, but simply because a small arbitrary preference, once established, led to runaway selection for ever more extreme preferences and ever longer eyestalks.

Is runaway selection the sole mechanism responsible for female preferences in stalk-eyed flies? We mentioned in the main text that the theories of female choice we have discussed are mutually compatible. Wilkinson and various colleagues have continued their research on stalk-eyed flies, looking for evidence of other mechanisms selecting on female preferences. Because males provide no parental care and offer no gifts to females, it seems unlikely that choosy females receive direct benefits—unless long-stalked males lay claim to better nighttime roosts. And Wilkinson, Heidi Kahler, and Richard Baker (1998) found no evidence that females had pre-existing sensory biases favoring long eyestalks before long eyestalks evolved in males. There is evidence, however, that choosy females get better genes for their offspring.

Choosy female stalk-eyed flies appear to get better genes for their offspring for at least two reasons. First, stalk-length in males is correlated with a trait biologists refer to as condition (David et al. 1998). Roughly speaking, condition is general health and vigor as demonstrated by the ability to gather and store energy. Wilkinson and Mark Taper (1999) found that condition is genetically variable. By choosing a male with long eyestalks, a female fly can give her offspring better genes for condition. Second, some male stalk-eyed flies carry an allele on their X-chromosome that causes them to have more daughters than sons, and some males carry an allele on their Y-chromosome that counteracts the allele on the X-chromosome, and causes the males to have more sons than daughters. Wilkinson, Daven Presgraves, and Lili Crymes (1998) found that the frequency of the X-chromosome allele does not vary across males with different stalk lengths,

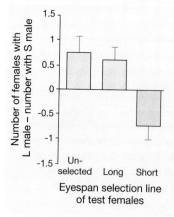

Figure 9.23   The results of Wilkinson and Reillo's paired choice tests for female preference   The height of each bar represents the average value (± standard error), for a number of trials, of the difference between the number of females that preferred the long-stalked male and the number that preferred the short-stalked male. Positive values indicate that more females preferred long-stalked males. Unselected females preferred long-stalked males ($P = 0.0033$), as did females from the long-selected line ($P = 0.005$). Females from the short-selected line preferred short-stalked males ($P = 0.023$). From Wilkinson and Reillo (1994). Copyright © 1994, The Royal Society.

Box 9.3 **Continued**

but the frequency of the Y-chromosome allele does. It is higher among males with long eyestalks. This matters because, in wild populations of stalk-eyed flies, females outnumber males and females can expect more grandoffspring through their sons than through their daughters. By choosing a mate with long eyestalks, a female fly can increase her chances of producing many sons.

In summary, long eyestalks appear to have evolved in stalk-eyed flies in response to a combination of male–male competition, a female preference for mates with good genes, and possibly a female preference reinforced by runaway selection. This combination of forces favoring long eyestalks raises a new question: Why are the males' eyestalks not even longer than they are now—for example, twice the length of the flies' bodies, or three times? One hypothesis is that if the eyestalks were any longer they would be a serious impediment to survival. As far as we know, this hypothesis has not been tested.

species (see Box 9.3 for an example). Another approach is to use the alternative hypotheses to develop testable predictions about how sexually selected traits will vary among closely related species on an evolutionary tree (see Prum 1997 for an example).

9.4 Diversity in Sex Roles

In all of the examples we have presented so far, the crucial fact explaining the roles taken by each sex is that access to mates limits the reproductive success of males more than it limits the reproductive success of females. This pattern is widespread, but it is by no means universal (Arnold and Duvall 1994). The pipefish species *Nerophis ophidion* and *Syngnathus typhle*, studied by Gunilla Rosenqvist, Anders Berglund, and their colleagues, provide a counterexample. These pipefish, which live in eelgrass beds, are relatives of the seahorses (Figure 9.24). As in seahorses, males provide all the parental care. In *N. ophidion*, the male has a brood patch on his belly; in *S. typhle*, the male has a brood pouch. In both species, the female lays her eggs directly onto or into the male's brood structure. The male supplies the eggs with oxygen and nutrients until they hatch.

Species in which males invest more in each offspring, and are thus a limiting resource for females, are the exceptions that can prove the rules of sexual selection.

Although the extensive parental care provided by male pipefish requires energy, the pivotal currency for pipefish reproduction is not energy but time (Berglund et al. 1989). Females of both *N. ophidion* and *S. typhle* can make eggs faster than males can rear them to hatching. As a result, access to male brood space limits female reproductive success. If the theory of sexual selection we have developed is correct, then in these pipefish the females should compete with each other over access to males, and the males should be choosy.

In *N. ophidion,* the females are larger than the males and have two traits the males lack: dark blue stripes and skin folds on their bellies. These traits appear to function primarily as advertisements for attracting mates. For example, females develop skin folds during the breeding season and lose them after, and in captivity females develop skin folds only when males are present (Rosenqvist 1990). In paired-choice tests (Figure 9.24a), *N. ophidion* males are choosy, preferring larger females (Figure 9.24b) and females with larger skin folds (Figure 9.24c). Females, in contrast, appear to be less choosy. In paired-choice tests, females showed no tendency to discriminate between males of different sizes (Berglund and Rosenqvist 1993).

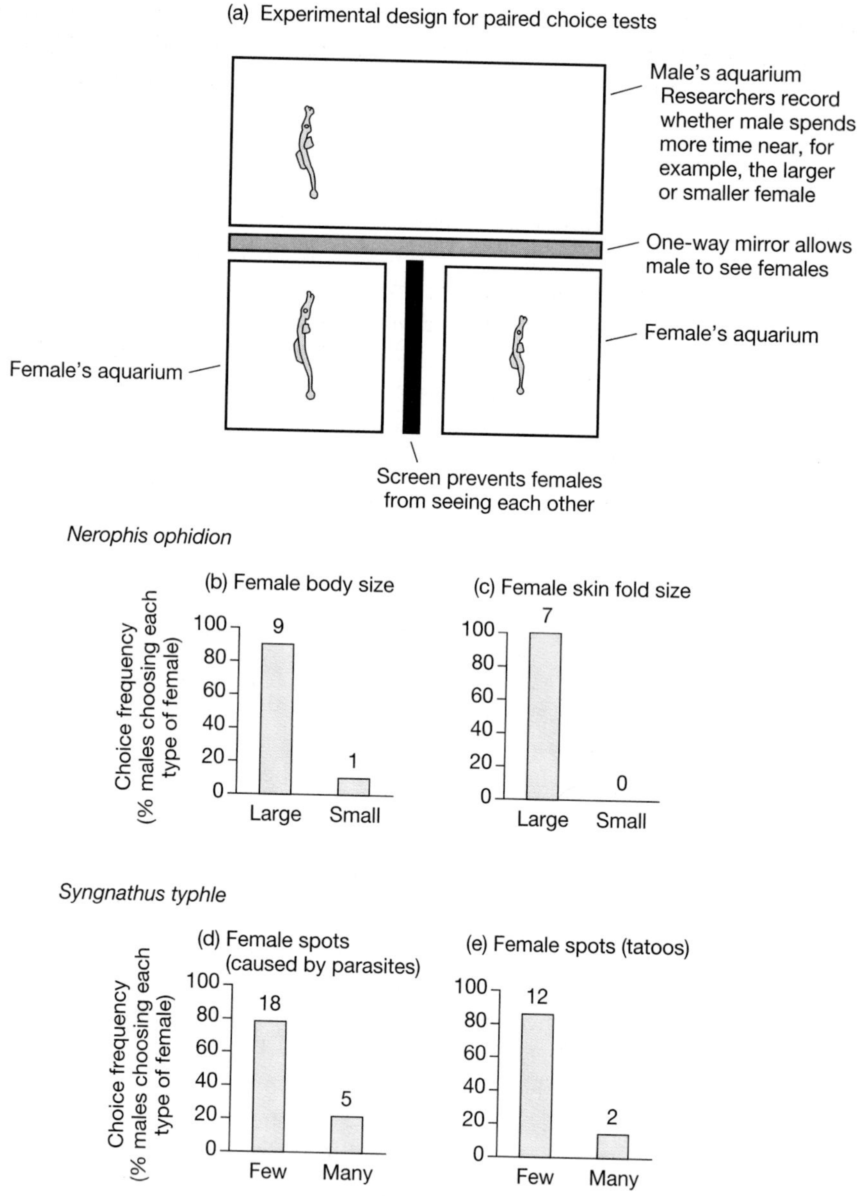

(a) Experimental design for paired choice tests

Male's aquarium Researchers record whether male spends more time near, for example, the larger or smaller female

One-way mirror allows male to see females

Female's aquarium

Female's aquarium

Screen prevents females from seeing each other

Figure 9.24   Male choice in pipefish   (a) In paired-choice tests, researchers place a male pipefish in an aquarium from which he can see two females. The researchers infer which female the male would prefer as a mate from where he spends more of his time. In (b–d) the numbers above the bars indicate the number of males tested. After Rosenqvist and Johansson (1995). (b) Given a choice between large or small females, male pipefish prefer large females (P = 0.022). Replotted from Rosenqvist (1990). (c) Given a choice between females with large or small skin folds, male pipefish prefer large-folded females (P = 0.016). Replotted from Rosenqvist (1990). (d) Given a choice between females with many black spots (caused by a parasite) or females with few black spots, male pipefish prefer females with few spots (P < 0.05). Replotted from Rosenqvist and Johansson (1995). (e) Males still prefer females with few spots, even when the spots are tattooed onto parasite-free females (P < 0.01). Replotted from Rosenqvist and Johansson (1995).

Nerophis ophidion

(b) Female body size

(c) Female skin fold size

Syngnathus typhle

(d) Female spots (caused by parasites)

(e) Female spots (tatoos)

Male pipefish brood their young, and access to males is a limiting resource for females. As predicted, females fight among themselves, and males are choosy.

In *S. typhle,* the males and females are similar in size and appearance. Females, however, can change their color to intensify the zigzag pattern on their sides (Berglund et al. 1997; Bernet et al. 1998). The females compete with each other over access to males (Berglund 1991), and while doing so display their dark colors. Females initiate courtship, and mate more readily than males (Berglund and Rosenqvist 1993). Males are choosy (Rosenqvist and Johansson 1995). In paired-choice tests (Figure 9.24a), male *S. typhle* prefer females showing fewer of the black spots that indicate infection with a parasitic worm, whether the black spots were actually caused by parasites (Figure 9.24d) or were tattooed onto the females (Figure 9.24e). This choosiness benefits the males directly, because females with fewer parasites lay more eggs for the males to fertilize and rear.

The mating behavior of pipefish males and females is consistent with the theory of sexual selection. Other examples of "sex-role reversed" species whose behavior appears to support the theory include moorhens (Petrie 1983), spotted sandpipers (Oring et al. 1991a,b, 1994), giant waterbugs (see Anderson 1994), and some species of katydids (Gwynne 1981; Gwynne and Simmons 1990).

9.5 Sexual Selection in Plants

Plants are often sexually dimorphic. Orchids in the genus *Catasetum* provide the most dramatic example. So different are the flowers of the two sexes that early orchid systematists placed the males (Figure 9.25a) in one genus and the females (Figure 9.25b) in another. The herb *Wurmbea dioica*, from Australia, provides a more typical example. The males make larger flowers than the females (Figure 9.25c). We have seen that sexual selection can explain sexual dimorphism in animals. Can it also explain sexual dimorphism in plants?

Many of the ideas we have developed about sexual selection in the context of animal mating can, in fact, be applied to plants (Bateman 1948; Willson 1979). In plants, mating involves the movement of pollen from one individual to another. The recipient of the pollen, the seed parent, must produce a fruit. As a result, the

Sexual selection theory can be applied to plants as well as animals.

Figure 9.25 Sexual dimorphism in plants (a) In the orcid *Catasetum barbatum*, males (a) and females (b) produce strikingly different flowers. (Sharon Dahl) In the herb *Wurmbea dioica* (c), males make larger flowers. Redrawn from Vaughton and Ramsey (1998). Copyright © 1998, Springer Verlag. Reprinted by permission.

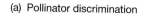

(a) Pollinator discrimination

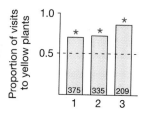

(b) Maternal function

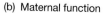

(c) Paternal function

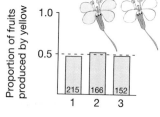

Population

Figure 9.26 Reproductive success through pollen donation is more stongly affected by the number of pollinator visits than is reproductive success through the production of seeds The numbers inside each bar represent the number of pollinator visits (a), the number of fruits (b), and the number of seeds (c) examined. Bars marked with an asterisk have heights significantly different from 0.5 ($P < 0.0001$). (a) In populations with equal numbers of white and yellow flowers, the yellow-flowered plants got most of the pollinator visits. (b) In spite of the inequality in pollinator visits, white- and yellow-flowered plants produced equal numbers of fruits. (c) The majority of the seeds, however, were fathered by yellow plants. From Stanton et al. (1986). Copyright © 1986, Association for the Advancement of Science.

seed parent may make a larger reproductive investment per seed than the pollen donor, which must only make pollen. When pollen is transported from individual to individual by animals, a plant's access to mates is a function of its access to pollinators. Based on the principles of sexual selection in animals, we can hypothesize that access to pollinators limits the reproductive success of pollen donors to a greater extent than it limits the reproductive success of seed parents.

Maureen Stanton and colleagues (1986) tested this hypothesis in wild radish (*Raphanus raphanistrum*). Wild radish is a self-incompatible annual herb that is pollinated by a variety of insects, including honeybees, bumblebees, and butterflies. Many natural populations of wild radish contain a mixture of white-flowered and yellow-flowered individuals. Flower color is determined by a single locus: White (*W*) is dominant to yellow (*w*). Stanton and colleagues set up a study population with eight homozygous white plants (*WW*) and eight yellow plants (*ww*). The scientists monitored the number of pollinator visits to plants of each color, then measured reproductive success through female and male function.

Measuring reproductive success through female function was easy: The researchers just counted the number of fruits produced by each plant of each color. Measuring reproductive success through male function was harder; in fact, it was not possible at the level of individual plants. Note, however, that a yellow seed parent (*ww*) will produce yellow offspring (*ww*) if it mated with a yellow pollen donor (*ww*), but white offspring (*Ww*) if it mated with a white pollen donor (*WW*). Thus by rearing the seeds produced by the yellow seed parents and noting the color of their flowers, Stanton and colleagues could compare the population-level reproductive success of white versus yellow pollen donors. The relative reproductive success of pollen donors through yellow seed parents should be a reasonable estimate of the pollen donors' relative reproductive success through seed parents of both colors. The scientists repeated their experiment three times.

As Stanton and colleagues expected from previous research, the yellow-flowered plants got about 3\4 of the pollinator visits (Figure 9.26a). If reproductive success is limited by the number of pollinator visits, then the yellow-flowered plants should also have gotten about 3\4 of the reproductive success. This was true for reproductive success through pollen donation (Figure 9.26c), but not for reproductive success through seed production (Figure 9.26b). Reproductive success through seed production was simply proportional to the number of plants of each type. These results are consistent with the typical pattern in animals: The reproductive success of males is more limited by access to mates than is the reproductive success of females. The results also suggest that the evolution of showy flowers that attract pollinators has been driven more by their effect on male reproductive success than on female reproductive success (Stanton et al. 1986).

If it is true in general that the number of pollinator visits is more important to male reproductive success than to female reproductive success, then in animal-pollinated plant species with separate male and female flowers, the flowers should be dimorphic and the male flowers should be more attractive. Lynda Delph (1996) and colleagues tested this hypothesis with a survey of animal- and wind-pollinated plants, including both **dioecious** species (separate male and female individuals) and **monoecious** species (separate male and female flowers on the same individual).

Delph and her coauthors first noted that the showiest parts of a flower, the petals and sepals that together form the perianth, serve not only to attract pollinators, but also to protect the reproductive structures when the flower is developing in the bud. If protection were the only function of the perianth, then the sex that has the bigger reproductive parts should always have the bigger perianth. This was indeed the case in all 11 wind-pollinated species Delph and colleagues measured (Figure 9.27a, right). If, however, pollinator attraction is also important, and more important to males than to females, then there should be a substantial number of species in which the female flowers have bigger reproductive parts, but the male flowers have bigger perianths. This was the case in 29% of the 42 animal-pollinated plants Delph and colleagues measured (Figure 9.27a, left). Furthermore, in species that are sexually dimorphic, male function tends to draw a greater investment in number of flowers per inflorescence and in strength of floral odor, although not in quantity of nectar (Figure 9.27b). These results are consistent with the hypothesis that sexual selection, via pollinator attraction, is often stronger for male flowers than for female flowers.

Can sexual selection explain the particular examples of sexual dimorphism we introduced at the beginning of this section? Recall that in the herb *Wurmbea dioica*, males make larger flowers than females. This plant is pollinated by bees, butterflies, and flies. Glenda Vaughton and Mike Ramsey (1998) found that bees and butterflies visit larger flowers at higher rates than smaller flowers. As a result, pollen is removed from large flowers more quickly than from small flowers. Males with large flowers may benefit from exporting their pollen more quickly if a head start allows their pollen to beat the pollen of other males in the race to females' ovules. In addition, larger male flowers make more pollen, giving the pollen donor more chances to win. For females, larger flowers probably do not confer any benefit. Female flowers typically receive more than four times the pollen needed to fertilize all their ovules, and seed production is therefore not limited by pollen. These patterns are consistent with the hypothesis that sexual selection on males is responsible for the sexual dimorphism in flower size.

When male reproductive success is limited by access to pollinators, but female reproductive success is not, male flowers may evolve showier displays than female flowers.

(a) **Animal-pollinated species**

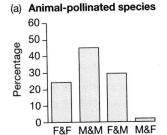

Wind-pollinated species

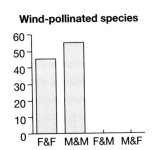

F&F: Female flower has larger reproductive parts and the larger perianth.
M&M: Male flower has larger reproductive parts and the larger perianth.
F&M: Female flower has larger reproductive parts, but male has the larger perianth.
M&F: Male flower has larger reproductive parts, but female has the larger perianth.

(b)

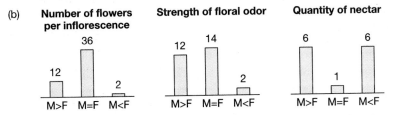

M>F: Male investment is greater than female investment.
M=F: Male investment and female investment are equal.
M<F: Male investment is less than female investment.

Figure 9.27 Patterns of sexual dimorphism in plants with separate male and female flowers (a) In all 11 wind-pollinated species measured (right), the sex with larger reproductive parts has the larger perianth. In 29% of the 42 animal-pollinated species measured (left), the female has larger reproductive parts, but the male has the larger perianth, a pattern significantly different from that for wind-pollinated species ($P < 0.001$). From Delph et al. (1996). (b) When animal-pollinated plants have flowers that are sexually dimorphic for investment in pollinator attraction, investment by males tends to be larger for two of the three traits studied ($P < 0.01$; $P = 0.01$; N.S.). Drawn from data in Delph et al. (1996). Copyright © 1996, American Naturalist. Reprinted by permission of The University of Chicago Press.

Orchids in the genus *Catasetum*, the plants with the dramatically dimorphic flowers, have an unusual pollination system. They are pollinated exclusively by male euglossine bees. The orchids attract the bees with fragrant chemicals, such as cineole, which the bees collect and use in their own attempts to attract mates. The flowers of male *Catasetum* orchids are loaded with a single pollen-bearing structure, called a pollinarium. When a bee trips the trigger in a male flower, the flower shoots the pollinarium at the bee like a rubber band off a finger. The pollinarium sticks to the back of the bee with an adhesive that makes it impossible for the bee to remove. When the bee later visits a female flower, one of the pollen masses on the pollinarium lodges in the receptive structure on the female flower, called the stigmatic cleft, and is torn from the pollinarium. The stigmatic cleft quickly swells shut. This means that a female flower typically receives pollen from just one male.

Gustavo Romero and Craig Nelson (1986) observed bees pollinating the flowers of *Catasetum ochraceum*. The researchers found that after being shot with a pollinarium by one male flower, the bees avoided visiting other male flowers but continued to forage in female flowers. Romero and Nelson offer the following scenario to account for the sexual dimorphism in the flowers of *Catasetum ochraceum*. At any given time, there are many more male flowers blooming than female flowers. This, in combination with the fact that female flowers accept pollen from only one male, means that there is competition among male flowers over opportunities to mate. The competition is further intensified by the fact that a second pollinarium attached to a bee would probably interfere with the first. A male flower that has attracted a bee and loaded it with a pollinarium would be at a selective advantage if it could prevent the bee from visiting another male flower. It is therefore adaptive for male flowers to train bees to avoid other male flowers, so long as they do not also train the bees to avoid female flowers. If this scenario is correct, forcible attachment of the pollinarium to the bee and sexually dimorphic flowers make sense together, and both are due to competition for mates—that is, to sexual selection.

9.6 Sexual Dimorphism in Body Size in Humans

One of the examples of sexual dimorphism that we cited at the beginning of this chapter was body size in humans (Figure 9.2). We now ask whether the sexual dimorphism in human size is the result of sexual selection. It is a difficult question to answer, because sexual selection concerns mating behavior. The evolutionary significance of human behavior is hard to study for at least two reasons:

- Human behavior is driven by a complex combination of culture and biology. Studies based on the behavior of people in any one culture provide no means of disentangling these two influences. Cross-cultural studies can identify universal traits or broad patterns of behavior, either of which may warrant biological explanations. Cultural diversity is rapidly declining, however, and some biologists feel that it is no longer possible to do a genuine cross-cultural study.
- Ethical and practical considerations prohibit most of the kinds of experiments we might conduct on individuals of other species. This means that most studies of human behavior are observational. Observational studies can identify correlations between variables, but they offer little evidence of cause and effect.

Human behavior is inherently fascinating, however, and we therefore proceed, with caution, to briefly consider the question of sexual selection and body size in humans.

The most basic knowledge of human reproductive biology indicates that the opportunity for sexual selection is greater in men than in women. Data from a single culture will suffice to illustrate this point. Research by Monique Borgerhoff Mulder (1988) on the Kipsigis people of southwestern Kenya revealed that the men with highest reproductive success had upwards of 25 children, while the most prolific women rarely had more than 10 (Figure 9.28). In Kipsigis culture, it appears that the reproductive success of men was limited by mating opportunities to a greater extent than was the reproductive success of women. But is there any evidence that reproductive competition, either via male–male interactions or female choice, selects for larger body size in men?

The most obvious kind of sexual selection to look at is male–male competition, because it drives the evolution of large male size in a great variety of other species. Men do, on occasion, compete among themselves over access to mates, but so do women. Do men compete more intensely? On the reasoning that homicide is an unambiguous indication of conflict, and that virtually all homicides are reported to the police, Martin Daly and Margo Wilson (1988) assembled data on rates of same-sex homicide from a variety of modern and traditional cultures. In all of these cultures, men kill men at much higher rates than women kill women. In the culture with the most *balanced* rates of male–male vs. female-female killings, men committed 85% of the same-sex homicides. In several cultures, men committed all of the same-sex homicides. Data from the United States and Canada show that the majority of perpetrators, and victims, of male–male homicides are in their late teens, twenties, and early thirties. On these and other grounds, Daly and Wilson interpret much male–male homicide as a manifestation of sexually selected competition among men.

If Daly and Wilson's interpretation is correct, then men who are more successful in male–male combat should have higher mating success and higher fitness, at least in pre-modern cultures without formal police and criminal justice systems. Napoleon Chagnon (1988) reported data on the Yąnomamö that confirm this prediction, at least for one culture. The Yąnomamö are a pre-modern people that live in the Amazon rain forest in Venezuela and Brazil. They take pride in their ferocity. Roughly 40% of the adult men in Chagnon's sample had participated in a homicide, and roughly 25% of the mortality among adult men was due to homicide. The Yąnomamö refer to men who have killed as *unokais*. Chagnon's data show that *unokais* have significantly more wives, and significantly more children, than non-*unokais* (Figure 9.29).

The Yąnomamö fight with clubs, arrows, spears, machetes, and axes. It would be reasonable to predict that *unokais* are larger that non-*unokais*. Chagnon (1988) reports, however, that "Personal, long-term familiarity with all the adult males in this study does not encourage me to conclude at this point that they could easily be sorted into two distinct groups on the basis of obvious biometric characters, nor have detailed anthropometric studies of large numbers of Yąnomamö males suggested this as a very likely possibility." Data on the relationship between male–male competition, body size, and mating success in other cultures are scarce.

B. Pawlowski and colleagues (2000) investigated the hypothesis that the sexual dimorphism in human body size is a result of female choice. The researchers gathered data from the medical records of 3201 Polish men. They used statistical techniques to remove the effects of a variety of confounding variables, including residence in cities versus rural areas, age, and education. Pawlowski and colleagues then com-

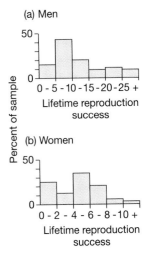

Figure 9.28   Variation in lifetime reproductive success among Kipsigis men and women   (a) For the men, the height of each bar represents the percentage of men who had 0 to 5 children, 6 to 10 children, and so on. (b) For the women, the height of each bar represents the percentage of women who had 0 to 2 children, 3 or 4 children, 5 or 6 children, and so on. Some of the men had more than 25 children; few of the women had more than 10. From Borgerhoff Mulder (1988). Copyright © 1988, University of Chicago Press. Reprinted by permission.

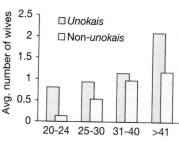

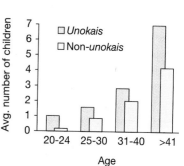

Figure 9.29 **Mating and reproductive success of *unokais* (killers) versus non-*unokais* among Yąnomamö men** These graphs show the average number of wives (top) and children (bottom) for adult men of various ages. Taken together, the data show that *unokais* are more successful than non-*unokais* ($P < 0.00001$). Plotted from data in Chagnon (1988).

pared bachelors to married men. The married men were taller by a small but statistically significant margin. In addition, men with one or more children were significantly taller than childless men. The exception to this pattern was the group of men in their fifties, within which there was no difference in height between fathers versus childless men. Pawlowski and colleagues note that the men in their fifties reached marrying age shortly after World War II, when the ratio of women to men in Poland was unusually high. The researchers speculate that the men in their fifties had experienced less intense sexual selection, via female choice, than is the norm.

The evolutionary significance of sexual size dimorphism in humans is unresolved. The observational studies we have reviewed provide mixed results, and evidence that is suggestive at best. It is also possible that we humans simply inherited our sexual size dimorphism from our ancestors, who were more sexually dimorphic in size than we are (McHenry 1992). What is really needed to settle the issue is data from a larger number of cultures on the relationship between body size, number of mates, survival, and reproductive success for both women and men. Preferably, the data would come from hunter-gatherer cultures, whose members live the life-style ancestral for our species. The most technically challenging factor to measure accurately is the reproductive success of men. Modern techniques for genetic analysis have made it feasible, in principle, to collect such data (Figure 9.15). However, the research remains to be done.

It is unclear whether sexual selection has played a role in maintaining the sexual dimorphism in body size in humans. Males compete for mates, but larger males do not necessarily win. Females are choosy, and limited data suggest a slight preference for taller men. More studies must be done on a greater variety of cultures.

Summary

Sexual dimorphism, a difference in form or behavior between females and males, is common. The difference often involves traits, like the enormous tail feathers of the peacock, that appear to be opposed by natural selection. To explain these puzzling traits, Darwin invoked sexual selection. Sexual selection is differential reproductive success resulting from variation in mating success.

Mating success is often a more important determinant of fitness for one sex than for the other. Usually, but by no means always, it is males whose reproductive success is limited by mating opportunities, and females whose reproductive success is limited by resources rather than matings.

The members of the sex experiencing strong sexual selection typically compete among themselves over access to mates. This competition may involve direct combat, gamete competition, infanticide, or advertisement.

The members of the sex whose reproductive success is limited by resources rather than matings are typically choosy. This choosiness may provide the chooser with direct or indirect benefits, such as food or better genes for its offspring, or it may be the result of a preexisting sensory bias.

The theory of sexual selection was developed to explain sexual dimorphism in animals, but it applies to plants as well. In plants, access to pollinators is often more limiting to reproductive success via pollen donation than to reproductive success via seed production. This can lead to the evolution of sexual dimorphism in which male flowers are showier than female flowers.

Questions

1. The graphs in Figure 9.30 show the variation in lifetime reproductive success of male vs. female elephant seals (Le Bouef and Reiter 1988). Note that the scales on the horizontal axes are different. Why is the variation in reproductive success so much more extreme in males than females? Draw a graph showing your hypothesis for the relationship between number of mates and reproductive success for male and female elephant seals. Why do you think male elephant seals are four times larger than female elephant seals? Why aren't males even bigger?

2. What sex is the sage grouse pictured in Figure 9.31? What is it doing and why? Do you think this individual provides parental care? What else can you guess about the social system of this species?

3. We used long-tailed widowbirds as an example of a dimorphic species at the beginning of this chapter. Suggest two hypotheses for why male widowbirds have such long tails. Design an experiment to test your ideas. (*Hint:* Anders Møller's experiments on barn swallows were inspired by Malte Anderson's research on widowbirds.) Look up Anderson's paper on widowbirds (Anderson

1982) and see if he designed the same experiment that you did.

4. Male butterflies and moths commonly drink from puddles, a behavior known as puddling. Scott Smedley and Thomas Eisner (1996) report a detailed physiological analysis of puddling in the moth *Gluphisia septentrionis*. A male *G. septentrionis* may puddle for hours at a time. He rapidly processes huge amounts of water, extracting the sodium and expelling the excess liquid in anal jets (see Smedley and Eisner's paper for a dramatic photo). The male moth will later give his harvest of sodium to a female during mating. The female will then put much of the sodium into her eggs. Speculate on the role this gift plays in the moth's mating ritual, and in the courtship roles taken by the male and the female. How would you test your ideas?

5. Males in many species often attempt to mate with strikingly inappropriate partners. Ryan (1985), for example, describes male túngara frogs clasping other males. Some orchids mimic female wasps and are pollinated by amorous male wasps—who have to be fooled twice for the strategy to work. Would a female túngara or a female wasp make

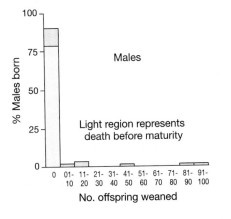

No. offspring weaned

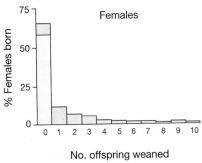

No. offspring weaned

Figure 9.30 Distributions of lifetime reproductive success in male and female elephant seals From Le Boeuf and Reiter (1988). Copyright © 1988, The University of Chicago Press. Reprinted by permission.

Figure 9.31   Sage grouse

the same mistake? Why or why not? (More general answers—applicable to a wider range of species—are better.)

6. Do you think there is any association in humans between infection with parasites and physical appearance? The scatterplot in Figure 9.32 shows the relationship between the importance of attractiveness in mate choice (as reported by subjects responding to a questionnaire) and the prevalence of six species of parasites (including leprosy, malaria, and filaria) in 29 cultures (Gangestad 1993; Gangestad & Buss 1993). (Note that statistical techniques have been used to remove the effects of latitude, geographic region, and mean income). What is the pattern in the graph? Does this pattern make sense from an evolutionary perspective?

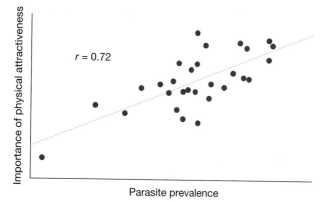

Figure 9.32   Importance of physical attractiveness in mate choice versus parasite prevalence in 29 human cultures

One of the parasitic diseases is schistosomiasis. We presented evidence in Chapter 4 that resistance to schistosomiasis is heritable. What do women gain (evolutionarily) by choosing an attractive mate? What do men gain (evolutionarily) by choosing an attractive mate? Can you offer a cultural explanation that could also account for this pattern?

7. In many katydids, the male delivers his sperm to the female in a large spermatophore which contains nutrients the female eats (for a photo, see Gwynne 1981). The female uses these nutrients in the production of eggs. Darryl Gwynne and L.W. Simmons (1990) studied the behavior of caged populations of an Australian katydid under low food (control) and high food (extra) conditions. Some of their results are graphed in Figure 9.33. (The graph shows the results from four sets of replicate cages; calling males = average number of males calling at any given time; matings/female = average number of times each female mated; % reject by M = fraction of the time a female approached a male for mating and was rejected; % reject by F = fraction of the time a female approached a male but then rejected him before copulating; % with F–F comp = fraction of matings in which one or more females were seen fighting over the male.) When were the females choosy and the males competitive? When where the males choosy and the females competitive? Why?

8. In some species of deep sea anglerfish, the male lives as a symbiont permanently attached to the female (see Gould 1983, essay 1). The male is tiny compared to the female. Many of the male's organs, including the eyes, are reduced, though the testes remain large. Others, such as the jaws and teeth, are modified for attachment to the female. The circulatory systems of the two sexes are fused, and the male receives all of his nutrition from the female via the shared bloodstream. Often, two or more males are attached to a single female. What are the costs and benefits of the male's symbiotic habit for the male? For the female? What limits the lifetime reproductive

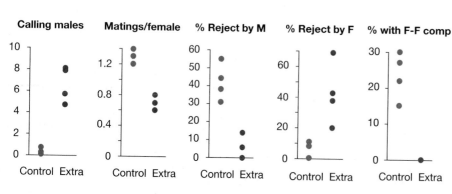

Food Level

Figure 9.33   Behavior of male and female katydids under control versus extra-food conditions

success of each sex—the ability to gather resources, or the ability to find mates? Do you think that the male's symbiotic habit evolved as a result of sexual selection, or natural selection? (It may be helpful to break the male symbiotic syndrome into separate features, such as staying with a single female for life, physical attachment to the female, reduction in body size, and nutritional dependence on the female.)

Exploring the Literature

9. If a single insemination provides all the sperm necessary to fertilize an entire clutch of eggs, then what do females gain by engaging in extra-pair copulations? For hypotheses and tests, see

   Kempenaers, B., G. R. Verheyn, M. van den Broeck, T. Burke, C. van Broeckhoven, and A. A. Dhondt. 1992. Extra-pair paternity results from female preference for high-quality males in the blue tit. *Nature* 357: 494–496.

   Madsen, T., R. Shine, J. Loman, and T. Hakansson. 1992. Why do female adders copulate so frequently? *Nature* 355: 440–441.

   Gray, E. M. 1996. Female control of offspring paternity in a western population of red-winged blackbirds (*Agelaius phoeniceus*). *Behavioral Ecology and Sociobiology* 38: 267–278.

   Gray, E. M. 1997. Do female red-winged blackbirds benefit genetically from seeking extra-pair copulations? *Animal Behaviour* 53: 605–623.

   Gray, E. M. 1997. Female red-winged blackbirds accrue material benefits from copulating with extra-pair males. *Animal Behaviour* 53: 625–629.

10. Why do females sometimes copulate more than once with the same male?

    Petrie, M. 1992. Copulation frequency in birds: Why do females copulate more than once with the same male? *Animal Behaviour* 44: 790–792.

11. The testes in many mammals, including humans, are positioned in a scrotum outside the abdominal cavity. This dangerous arrangement has long defied adequate evolutionary explanation. One hypothesis is that the evolution of scrotal testes was driven by sperm competition. See

    Freeman, S. 1990. The evolution of the scrotum: A new hypothesis. *Journal of Theoretical Biology* 145: 429–445.

12. In plants, the analog of sperm competition is a race among pollen tubes to reach the ovules. For an exploration of whether the pollen of some donors is consistently superior in competition with the pollen from other donors, see

    Snow, A. A., and T. P. Spira. 1991. Pollen vigor and the potential for sexual selection in plants. *Nature* 352: 796–797.

    Snow, A. A., and T. P. Spira. 1996. Pollen-tube competition and male fitness in *Hibiscus moscheutos*. *Evolution* 50: 1866–1870.

13. Peacocks are among the most famous animals with an elaborate male mating display. For research on sexual selection in peacocks, see

    Manning, J. T., and M. A. Hartley. 1991. Symmetry and ornamentation are correlated in the peacock's train. *Animal Behaviour* 42: 1020–1021.

    Petrie, M. 1992. Peacocks with low mating success are more likely to suffer predation. *Animal Behaviour* 44: 585–586.

    Petrie, M., T. Halliday, and C. Sanders. 1991. Peahens prefer peacocks with elaborate trains. *Animal Behaviour* 41: 323–331.

Citations

Anderson, M. 1982. Female choice selects for extreme tail length in a widowbird. *Nature* 299: 818–820.

Anderson, M. 1994. *Sexual Selection*. Princeton, NJ: Princeton University Press.

Arnold, S. J. 1983. Sexual selection: The interface of theory and empiricism. In P. Bateson, ed. *Mate Choice*. Cambridge: Cambridge University Press, 67–107.

Arnold, S. J., and D. Duvall. 1994. Animal mating systems: A synthesis based on selection theory. *American Naturalist* 143: 317–348.

Bateman, A. J. 1948. Intra-sexual selection in Drosophila. *Heredity* 2: 349–368.

Berglund, A. 1991. Egg competition in a sex-role reversed pipefish: Subdominant females trade reproduction for growth. *Evolution* 45: 770–774.

Berglund, A., and G. Rosenqvist. 1993. Selective males and ardent females in pipefish. *Behavioral Ecology and Sociobiology* 32: 331–336.

Berglund, A., G. Rosenqvist, and P. Bernet. 1997. Ornamentation predicts reproductive success in female pipefish. *Behavioral Ecology and Sociobiology* 40: 145–150.

Berglund, A., G. Rosenqvist, and I. Svensson. 1989. Reproductive success of females limited by males in two pipefish species. *American Naturalist* 133: 506–516.

Bernet, P., G. Rosenqvist, and A. Berglund. 1998. Female-female competition affects female ornamentation in the sex-role reversed pipefish *Syngnathus typhle*. *Behaviour* 135: 535–550.

Bertram, C. R. 1975. Social factors influencing reproduction in wild lions. *Journal of Zoology* 177: 463–482.

Boellstorff, D. E., D. H. Owings, M. C. T. Penedo, and M. J. Hersek. 1994. Reproductive behavior and multiple paternity of California ground squirrels. *Animal Behaviour* 47: 1057–1064.

Borgerhoff Mulder, M. 1988. Reproductive success in three Kipsigis cohorts. In T.H. Clutton-Brock, ed. *Reproductive Success*. Chicago: University of Chicago Press, 419–435.

Burkhardt, D., and I. de la Motte. 1983. How stalk-eyed flies eye stalk-eyed flies: Observations and measurements of the eyes of *Cyrtodiopsis whitei* (Dopsidae, Diptera). *Journal of Comparative Physiology* 151: 407–421.

Burkhardt, D., and I. de la Motte. 1987. Physiological, behavioural, and morphometric data elucidate the evolutive significance of stalked eyes in Diopsidae (Diptera). *Entomologia Generalis* 12: 221–233.

Burkhardt, D., and I. de la Motte. 1988. Big "antlers" are favored: Female choice in stalk-eyed flies (Diptera, Insecta), field collected harems and laboratory experiments. *Journal of Comparative Physiology* A 162: 649–652.

Chagnon, N. A. 1988. Life histories, blood revenge, and warfare in a tribal population. *Science* 239: 985–992.

Clutton-Brock, T. H. 1985. Reproductive Success in Red Deer. *Scientific American* 252(February): 86–92.

Daly, M., and M. Wilson. 1988. *Homicide*. New York: Aldine de Gruyter.

Darwin, C. 1871. *The Descent of Man, and Selection in Relation to Sex*. London: John Murray.

David, P., A. Hingle, et al. 1998. Male sexual ornament size but not asymmetry reflects condition in stalk-eyed flies. *Proceedings of the Royal Society London*, Series B 265: 2211–2216.

Delph, L. F., L. F. Galloway, and M. L. Stanton. 1996. Sexual dimorphism in flower size. *American Naturalist* 148: 299–320.

Enquist, M., and A. Arak. 1993. Selection of exaggerated male traits by female aesthetic senses. *Nature* 361: 446–448.

Falconer, D. S. 1989. *Introduction to Quantitative Genetics*. New York: John Wiley & Sons.

Fisher, R. A. 1915. The evolution of sexual preference. *Eugenics Review* 7: 184–192.

Fisher, R. A. 1958. *The Genetical Theory of Natural Selection,* 2nd ed. New York: Dover.

Gage, M. J. G. 1991. Risk of sperm competition directly affects ejaculate size in the Mediterranean fruit fly. *Animal Behaviour* 42: 1036–1037.

Gangestad, S. W. 1993. Sexual selection and physical attractiveness: Implications for mating dynamics. *Human Nature* 4: 205–235.

Gangestad, S. W., and D. M. Buss. 1993. Pathogen prevalence and human mate preferences. *Ethology and Sociobiology* 14: 89–96.

Gerhardt, H. C., M. L. Dyson, and S. D. Tanner. 1996. Dynamic properties of the advertisement calls of gray tree frogs: Patterns of variability and female choice. *Behavioral Ecology* 7: 7–18.

Gibbs, H. L., P. J. Weatherhead, P. T. Boag, B. N. White, L. M. Tabak, and D. J. Hoysak. 1990. Realized reproductive success of polygynous red-winged blackbirds revealed by DNA markers. *Science* 250: 1394–1397.

Gilbert, L. E. 1976. Postmating female odor in *Heliconius* butterflies: A male-contributed anti-aphrodisiac? *Science* 193: 419–420.

Gould, S. J. 1983. *Hen's Teeth and Horse's Toes*. New York: W. W. Norton & Company.

Gray, E. M. 1997. Do female red-winged blackbirds benefit genetically from seeking extra-pair copulations? *Animal Behaviour* 53: 605–623.

Gross, M. R. 1984. Sunfish, salmon, and the evolution of alternative reproductive strategies and tactics in fishes. In G. W. Potts and R. J. Wootton, eds. *Fish Reproduction: Strategies and Tactics*. London: Academic Press, 55–75.

Gross, M. R. 1985. Disruptive selection for alternative live histories in salmon. *Nature* 313: 47–48.

Gross, M. R. 1991. Salmon breeding behavior and life history evolution in changing environments. *Ecology* 72: 1180–1186.

Gwynne, D. T. 1981. Sexual difference theory: Mormon crickets show role reversal in mate choice. *Science* 213: 779.

Gwynne, D. T., and L. W. Simmons. 1990. Experimental reversal of courtship roles in an insect. *Nature* 346: 172–174.

Hooper, R. E., and M. T. Siva-Jothy. 1996. Last male sperm precendence in a damselfly demonstrated by RAPD profiling. *Molecular Ecology* 5: 449–452.

Lande, R. 1981. Models of speciation by sexual selection on polygenic traits. *Proceedings of the National Academy of Sciences, USA* 78: 3721–3725.

Le Boeuf, B. J., and J. Reiter. 1988. Lifetime reproductive success in northern elephant seals. In T.H. Cutton-Brock, ed. *Reproductive Success*. Chicago: University of Chicago Press, 344–362.

McHenry, H. M. 1992. Body size and proportions in early hominids. *American Journal of Physical Anthropology* 87: (4) 407–431 Apr 1992

Møller, A. P. 1988. Female choice selects for male sexual tail ornaments in the monogamous swallow. *Nature* 332: 640–642.

Møller, A. P. 1991. Sexual selection in the monogamous barn swallow (*Hirundo rustica*). I. Determinants of tail ornament size. *Evolution* 45: 1823–1836.

Nakatsuru, K., and D. L. Kramer. 1982. Is sperm cheap? Limited male fertility and female choice in the lemon tetra (Pisces, Characidae). *Science* 216: 753–755.

Nowak, R. M. 1991. *Walker's Mammals of the World*. Baltimore: Johns Hopkins University Press.

Olsson, M., A. Gullberg, and H. Tegelstrom. 1994. Sperm competition in the sand lizard, *Lacerta agilis*. *Animal Behaviour* 48: 193–200.

Oring, L. W., M. A. Colwell, J. M. Reed. 1991a. Lifetime reproductive success in the spotted sandpiper (*Actitis macularia*)—sex-differences and variance-components. *Behavioral Ecology and Sociobiology* 28: 425–432.

Oring L. W., J. M. Reed, et al. 1991b. Factors regulating annual mating success and reproductive success in spotted sandpipers (*Actitis macularia*). *Behavioral Ecology and Sociobiology* 28: 433–442.

Oring, L. W., J. M. Reed, and S. J. Maxson. 1994. Copulation patterns and mate guarding in the sex-role reversed, polyandrous spotted sandpiper, *Actitis macularia*. *Animal Behaviour* 47: (5) 1065–1072.

Packer, C., L. Herbst, A. E. Pusey, J. D. Bygott, J. P. Hanby, S. J. Cairns, and M. Borgerhoff Mulder. 1988. Reproductive success of lions. In T. H. Clutton-Brock, ed. *Reproductive Success: Studies of Individual Variation in Contrasting Breeding Systems*. Chicago: University of Chicago Press, 263–283.

Packer, C., and A. E. Pusey. 1983. Adaptations of female lions to infanticide by incoming males. *American Naturalist* 121: 716–728.

Panhuis, T. M., and G. S. Wilkinson. 1999. Exaggerated male eye span influences contest outcome in stalk-eyed flies (Diopsidae). *Behavioral Ecology and Sociobiology* 46: 221–227.

Pawlowski, B., R. I. M. Dunbar, and A. Lipowicz. 2000. Tall men have more reproductive success. *Nature* 403: 156.

Petrie, M. 1983. Female moorhens compete for small fat males. *Science* 220: 413–415.

Proctor, H. C. 1991. Courtship in the water mite, *Neumania papillator.* Males capitalize on female adaptations for predation. *Animal Behaviour* 42: 589–598.

Proctor, H. C. 1992. Sensory exploitation and the evolution of male mating behaviour: a cladistic test using water mites (Acari: Parasitengona). *Animal Behaviour* 44: 745–752.

Prum, Richard O. 1997. Phylogenetic tests of alternative intersexual selection mechanisms: Trait macroevolution in a polygynous clade (*Aves: Pipridae*). *American Naturalist* 149: 668–692.

Rauch, N. 1985. Female habitat choice as a determinant of the reproductive success of the territorial male marine iguana (*Amblyrhynchus cristatus*). *Behavioral Ecology and Sociobiology* 16: 125–134.

Rauch, N. 1988. Competition of marine iguana females *Amblyrhynchus cristatus* for egg-laying sites. *Behavior* 107: 91–106.

Rogers, A. R., and A. Mukherjee. 1992. Quantitative genetics of sexual dimorphism in human body size. *Evolution* 46: 226–234.

Romero, G. A., and C. E. Nelson. 1986. Sexual dimorphism in *Catasetum* orchids: Forcible pollen emplacement and male flower competition. *Science* 232: 1538–1540.

Rosenqvist, G. 1990. Male mate choice and female-female competition for mates in the pipefish *Nerophis ophidion*. *Animal Behaviour* 39: 1110–1115.

Rosenqvist, G., and K. Johansson. 1995. Male avoidance of parasitized females explained by direct benefits in a pipefish. *Animal Behaviour* 49: 1039–1045.

Ryan, M. J. 1985. *The Túngara Frog: A Study in Sexual Selection and Communication.* Chicago: University of Chicago Press.

Schenk, A., and K. M. Kovacs. 1995. Multiple mating between black bears revealed by DNA fingerprinting. *Animal Behaviour* 50: 1483–1490.

Sillén-Tullberg, B. 1981. Prolonged copulation: A male "postcopulatory" strategy in a promiscuous species, *Lygaeus equestris* (Heteroptera: Lygaeidae). *Behavioral Ecology and Sociobiology* 9: 283–289.

Smedley, S. R., and T. Eisner. 1996. Sodium: A male moth's gift to its offspring. *Proceedings of the National Academy of Sciences, USA* 93: 809–813.

Smith, R. L. 1984. Human sperm competition. In R. L. Smith, ed. *Sperm Competition and the Evolution of Animal Mating Systems.* Orlando: Academic Press, 601–659.

Stanton, M. L., A. A. Snow, and S. N. Handel. 1986. Floral evolution: Attractiveness to pollinators increases male fitness. *Science* 232: 1625–1627.

Thornhill, R. 1976. Sexual selection and nuptial feeding behavior in *Bittacus apicalis* (Insecta: Mecoptera). *American Naturalist* 110: 529–548.

Thornhill, R., and J. Alcock. 1983. *The Evolution of Insect Mating Systems.* Cambridge, MA: Harvard University Press.

Trillmich, K. G. K. 1983. The mating system of the marine iguana (*Amblyrhynchus cristatus*). *Zeitschrift für Tierpsychologie* 63: 141–172.

Trivers, R. L. 1972. Parental investment and sexual selection. In B. Campbell, ed. *Sexual Selection and the Descent of Man 1871–1971.* Chicago: Aldine, 136–179.

Trivers, R. 1985. *Social Evolution.* Menlo Park, CA: Benjamin/Cummings.

Vaughton, G. and M. Ramsey. 1998. Floral display, pollinator visitation, and reproductive success in the dioecious perennial herb *Wurmbea dioica* (Liliaceae). *Oecologia* 115: 93–101.

Waage, J. K. 1984. Sperm competition and the evolution of Odonate mating systems. In R. L. Smith, ed. *Sperm Competition and the Evolution of Animal Mating Systems.* Orlando: Academic Press, 251–290.

Waage, J. K. 1986. Evidence for widespread sperm displacement ability among Zygoptera (Odonata) and the means for predicting is presence. *Biological Journal of the Linnean Society* 28: 285–300.

Watson, P. J. 1991. Multiple paternity as genetic bet-hedging in female sierra dome spiders, *Linyphia litigiosa* (Linyphiidae). *Animal Behaviour* 41: 343–360.

Welch, Allison, R. D. Semlitsch, and H. Carl Gerhardt. 1998. Call duration as an indicator of genetic quality in male gray tree frogs. *Science* 280: 1928–1930.

Wikelski, M., and S. Bäurle. 1996. Precopulatory ejaculation solves time constraints during copulations in marine iguanas. *Proceedings of the Royal Society of London,* Series B 263: 439–444.

Wikelski, M., C. Carbone, and F. Trillmich. 1996. Lekking in marine iguanas: Female grouping and male reproductive strategies. *Animal Behaviour* 52: 581–596.

Wikelski, M., V. Carrillo, and F. Trillmich. 1997. Energy limits to body size in a grazing reptile, the Galapagos marine iguana. *Ecology* 78: 2204–2217.

Wikelski, M., and C. Thom. 2000. Marine iguanas shrink to survive El Niño. *Nature* 403: 37.

Wikelski, M., and F. Trillmich. 1997. Body size and sexual size dimorphism in marine iguanas fluctuate as result of opposing natural and sexual selection: An island comparison. *Evolution* 51: 922–936.

Wilkinson, G. S., H. Kahler, and R. H. Baker. 1998. Evolution of female mating preferences in stalk-eyed flies. *Behavioral Ecology* 9: 525–533.

Wilkinson, G. S., D. C. Presgraves, and L. Crymes. 1998. Male eye span in stalk-eyed flies indicates genetic quality by meiotic drive suppression. *Nature* 391: 276–279.

Wilkinson, G. S., and P. R. Reillo. 1994. Female choice response to artificial selection on an exaggerated male trait in a stalk-eyed fly. *Proceedings of the Royal Society of London,* Series B 255: 1–6.

Wilkinson, G. S., and M. Taper. 1999. Evolution of genetic variation for condition-dependent traits in stalk-eyed flies. *Proceedings of the Royal Society London,* Series B 266: 1685–1690.

Williams, G. C. 1966. *Adaptation and Natural Selection: A Critique of Some Current Evolutionary Thought.* Princeton University Press, Princeton, NJ.

Willson, M. F. 1979. Sexual selection in plants. *American Naturalist* 113: 777–790.

Woodroffe, R., and A. Vincent. 1994. Mother's little helpers: Patterns of male care in mammals. *Trends in Ecology and Evolution* 9: 294–297.

Zahavi, A. 1975. Mate selection—A selection for a handicap. *Journal of Theoretical Biology* 53: 205–214.

CHAPTER 10

Kin Selection and Social Behavior

One of these crows has a fish; the other two appear to want it. In many cases, the outcome of a social interaction like this depends on the genetic relationship of the participants. (Gregory K. Scott/Photo Researchers, Inc.)

SOCIAL INTERACTIONS CREATE THE POSSIBILITY FOR CONFLICT AND COOPERATION. Consider two American crows (*Corvus brachyrhynchos*) patrolling the edge of their adjacent nesting territories. If one moves across the established boundary, its action may trigger aggressive calls, a flight chase, or even physical combat. But if a hawk flies by, the two antagonists will cooperate in chasing the predator away. Later in the day, these same individuals may spend considerable time and effort feeding the young birds in their respective nests, even though the nestlings are siblings or half-siblings and not their own offspring.

When and why do these individuals cooperate with each other, and why do they help their parents raise their siblings instead of raising their own offspring? What conditions lead to conflicts with each other and with their parents, and how are these conflicts resolved? These are the types of questions addressed in this chapter.

In fitness terms, an interaction between individuals has four possible outcomes (Table 10.1). Cooperation (or **mutualism**) is the term for actions that result in fitness gains for both participants. **Altruism** represents cases in which the individual instigating the action pays a fitness cost and the individual on the receiving end benefits. **Selfishness** is the opposite: The actor gains and the recipient loses. **Spite** is the term for behavior that results in fitness losses for both participants.

331

Table 10.1   Types of social interactions

The "actor" in any social interaction affects the recipient of the action as well as itself. The costs and benefits of interactions are measured in units of surviving offspring (fitness).

	Actor benefits	Actor is harmed
Recipient benefits	Cooperative	Altruistic
Recipient is harmed	Selfish	Spiteful

Understanding the evolution of these four interactions is made simpler because there are no clear-cut examples of spite in nature (Keller et al. 1994). It is straightforward to understand why spite has not evolved: An allele that results in fitness losses for both actor and recipient would quickly be eliminated by natural selection. But altruism would seem equally difficult to explain, because one of the participants suffers a fitness loss. Altruistic behavior appears to be common, however. Examples range from the crows that help at their parents' nests to a human who dives into a river and saves a drowning child. This is the first question we need to address: Why does altruism exist in nature?

10.1   Kin Selection and the Evolution of Altruism

Explaining altruistic behavior is a challenge for the Theory of Evolution by Natural Selection.

Altruism is a central paradox of Darwinism. It would seem impossible for natural selection to favor an allele that results in behavior benefiting other individuals at the expense of the individual bearing the allele. For Darwin (1859: 236), the apparent existence of altruism presented a "special difficulty, which at first appeared to me insuperable, and actually fatal to my whole theory." Fortunately he was able to hint at a resolution to the paradox: Selection could favor traits that result in decreased personal fitness if they increase the survival and reproductive success of close relatives. Over a hundred years passed, however, before this result was formalized and widely applied.

Inclusive Fitness

In 1964, William Hamilton developed a genetic model showing that an allele that favors altruistic behavior could spread under certain conditions. The key parameter in Hamilton's formulation is the **coefficient of relationship**, r. This is the probability that the homologous alleles in two individuals are identical by descent (Box 10.1). The parameter is closely related to F, the coefficient of inbreeding, which we introduced in Chapter 6. F is the probability that homologous alleles in the same individual are identical by descent.

Given r, the coefficient of relatedness between the actor and the recipient, **Hamilton's rule** states that an allele for altruistic behavior will spread if

$$Br - C > 0$$

where B is the benefit to the recipient and C is the cost to the actor. Both B and C are measured in units of surviving offspring. This simple law means that altruism is more likely to spread when the benefits to the recipient are great, the cost to the actor is low, and the participants are closely related.

BOX 10.1 Calculating coefficients of relatedness

Calculating r, the coefficient of relatedness, requires a pedigree that includes the actor (the individual dispensing the behavior) and the recipient (the individual receiving the behavior). The researcher then performs a path analysis. Starting with the actor, all paths of descent are traced through the pedigree to the recipient. For example, half-siblings share one parent and have two genealogical connections, as indicated in Figure 10.1a. Parents contribute half their genes to each offspring, so the probability that genes are identical by descent (ibd) in each step in the path is 1/2. Put another way, the probability that a particular allele was transmitted from parent to actor is 1/2. The probability that the same allele was transmitted from parent to recipient is 1/2. The probability that this same allele was transmitted to both the actor and the recipient (meaning that the alleles in actor and recipient are ibd) is the product of these two independent probabilities, or 1/4.

Full siblings, on the other hand, share genes inherited from both parents. To calculate r when actor and recipient are full-sibs, we have to add the probabilities that genes are ibd through each path in the pedigree. In this case, we add the probability that genes are ibd through the mother to the probability that they are ibd through the father (see Figure 10.1b). This is $\frac{1}{4} + \frac{1}{4} = \frac{1}{2}$.

Using this protocol results in the following coefficients:

- First cousins, $\frac{1}{8}$ (Figure 10.1c)
- Parent to offspring, $\frac{1}{2}$
- Grandparent to grandchild, $\frac{1}{4}$
- Aunt or uncle to niece or nephew, $\frac{1}{4}$

The analyses we have just performed work for autosomal loci in sexual organisms, and assume that no inbreeding has occurred. If the population is inbred then coefficients will be higher. But when studying populations in the field, investigators usually have no data on inbreeding and have to assume that individuals are completely outbred. On this basis, coefficients of relationship that are reported in the literature should be considered minimal estimates. Another uncertainty in calculating r's comes in assigning paternity in pedigrees. As we indicated in Chapter 9, extra-pair copulations are common in many species. If paternity is assigned on the basis of male-female pairing relationships and extra-pair copulations go undetected, estimates of r may be inflated.

When constructing genealogies is impractical, coefficients of relatedness can be estimated directly from genetic data (Queller and Goodnight 1989). The microsatellite loci introduced in Chapter 18 are proving to be extremely useful markers for calculating r in a wide variety of social insects (e.g., Peters et al. 1999).

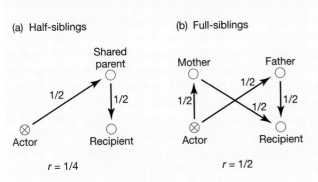

(a) Half-siblings $\qquad$ $r = 1/4$

(b) Full-siblings $\qquad$ $r = 1/2$

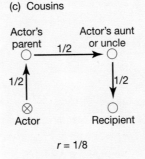

(c) Cousins $\qquad$ $r = 1/8$

Figure 10.1 Path analysis with pedigrees The arrows describe paths by which genes can be identical by descent. The text explains how these paths are used to calculate r, the coefficient of relatedness.

To generalize this result, Hamilton created the concept of **inclusive fitness**. He pointed out that an individual's fitness can be partitioned into two components, which he called direct and indirect. **Direct fitness** results from personal reproduction. **Indirect fitness** results from additional reproduction by relatives that is made possible by an individual's actions. Indirect fitness accrues when relatives achieve reproductive success above and beyond what they would have achieved on their own— meaning, without aid. When natural selection favors the spread of alleles that increase

Inclusive fitness consists of direct fitness due to personal reproduction and indirect fitness due to additional reproduction by relatives. Behavior that results in indirect fitness gains is favored by kin selection.

the indirect component of fitness, **kin selection** occurs. As we will see, most instances of altruism in nature are the result of kin selection.

Robert Trivers (1985:47) called Hamilton's rule and the concept of inclusive fitness "the most important advance in evolutionary theory since the work of Charles Darwin and Gregor Mendel." To see why, we will apply the theory by venturing to the Sierra Nevada of California and observing an intensely social mammal: Belding's ground squirrel (*Spermophilus beldingi*).

Alarm Calling in Belding's Ground Squirrels

Explaining alarm calling in birds and mammals is a classical application of inclusive fitness theory. When flocks or herds are stalked by a predator, prey individuals that notice the intruder sometimes give loud, high-pitched calls. These warnings alert nearby individuals and allow them to flee or dive for cover. They may also expose the calling individual to danger. In Belding's ground squirrels, 13% of callers are stalked or chased by predators while only 5% of non-calling individuals are (Sherman 1977).

Paul Sherman (1977, 1980) studied patterns in alarm calls given by Belding's ground squirrels to determine why such seemingly altruistic behavior evolved. Belding's ground squirrels are rodents that breed in colonies established in alpine meadows. Males disperse far from the natal burrow, while female offspring tend to remain and breed close by. As a result, females in proximity tend to be closely related. Because Sherman had individually marked many individuals over the course of the study, he was able to construct pedigrees and calculate coefficients of relationship for most members of the colony.

When Sherman compiled data on which squirrels called at the approach of a weasel, coyote, or badger, two outstanding patterns emerged: Females were much more likely to call than males (Figure 10.2), and females were much more likely

(a)

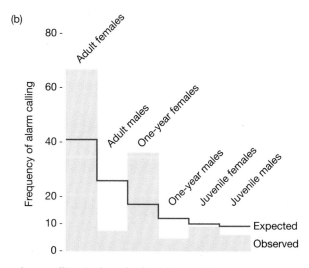
(b)

Figure 10.2 In ground squirrels, most alarm calling is done by females (a) This female Belding's ground squirrel is giving an alarm call. (Richard R. Hansen/Photo Researchers, Inc.) (b) This bar chart reports the observed and expected frequencies of alarm calling by different sex and age classes of Belding's ground squirrels, based on 102 encounters with predatory mammals. The expected values are indicated by the blue line and are calculated by assuming that individuals call randomly—that is, in proportion to the number of times they are present when the predator approaches. The observed and expected values are significantly different ($P = 0.001$). Reprinted with permission from Sherman (1977). Copyright © 1977, American Association for the Advancement of Science.

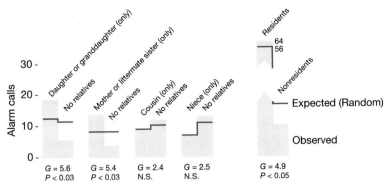

Figure 10.3 **Female ground squirrels are more likely to give alarm calls when close kin are nearby** This bar chart summarizes data from 119 cases in which a mammalian predator approached a ground squirrel colony. Each paired comparison in the figure represents the occasions when at least one female in each category was present, but no others. The expected values are computed as in Figure 10.2. The G values reported here represent a modified form of the χ^2 statistic introduced in Chapter 5. "N.S." stands for not significant. From Sherman (1980).

to call when they had close relatives within earshot (Figure 10.3). These data strongly support the hypothesis that kin selection is responsible for the evolution of alarm calling. Sherman (1981) has also been able to show that mothers, daughters, and sisters are much more likely to cooperate when chasing trespassing squirrels off their territory than are more distant kin or nonrelatives (Figure 10.4).

The data show that altruistic behavior is not dispensed randomly. It is nepotistic. Self-sacrificing behavior is directed at close relatives and should result in indirect fitness gains.

Individuals are more likely to give alarm calls when close relatives are nearby.

White-Fronted Bee-Eaters

Another classical system for studying kin selection in vertebrates is helping behavior in birds (see Brown 1987; Stacey and Koenig 1990). In species from a wide variety of bird families, young that are old enough to breed on their own will instead remain and help their parents rear their brothers, sisters, or half-siblings. Helpers

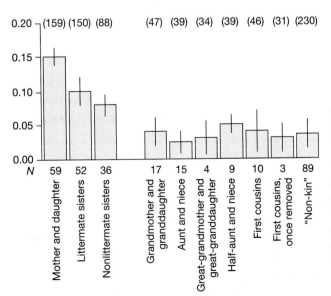

Figure 10.4 **Closely related female ground squirrels are more likely to cooperate than distant kin** This bar chart reports how frequently territory-owning females were joined by different categories of relatives and nonrelatives in chasing away trespassing ground squirrels. The number in parentheses indicates the number of chases that occurred when both types of individuals were present. *N* gives the number of different dyads of each kind that were observed. The horizontal bars give the standard deviations of the frequencies. There is a significant difference in the frequency of cooperation between the three categories on the left and the seven categories on the right ($P < 0.01$), but no significant difference among the seven kinship categories on the right ($P > 0.09$). From Sherman (1981).

Figure 10.5 **White-fronted bee-eaters** The individual in the middle is performing a wing-waving display, and may be soliciting a feeding. (Gerard Lacz/Animals Animals/Earth Scenes)

(a)

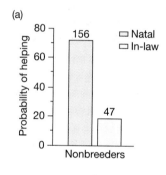

(b)

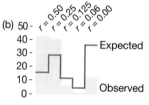

Figure 10.6 **In bee-eaters, helpers assist close relatives** (a) Bee-eater clans often contain nonbreeders that have paired with members of the clan. Their r with the offspring being raised that season is 0. This bar chart shows that they are much less likely to help than are clan members ($P < 0.01$). (b) In this bar chart, the expected probability of helping is calculated by assuming that helpers assist clan members randomly, in proportion to the r's of nestlings in clan nests. A G-test rejects the null hypothesis that helping is directed randomly with respect to kinship ($P < 0.01$). From Emlen and Wrege (1988).

assist with nest building, nest defense, or food delivery to incubating parents and the nestlings.

Helping at the nest is usually found in species where breeding opportunities are extremely restricted, either because habitats are saturated with established breeding pairs or because suitable nest sites are difficult to obtain. In these cases, gaining direct fitness is almost impossible for young adults. Gaining indirect fitness by helping becomes a best-of-a-bad-job strategy.

Steve Emlen, Peter Wrege, and Natalie Demong have completed an intensive study of helping behavior in the white-fronted bee-eater (*Merops bullockoides*). This colonial species, native to East and central Africa, breeds in nesting chambers excavated in sandy riverbanks (Figure 10.5). The 40–450 individuals in a colony are subdivided into groups of 3 to 17, each of which defends a feeding territory up to seven kilometers away. These clans may include several sets of parents and offspring.

Many year-old bee-eaters stay to help at the nest during what would otherwise be their first breeding season. Clan members are related, so helpers usually have a choice of nestlings with different degrees of kinship as recipients of their helping behavior (Hegner et al. 1982; Emlen et al. 1995). This choice is a key point: Because kinship varies among the potential recipients of altruistic behavior, white-fronted bee-eaters are an excellent species for researchers to use in testing theories about kin selection.

After marking large numbers of individuals and working out genealogies over an eight-year study period, Emlen and Wrege (1988, 1991) found that bee-eaters conform to predictions made by Hamilton's rule. They determined, for example, that the coefficient of relatedness with recipients has a strong effect on whether a nonbreeding member of the clan helps (Figure 10.6a). Further, nonbreeders actively decide to help the most closely related individuals available (Figure 10.6b). That is, when young with different coefficients of relationship are being reared within their clan, helpers almost always chose to help those with the highest r (Box 10.2). Their assistance is an enormous benefit to parents. More than half of bee-eater young die of starvation before leaving the nest. On average, the presence of each helper results in an additional 0.47 offspring being reared to fledging (Figure 10.7). For young birds, helping at the nest results in clear benefits for inclusive fitness.

BOX 10.2 Kin recognition

The data in Figures 10.2–6 suggest that individuals have accurate mechanisms for assessing their degree of kinship with members of their own species, or conspecifics. This phenomenon, called kin recognition, has been divided into two broad categories: direct and indirect (Pfennig and Sherman 1995). Indirect kin recognition is based on cues like the timing or location of interactions. Many species of adult birds rely on indirect kin recognition when their chicks are young, and will feed any young bird that appears in their nest. Direct kin recognition, in contrast, is based on specific chemical, vocal, or other cues.

There is currently a great deal of interest in determining whether loci in the major histocompatibility complex (MHC) function in direct kin recognition. In Chapter 5, we introduced the MHC and its role in self-nonself-recognition by cells in the immune system. Although loci in the MHC clearly evolved to function in disease prevention, polymorphism is so extensive that non-kin share very few alleles. As a result, these genes can serve as reliable markers of kinship (see Brown and Eklund 1994). Could similarity in MHC provide a reliable cue of kinship and offer a criterion for dispensing altruistic behavior?

Jo Manning and colleagues (1992) addressed this question in a population of house mice (*Mus musculus domesticus*). A kin recognition system requires three components: production of the signal, recognition of the signal by conspecifics, and action based on that recognition. Previous work had shown that glycoproteins coded for by MHC loci are released in the urine of mice, and that mice can distinguish these molecules by smell. Mice are, for example, able to distinguish full siblings from half-siblings on the basis of their MHC genotypes. But do mice dispense altruistic behavior accordingly?

House mice form communal nests and nurse each others' pups. Because individuals could take advantage of this cooperative system by contributing less than their fair share of milk, Manning et al. predicted that mothers would prefer to place their young in nests containing close relatives. The logic here is that close kin should be less likely to cheat on one another because of the cost to their indirect fitness. Through a program of controlled breeding in which wild-caught mice were crossed with laboratory strains, Manning et al. created a population of mice with known MHC genotypes. This population was allowed to establish itself in a large barn. The researchers then recorded where mothers in this population placed their newborn pups after birth. The null hypothesis was that mothers would choose to rear their offspring randomly with respect to the MHC genotypes present in the communal nests available at the time. Contrary to the null expectation, mothers showed a strong preference for rearing their young in nests containing offspring with similar MHC genotypes. This result confirms a role for MHC as a signal used in direct kin recognition, and shows that mice are capable of dispensing altruistic behavior on the basis of MHC genotypes.

10.2 Evolution of Eusociality

Darwin (1859) recognized that social insects represent the epitome of altruism, and thus a special challenge to the theory of evolution by natural selection. Many worker ants and bees, for example, do not reproduce at all. They are helpers at the nests of their parents, for life. This is an extreme form of reproductive altruism.

Eusociality (true sociality) is used to describe social systems with three characteristics (Michener 1969; Wilson 1971; Alexander et al. 1991): (1) overlap in generations between parents and their offspring, (2) cooperative brood care, and (3) specialized castes of nonreproductive individuals. Eusocial species are found in a variety of insect orders (Table 10.2), snapping shrimp (Duffy 1996), and one family of rodents (the mammal family Bathyergidae, or mole-rats).

As an entree to the extensive literature on eusociality, in this section we consider how reproductive altruism evolved in two very different groups: the Hymenoptera (ants, bees, and wasps) and mole-rats.

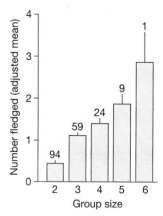

Figure 10.7 Fitness gains due to helping From Emlen and Wrege (1991).

Haplodiploidy and Eusocial Hymenoptera

The Hymenoptera represent the pinnacle of social evolution. A single ant colony may number millions of individuals, each appearing to function more like a cell in a superorganism than an individual pursuing its own reproductive interests. Worker, soldier, and reproductive castes, which seem analogous to tissues in a body, can be identified on the basis of their morphology and the tasks they perform. But unlike cells and tissues, individuals in the colony are not genetically identical. What factors laid the groundwork for such extensive altruism? Why is eusociality so widespread in Hymenoptera?

William Hamilton (1972) proposed that the unique genetic system of ants, wasps, and bees predisposes them to eusociality. Hymenoptera have an unusual form of sex determination: Males are haploid and females are diploid. Males develop from unfertilized eggs; females develop from fertilized eggs. As a result of this system, called **haplodiploidy**, female ants, bees, and wasps are more closely related to their sisters than they are to their own offspring. This follows because sisters share all of the genes they inherited from their father, which is half their genome, and half the genes they inherited from their mother (the colony's queen), which is the other half of their genome. Thus, the probability that homologous alleles in hymenopteran sisters are identical by descent is $(1 \times 1/2) + (1/2 \times 1/2) = 3/4$. To their own offspring, however, females are related by the usual r of $1/2$. This unique system favors the production of reproductive sisters over daughters, sons, or brothers. (Females are related to their brothers by $r = 1/4$; see Figure 10.8). Thus, females will maximize their inclusive fitness by acting as workers rather than as reproductives (Hamilton 1972). Specifically, their alleles will increase in the population faster when they invest in the production of sisters rather than producing their own offspring. This is the haplodiploidy hypothesis for the evolution of eusociality in Hymenoptera.

In haplodiploid species, females are more closely related to their sisters than they are to their own offspring.

Testing the Haplodiploidy Hypothesis

In addition to offering an explanation for why workers prefer to invest in sisters rather than their own offspring, the haplodiploidy hypothesis predicts that workers prefer to invest in sisters over brothers. Because their r with sisters is $3/4$ and only $1/4$ with brothers, workers should favor a 3:1 female-biased sex ratio in reproductive offspring (meaning, offspring that are not destined to become sterile workers or soldiers; Trivers and Hare 1976). Queens, in contrast, are equally related to their sons and daughters and should favor a 1:1 sex ratio in the reproductives produced (see Box 10.3). The fitness interests of workers and queens are not the same. The question is: Who wins the conflict? Do queens or workers control the sex ratio of reproductive offspring?

Liselotte Sundström and coworkers (1996) set out to answer this question by determining the sex ratio of reproductive offspring in wood ant (*Formica exsecta*) colonies. They found that queens laid a roughly equal number of male and female eggs, but that sex ratios were heavily female-biased at hatching. To make sense of this result, the researchers hypothesize that workers are able to determine the sex of eggs and that they selectively destroy male offspring.

Based on results from similar studies, most researchers acknowledge that female-biased sex allocation is widespread among eusocial hymenoptera. (For recent reviews, see Bourke and Franks 1995; Crozier and Pamilo 1996.) In the tug-of-war over the fitness interests, workers appear to have the upper hand over queens.

Table 10.2 **Sociality in insects**

This table summarizes the taxonomic distribution of eusociality in insects. Species are called "primitively eusocial" if queens are not morphologically differentiated from other individuals.

Order	Family	Subfamily	Eusocial species
Hymenoptera	Anthophoridae (carpenter bees)		In seven genera
	Apidae	Apinae (honeybees)	Six highly eusocial species
		Bombinae (bumble bees)	300 primitively eusocial species
		Euglossinae (orchid bees)	None
		Meliponinae (stingless bees)	200 eusocial species
	Halictidae (sweat bees)		In six genera
	Sphecidae (sphecoid wasps)		In one genus
	Vespidae (paper wasps, yellow jackets)	Polistinae	Over 500 species, all eusocial
		Stenogastrinae	Some primitively eusocial species
		Vespinae	Ca. 80 species, all eusocial
	Formicidae (ants)	11 subfamilies	Over 8,800 described species, all eusocial or descended from eusocial species
	Many other families		None
Isoptera (termites)	Nine families		All species (over 2,288) are eusocial
Homoptera (plant bugs)	Pemphigidae		Sterile soldiers found in six genera
Coleoptera (beetles)	Curculionidae		*Austroplatypus incompertus*
Thysanoptera (thrips)	Phlaeothripidae		Subfertile soldiers are found in *Oncothrips*

Source: From Crozier and Pamilo (1996).

Perhaps the more important general message of this work, however, is that colonies of ants, bees, and wasps are not harmonious "superorganisms." The asymmetry in relationship between queens and offspring versus workers and offspring produces a sharp conflict of interest.

Does the Haplodiploidy Hypothesis Explain Eusociality?

The prediction and affirmation of 3:1 sex ratios in reproductive offspring, at least in some hymenopterans, confirms that the haplodiploid system of sex determination has a strong effect on how workers behave. But is haplodiploidy the reason that so many hymenopteran species are eusocial? Most researchers are concluding that the answer is no. There are several reasons for this.

First, the prediction that workers favor the production of sisters over the production of their own offspring is based on an important assumption: that all of the female workers in the colony have the same father. In many species this is not true. Multiple mating is common in certain groups of eusocial Hymenoptera. Honeybee queens, for example, mate an average of 17.25 times before founding a colony (Page and Metcalf 1982). As a result, it is common to find that the average coefficient of relatedness among honeybee workers is under 1/3 (Oldroyd et

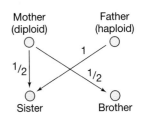

Figure 10.8 Haplodiploidy produces unusual coefficients of relationship The arrows describe the paths by which genes can be identical by descent in hymenopterans. Note that there is no path of shared descent between sisters and brothers through their father, because males have no father.

BOX 10.3 The evolution of the sex ratio

In many species, the sex ratio at hatching, germination, or birth is 1:1. Ronald Fisher (1930) explained why this should be so. Fisher pointed out that if one sex is in short supply in a population, then an allele that leads to the production of the rarer sex will be favored. This is because individuals of the rarer sex will have more than one mate on average when they mature, simply because in a sexual species every individual has one mother and one father. Members of the rarer sex will experience increased reproductive success relative to individuals of the more common sex. Indeed, whenever the sex ratio varies from 1:1, selection favoring the rarer sex will exist until the ratio returns to unity. Fisher's explanation is a classic example of frequency-dependent selection—a concept we introduced in Chapter 5 with the example of left- and right-handed scale-eating fish.

Fisher's argument is based on an important assumption: that parents invest equally in each sex. When one sex is more costly than the other, parents should adjust the sex ratio to even out the investment in each. For this reason evolutionary biologists distinguish the numerical sex ratio from the investment sex ratio and speak, in general terms, about the issue of sex allocation (Charnov 1982).

Robert Trivers and Dan Willard (1973) came up with an important extension to Fisher's model. They suggested that when females are in good physiological condition and are better able to care for their young, and when differences in the condition of young are sustained into adulthood, then they should preferentially invest in male offspring. This is because differences in condition affect male reproductive success RS more than female RS (see Chapter 9). This prediction, called condition-dependent sex allocation, has been confirmed in a wide variety of mammals, including humans. (For examples, see Clutton-Brock et al. 1984; Betzig and Turke 1986.)

A third prominent result in sex-ratio theory is due to William Hamilton (1967). In insects that lay their eggs in fruit or other insects, the young often hatch, develop, and mate inside the host. Frequently, hosts are parasitized by a single female. Given this situation, Hamilton realized that selection should favor females that produce only enough males to ensure fertilization of their sisters, resulting in a sex ratio with a strong female bias. This phenomenon, known as local mate competition, has been observed in a variety of parasitic insects. (For examples, see Hamilton 1967; Werren 1984.)

---

al. 1997, 1998). In these colonies, workers are *not* more closely related to their sisters than they are to their own offspring.

Second, in many species more than one queen is active in founding the nest. If they have neither parent in common, then workers in these colonies have a coefficient of relatedness of 0.

Haplodiploidy affects the behavior of eusocial species, but it is not the most important factor leading to the evolution of eusociality.

Third, many eusocial species are not haplodiploid, and many haplodiploid species are not eusocial. Nonreproductive castes are found in all termite species, for example, even though termites are diploid and have a normal chromosomal system of sex determination (Thorne 1997). And although eusociality is common among hymenopterans, it is by no means universal. Reviewing recent work on the phylogeny of the hymenoptera will help drive this last point home.

Using Phylogenies to Analyze Social Evolution

To understand which traits are most closely associated with the evolution of eusociality in hymenoptera, James Hunt (1999) analyzed the evolutionary trees shown in Figure 10.9. Because all hymenopterans are haplodiploid, Hunt could infer that this system of sex determination evolved early in the evolution of the group, at the point marked A on the tree. Eusociality is found in just a few families of hymenopterans, however. Because these families are scattered around the tree, it is

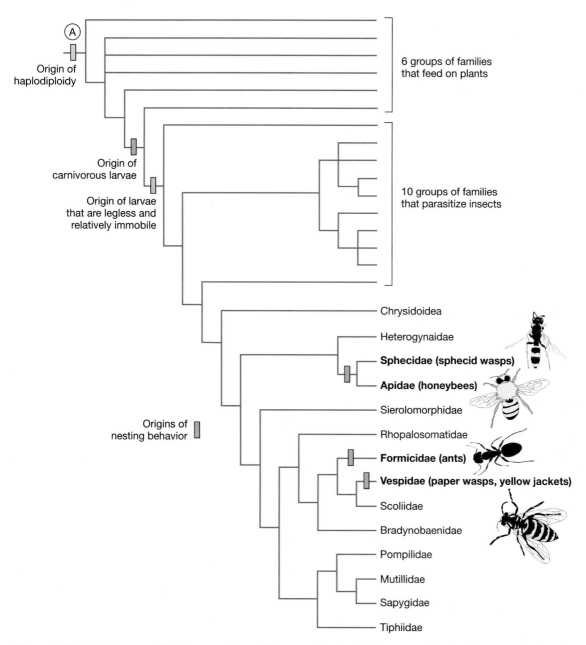

Figure 10.9 **A phylogeny of the hymenoptera** The taxa at the tips of this tree are either families or groups of families. Families that include eusocial species are indicated in bold type. (Not all of the species in these families are eusocial, however.) The arrows indicate points where certain key traits evolved. Modified from Hunt (1999). Copyright © 1999 Evolution. Reprinted by permission of Evolution.

likely that eusociality evolved not just once, but several times independently. Most importantly, Hunt noted that eusociality only evolved in groups that build complex nests and that care for their larvae for extended periods.

The association between nest building, care of larvae, and eusociality is important because it suggests that the primary agent favoring reproductive altruism in insects is ecological in nature—not genetic as proposed by the haplodiploidy hypothesis. The logic here is similar to the "best-of-a-bad-job" explanation for helping behavior in birds reviewed in Section 10.1. Nest building and the need to supply larvae with a continuous supply of food make it difficult or impossible for a female to breed on her own (see Alexander et al. 1991). Also, when predation rates are high but young are dependent on parental care for a long period, then individuals who breed alone are unlikely to survive long enough to bring their young to adulthood (Queller 1989; Queller and Strassmann 1998). In short, to explain the evolution of eusociality we clearly need to consider ecological factors that affect B and C as well as genetic factors that dictate r.

Facultative Strategies in Paper Wasps

Paper wasps in the genus *Polistes* have been an especially productive group for research into the costs and benefits of reproductive altruism. Unlike workers and soldiers in ants and termites, paper wasp workers are not sterile. Instead of being obligate helpers, *Polistes* females are capable of reproducing on their own. This contrast is important. To achieve reproductive success, worker and soldier ants and termites have no choice but to assist relatives—the nutrition they received as larvae guarantees that they are sterile. But in paper wasps, females have the option of helping relatives or breeding on their own.

> *In paper wasps, reproductive altruism is facultative. Females can choose between helping at a nest or breeding on their own.*

In *Polistes dominulus,* Peter Nonacs and Hudson Reeve (1995) found that females pursue one of three distinct strategies: They either initiate their own nest, join a nest as a helper, or wait for a breeding opportunity. Each option is associated with costs and benefits.

What are the costs and benefits of founding a nest? In the population that Nonacs and Reeve studied, nests were founded by single females or by multifemale groups. Earlier studies had shown that single foundresses are at a distinct disadvantage compared to multifemale coalitions. Adult mortality is high, and nests with multiple foundresses are less likely to fail because surviving females keep the nest going. Nonacs and Reeve also found that multifoundress coalitions are more likely to renest after a nest is destroyed. When they analyzed 106 instances of nest failure due to predation or experimental removal, they determined that only 5 of 54 single foundresses rebuilt while 21 of 51 multifoundress groups did.

Although the success rate of multifemale nests is high when compared to single-foundress nests, multifemale coalitions are not free of conflicts. Fights between wasps are decided by body size. As the graph in Figure 10.10 shows, multifoundress nests grew fastest when there was a large difference in the body size of the dominant female and her subordinate helpers. To interpret this result, Nonacs and Reeve suggest that productivity is low in coalitions where body size is similar be-

Figure 10.10   In paper wasps, the success of female coalitions varies   This graph plots the growth rate of *Polistes dominulus* nests as a function of the size difference between cofoundresses. Nests grow fastest when the founding females are markedly different in size. Modified from Nonacs and Reeve (1995). Copyright © 1995, Ecological Society of America. Reprinted with permission.

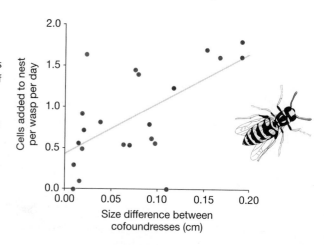

cause subordinate females frequently challenge for control of the nest and the right to lay most of the eggs.

Why would females join a coalition and help rear offspring that are not their own? Subordinates gain indirect fitness benefits because they are usually closely related to the dominant female. They may also gain direct fitness benefits if the dominant individual dies and they are able to take over the nest. Thus, the costs and benefits of helping depend on a female's body size and her coefficient of relatedness with other members of the coalition.

Nonacs and Reeve also found that a "sit-and-wait" strategy could make sense in fitness terms, because females that do not participate in nest initiation are able to adopt orphaned nests (after all of the adult females have died) or usurp small nests later in the season by defeating the attending female(s) in combat. In *Polistes fuscatus,* Reeve and colleagues (1998) found that some females pursue an interesting twist on these sit-and-wait tactics: They leave the nest early in the spring, enter a dormant state in a sheltered location, and wait until the following breeding season before attempting to nest.

The fundamental message of these studies is that reproductive altruism is facultative. It is an adaptive response to environmental conditions. In the case of the population studied by Nonacs and Reeve, the conditions that are relevant to a female are its body size relative to its competitors, its coefficient of relatedness to members of a nesting coalition, and the availability of other nests or nest-sites. Genetic, social, and ecological factors have also been invoked to explain the evolution of eusociality in naked mole-rats.

For female paper wasps, the decision to join an existing nest or to breed independently hinges on a series of costs of benefits. These costs and benefits are dicated by environmental and social conditions, and may change through time.

Naked Mole-Rats

Naked mole-rats (*Heterocephalus glaber*) are one of the great oddities of the class Mammalia (Figure 10.11). They are neither moles nor rats, but are members of the family Bathyergidae, native to desert regions in the Horn of Africa. They eat tubers, live underground in colonies of 70–80 members, and construct tunnel systems up to two miles long by digging cooperatively in the fashion of a bucket brigade. Mole-rats are nearly hairless and ectothermic ("cold-blooded") and, like termites, can digest cellulose with the aid of specialized microorganisms in their intestines.

Figure 10.11 Naked mole-rats This photo shows a naked mole-rat queen threatening a worker. For superb introductions to the biology of naked mole-rats, see Honeycutt (1992) and Sherman et al. (1992). (Raymond A. Mendez/Animals Animals/Earth Scenes)

Naked mole–rats are also eusocial. All young are produced by a single queen and all fertilizations are performed by a group of 2–3 reproductive males. As other members of the colony grow older and increase in size, their tasks change from tending young and working in the tunnels to specializing in colony defense. For unknown reasons, there is a slight male bias in the colony sex ratio, of 1.4:1. Naked mole–rats are diploid and have an XY-chromosome system of sex determination.

In naked mole-rats, helpers gain indirect fitness benefits because they are very closely related to the queen's offspring.

The leading hypothesis to explain why naked mole–rats are eusocial centers on inbreeding. Analyses of microsatellite loci confirm that colonies are highly inbred (Reeve et al. 1990). Researchers studying colonies established in the lab have determined that approximately 85% of all matings are between parents and their offspring or between full siblings, and that the average coefficient of relationship among colony members is 0.81 (Sherman et al. 1992). These are among the highest coefficients ever recorded in animals.

Even extensive inbreeding does not mean that the reproductive interests of workers and reproductives are identical, however. Conflicts exist because workers are still more closely related to their own offspring than they are to their siblings and half-siblings. Queens are able to maintain control, however, through physical dominance. If nonreproductives slow their pace of work, mole-rat queens push them. These head-to-head shoves are aggressive and can move a worker more than a meter backward through a tunnel. Shoves are directed preferentially toward nonrelatives and toward relatives more distant than offspring and siblings of the queen (Figure 10.12). Workers respond to shoves by nearly doubling their work rate (Table 10.3). These data suggest that queens impose their reproductive interests on subordinates through intimidation.

Inbreeding has also been hypothesized as a key factor predisposing termites to eusociality (Bartz 1979; but see Pamilo 1984; Roisin 1994). Not all inbred species are eusocial, however. This means that inbreeding is just one of several factors that contribute to eusociality in naked mole-rats and termites. Ecological factors such as extended parental care, group defense against predation, and severely constrained breeding opportunities are also important in explaining the evolution of reproductive altruism.

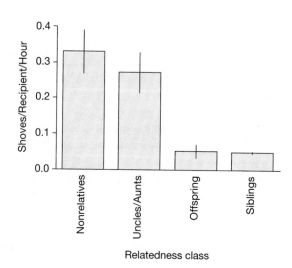

Figure 10.12 Naked mole-rat queens preferentially shove nonrelatives These data were collected from a captive colony of naked mole-rats. The bars indicate the average and standard errors of shoves given to different kin classes by a queen called three-bars. There is a statistically significant difference between shoving rates for nonrelatives and uncles/aunts versus the two closer kin classes. From Reeve and Sherman (1991). Copyright © 1991, Princeton University Press. Reprinted by permission of Princeton University Press.

Table 10.3 **Shoves from naked mole-rat queens motivate workers**

Working in captive colonies, Hudson Reeve (1992) performed regular scans and recorded the activity of all individuals in the colony. The work level reported in this table represents the proportion of scans during which individuals were performing work, with standard errors given in parentheses. Shoving events by queens that took place in the nestbox or tunnels were also recorded. There is a statistically significant difference between work rates before and after shoves, for both types of shoves ($P < 0.01$).

Shove recipient's work level	Before shove	After shove
All shoves	0.14 (0.03)	0.25 (0.06)
Tunnel shoves only	0.34 (0.05)	0.58 (0.07)

10.3 Parent–Offspring Conflict

The theory of kin selection has been remarkably successful in explaining the structure and dynamics of social groups such as bee-eater clans and wasp colonies. Now, we consider how the theory might inform questions about a more fundamental social unit: parents and offspring.

Parental care is a special case of providing fitness benefits for close relatives. Although kin selection can lead to close cooperation between related individuals such as parents and offspring, even close kin can be involved in conflicts when the costs and benefits of altruism change or when degrees of relatedness are not symmetrical. Robert Trivers (1974) was the first to point out that parents and offspring are *expected* to disagree about each other's fitness interests. Because parental care is so extensive in birds and mammals, conflicts over the amount of parental investment should be especially sharp.

Weaning Conflict

Weaning conflict is a well-documented example of parent–offspring strife. Aggressive and avoidance behaviors are common toward the end of nursing in a wide variety of mammals. Mothers will ignore or actively push young away when they attempt to nurse, and offspring will retaliate by screaming or by attacking their mothers (Figure 10.13).

The key to explaining weaning conflict is to recognize that the fitness interests of parents and offspring are not symmetrical. Offspring are related to themselves with $r = 1$, but parents are related to their offspring with $r = 1/2$. Further, parents are equally related to all their offspring and are expected to equalize their investment in each. Siblings, in contrast, are related by 1 to themselves but 1/2 to each other. The theory of evolution by natural selection predicts that each offspring will demand an unequal amount of parental investment for itself.

When these asymmetries are applied to nursing, conflicts arise. At the start of nursing, the benefit to the offspring is high relative to the cost to the parent (Figure 10.14a). As nursing proceeds, however, this ratio declines. Young grow and demand more milk, which increases the cost of care. At the same time, they are increasingly able to find their own food, which decreases the benefit. Natural selection should favor mothers who stop providing milk when the benefit-to-cost

Parents maximize their fitness by investing in all of their offspring equally. Offspring, in contrast, maximize their fitness by receiving more parental investment than their siblings.

(a)  (b)

Figure 10.13 Weaning conflict (a) The infant langur monkey on the left has just attempted to nurse from its mother, at the right. The mother refused to nurse. In response, the infant is screaming at her. Reproduced by permission from Trivers, *Social Evolution*, page 147, Fig. 7.2a. Menlo Park, CA: Benjamin Cummings Publishing Co. (1985). (b) The infant then dashes across the branch and slaps its mother. (Sarah Blaffer Hrdy/Anthro-Photo File)

ratio reaches 1 (this is time *P* in Figure 10.14a). From the mother's perspective, this is when weaning should occur. Offspring, on the other hand, devalue their mother's cost of providing care. They do this because the "savings" that a parent achieves through weaning will be invested in brothers or sisters with $r = 1/2$ instead of in themselves with $r = 1.0$. Natural selection should favor offspring who try to coerce continued parental investment until the benefit-cost ratio is $1/2$ (this is time *O* on Figure 10.14a). The period between time *P* and time *O* defines the interval of weaning conflict. Avoidance and aggressive behavior should be observed

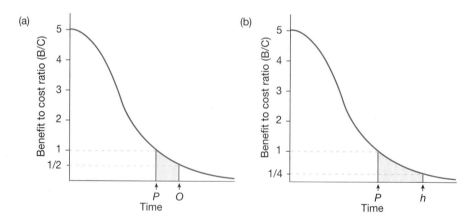

Figure 10.14 Parent–offspring conflict results from changes in the costs and benefits of parental care and asymmetries in relationship (a) This graph illustrates why parent–offspring conflict occurs. The *y*-axis plots the benefit-to-cost ratio (*B/C*) for an act of parental care such as providing milk. Benefit is measured in terms of increased survival by the offspring receiving the care, while cost is measured as decreased production of additional offspring by the parent. Time is plotted along the *x*-axis. The curve drawn here is hypothetical; its shape will vary from species to species. See the text for an explanation of how this curve is interpreted. (b) This is the same graph as in (a), modified to illustrate how the period of parent–offspring conflict is extended when parents produce half-siblings instead of full siblings. From Trivers (1985).

throughout this period. If mating systems are such that mothers routinely remate and produce half-siblings, the period of weaning conflict will extend to time *h,* when the ratio of benefit to cost $(B/C) = r = 1/4$ (Figure 10.14b). For field studies that confirm weaning conflict, see Trivers (1985, Chapter 7); for a theoretical treatment of other types of parent–offspring strife, see Godfrey (1995).

Harassment in White-Fronted Bee-Eaters

Another dramatic example of parent–offspring conflict occurs in the white-fronted bee-eaters introduced earlier. Steve Emlen and Peter Wrege (1992) have collected data suggesting that fathers occasionally coerce sons into helping to raise their siblings. They do this by harassing sons who are trying to raise their own young.

A variety of harassment behaviors are observed at bee-eater colonies. Individuals chase resident birds off their territory, physically prevent the transfer of food during courtship feeding, or repeatedly visit nests that are not their own before egg laying or hatching. During the course of their study, Emlen and Wrege observed 47 cases of harassment. Over 90% of the instigators were male and over 70% were older than the targeted individual. In 58% of the episodes, the instigator and victim were close genetic kin. In fact, statistical tests show that harassment behavior is not targeted randomly, but is preferentially directed at close kin ($P < 0.01$; χ^2 test).

Emlen and Wrege interpret this behavior by proposing that instigators are actively trying to break up the nesting attempts of close kin. Further, they suggest that instigators do this to recruit the targeted individuals as helpers at their own (the instigator's) nest.

What evidence do Emlen and Wrege present to support this hypothesis? In 16 of the 47 harassment episodes observed, the behavior actually resulted in recruitment: The harassed individuals abandoned their own nesting attempts and helped at the nest of the instigator. Of these successful events, 69% involved a parent and offspring and 62% involved a father and son. The risk of being recruited is clearly highest for younger males and for males with close genetic relatives breeding within their clan (Figure 10.15).

These data raise the question of why sons do not resist harassment more effectively. Emlen and Wrege suggest that harassment can be successful because sons are equally related to their own offspring and to their siblings. Parents, in contrast, are motivated to harass because they are more closely related to their own offspring ($r = 1/2$) than they are to their grandchildren ($r = 1/4$). We have already mentioned that on average, each helper is responsible for an additional 0.47 offspring being raised. In comparison, each parent at a nest unaided by relatives is able to raise 0.51 offspring. This means that for a first-time breeder, the fitness payoff from breeding on its own is only slightly greater than the fitness payoff from helping. The payoffs are close enough to suggest that parents can change the bottom line of the fitness accounting. Perhaps harassing a son tips the balance by increasing his cost of rearing young. Then helping becomes a more favorable strategy for the son than raising his own young. Emlen and Wrege's data imply that bee-eater fathers recognize sons and coerce them into serving the father's reproductive interests.

Siblicide

In certain species of birds and mammals, it is common for young siblings to kill each other while parents look on passively. How can this behavior be adaptive, given that the parents and siblings are related by an *r* of 1/2?

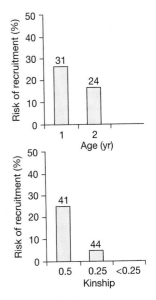

Figure 10.15 Bee-eaters recruit helpers who are younger and closely related Emlen and Wrege (1992) considered each paired male in the colony who had a same-age or older male present in its clan, and calculated the percentage of these individuals who were recruited as helpers after experiencing harassment. This probability is plotted on the *y*-axis of these two bar charts. Different age and kinship categories of targeted individuals are plotted on the *x*-axis. Here kinship represents the *r*-value between the targeted individual and the offspring in the instigator's nest.

Lynn Lougheed and David Anderson (1999) took an experimental approach to answering this question. Their research subjects were species of seabirds called the blue-footed booby and the masked booby (Figure 10.16). In both taxa, females normally lay a two-egg clutch. Because the eggs are laid 2–10 days apart, one chick hatches before the other. In the masked booby, the older offspring pushes its younger sibling from the nest within a day or two of hatching. There the smaller chick quickly dies of exposure or is taken by a predator.

Siblicide is more complex in the blue-footed booby, however. The older nestling does not always kill its younger sibling right after it hatches. During short-term food shortages, Anderson and Robert Ricklefs (1995) actually found that older chicks reduce their food intake. By doing so, they help their younger siblings survive. But if food shortages continue, the older chick attacks and kills its sibling. Presumably, this enhances the older chick's chance of survival by removing competition for food.

Lougheed and Anderson (1999) wanted to understand whether parents play a role in these events. In both masked boobies and blue-footed boobies, siblicide is sensible in light of the relatedness asymmetry between individuals (where $r = 1$) and their siblings (where $r = 1/2$). But parents are equally related to each chick and would be expected to intervene and prevent attacks.

To explore whether parental behavior differs between masked boobies and blue-footed boobies, Lougheed and Anderson performed a reciprocal transplant experiment. They placed newly hatched masked booby chicks in blue-footed booby nests, and vice versa. As controls, they also monitored the fate of masked booby chicks transferred to other masked booby nests and blue-footed booby broods transferred to other blue-footed booby nests.

Siblicide may increase the fitness of parents as well as the siblicidal offspring if the offspring that is killed is likely to die anyway.

As the data in Table 10.4 show, the fate of the chicks varied dramatically in the four treatments. Chicks were much more likely to die if they had a masked booby nestmate. This is consistent with the observation that siblicide is virtually universal in this species. But nestlings were also much more likely to die if they had masked booby parents. To explain this result, Lougheed and Anderson proposed that masked booby parents tolerate siblicidal chicks, while blue-footed booby parents attempt to intervene and prevent the death of their younger offspring. Their data set is the first to indicate that in some siblicidal species, parents act to defend their reproductive interests.

Why do masked booby and blue-footed boobies differ so strongly in their response to parent–offspring conflict? The leading hypothesis is that food shortages

Figure 10.16 Blue-footed and masked boobies These photos show masked boobies (left) and blue-footed boobies (right). The two species nest in adjacent colonies at the study site established by Lougheed and Anderson in the Galápagos islands off the northwest coast of South America. (Left: D. Cavagnaro/ Visuals Unlimited; right: Tui De Roy/Minden Pictures)

Table 10.4 **In boobies, the probability of siblicide varies with parent species and nestmate species**

These data show that siblicide is much more common in nests with masked booby parents or masked booby nestlings than in nests with blue-footed booby nestlings or blue-footed booby parents. To explain these patterns, Lougheed and Anderson hypothesize that masked booby nestlings are more siblicidal than blue-footed booby nestlings, and that blue-footed booby parents attempt to intervene and prevent siblicide.

Treatment	No siblicide	Siblicide
Masked booby nestlings with masked booby parents	0	25
Blue-footed booby nestlings with masked booby parents	12	8
Masked booby nestlings with blue-footed booby parents	4	16
Blue-footed booby nestlings with blue-footed booby parents	17	0

Source: Lougheed and Anderson (1999).

are much more likely in masked boobies, and that second chicks almost always starve to death even without siblicide. This hypothesis is still untested, however. Research into the dynamics of siblicide and other forms of parent–offspring conflict continues (see Mock and Parker 1997).

10.4 Reciprocal Altruism

Inclusive fitness theory has been remarkably successful in explaining a wide range of phenomena in social evolution. In many cases, altruistic acts can be understood in light of Hamilton's rule, and conflicts can be understood by analyzing asymmetries in coefficients of relatedness and differences in fitness payoffs. But the theory and data we have reviewed thus far are only relevant to interactions among kin. What about the frequent occurrence of cooperation among unrelated individuals?

Reciprocal altruism provides one theoretical framework for studying cooperation among non-kin. Robert Trivers (1971) proposed that individuals can be selected to dispense altruistic acts if equally valuable favors are later returned by the beneficiaries. According to Trivers, natural selection can favor altruistic behavior if the recipients reciprocate.

Two important conditions must be met for reciprocal altruism to evolve. First, selection can favor altruistic acts only if the cost to the actor is smaller than or equal to the benefit to the recipient. Alleles that lead to high-cost, low-benefit behavior cannot increase in the population even if this type of act is reciprocated. (As with kin selection, the costs and benefits of altruistic acts are measured by the numbers of surviving offspring.) Second, individuals that fail to reciprocate must be punished in some way. If they are not, then altruistic individuals suffer fitness losses with no subsequent return. Alleles that lead to cheating behavior would increase in the population and altruists would quickly be eliminated. As a result, the theory predicts that altruists will be selected to detect and punish cheaters by physically assaulting them or by withholding future benefits (Box 10.4).

BOX 10.4 Prisoner's dilemma: analyzing cooperation and conflict using game theory

Robert Trivers (1971) recognized that a classical problem from the branch of mathematics called game theory closely simulates the problems faced by nonrelatives in making decisions about their interactions. The central idea in game theory is that the consequences of any move in a game are contingent: The result or payoff from an action depends on the move made by the opponent. When players in a game pursue contrasting strategies, game theory provides a way to quantify the outcomes and decide which strategy works best.

Game theory was invented in the 1940s to analyze contrasting strategies in games like poker and chess. Later, the approach was applied by economists to a variety of problems in market economics and business competition. John Maynard Smith (1974, 1982) pioneered the use of game theory in evolutionary biology in analyses of animal contests. His work inspired a series of productive studies on the evolution of display behavior and combat (e.g., Sigurjónsdóttir and Parker 1981; Hammerstein and Reichert 1988).

The game that Trivers employed to analyze cooperation is called Prisoner's Dilemma. Prisoner's Dilemma models the following situation: Two prisoners who have been charged as accomplices in a crime are locked in separate cells. The punishment they suffer depends on whether they cooperate with one another in maintaining their innocence or implicate the other in the crime. Each prisoner has to choose his strategy without knowing the other prisoner's choice. The payoffs to Player A in this game are as follows:

		Player B's action	
		C **Cooperation**	**D** **Defection**
Player A's **action**	**C** **Cooperation**	R (reward for cooperation—both receive light sentences)	S (sucker gets longer sentence if partner defects)
	D **Defection**	T (temptation—reduced sentence for defector)	P (punishment for mutual defection—both receive intermediate sentences)

where $T > R > P > S$ and $R > (S + T)/2$. The highest payoff in the game comes when Players A and B cooperate by maintaining silence, but Player A does best when A defects and B cooperates. When Players A and B interact just once, the best strategy for each player is to defect.

What happens when the two players interact repeatedly? Robert Axelrod and William Hamilton (1981) performed a widely cited analysis of an iterated Prisoner's Dilemma. They invited game theorists from all over the world to submit strategies for players competing in a computerized simulation of the game. Each round in this tournament had the following payoffs: $R = 3$, $T = 5$, $S = 0$, and $P = 1$. Axelrod and Hamilton let each strategy play against all of the other strategies submitted, and computed the outcome of every one-on-one game over many interactions. Most of the theorists submitted complicated decision-making algorithms, but the winner was always the simplest strategy of all, called tit for tat, TFT. An individual playing TFT starts by cooperating, then simply does whatever the opponent did in the previous round. This strategy has three prominent features: (1) It is never the first to defect, (2) it is provoked to immediate retaliation by defection, and (3) it is willing to cooperate again after just one act of retaliation for a defection.

In analyzing the outcome of games like this, researchers use the concept of an evolutionarily stable strategy, ESS. A strategy is an ESS if a population of individuals using it cannot be invaded by a rare mutant adopting a different strategy. Axelrod and Hamilton's tournament showed that TFT is an evolutionarily stable strategy with respect to other strategies employed in the tournament. Their result offers an explanation for the evolution of cooperative behavior in unrelated individuals. Laboratory experiments with guppies and sticklebacks suggest that animals may actually play TFT when they interact (see Milinski 1996; Dugatkin 1998).

Trivers pointed out that reciprocal altruism is most likely to evolve when

*Reciprocal altruism can evolve
only under a restricted set of
conditions.*

- each individual repeatedly interacts with the same set of individuals (groups are stable);
- many opportunities for altruism occur in an individual's lifetime;
- individuals have good memories; and
- potential altruists interact in symmetrical situations.

This means that interacting individuals are able to dispense roughly equivalent benefits at roughly equivalent costs.

Accordingly, we expect reciprocal altruism to be characteristic of long-lived, intelligent, social species with small group size, low rates of dispersal from the group, and a high degree of mutual dependence in group defense, foraging, or other activities. Reciprocal altruism should be less likely to evolve in species where strong dominance hierarchies are the rule. In these social systems, subordinate individuals are rarely able to provide benefits in return for altruistic acts dispensed by dominant individuals.

Based on these characteristics, Trivers (1971, 1985; see also Packer 1977) has suggested that reciprocal altruism is responsible for much of the cooperative behavior observed in primates like baboons, chimpanzees, and humans. Indeed, Trivers has proposed that human emotions like moralistic aggression, gratitude, guilt, and trust are adaptations that have evolved in response to selection for reciprocal altruism. He suggests that these emotions function as "scorekeeping" mechanisms useful in moderating transactions among reciprocal altruists.

Studying reciprocal altruism in natural populations is exceptionally difficult, however. For example, it is likely that kin selection and reciprocal altruism interact and are mutually reinforcing in many social groups. This makes it difficult for researchers to disentangle the effect that each type of selection has independently of the other. Also, the fitness effects of some altruistic actions can be difficult to quantify. When a young male baboon supports an older, unrelated male in his fight over access to a female, or when a young lioness participates in group defense of the territory, how do we quantify the fitness costs and benefits for each participant? What are our chances of observing the return behavior, and quantifying its costs and benefits as well? Finally, it can be difficult to distinguish reciprocal altruism from what biologists call by-product mutualism. This is cooperative behavior that benefits both individuals more or less equally. The critical difference between reciprocity and mutualism is that there is a time lag between the exchange of benefits in reciprocal altruism.

For these reasons, it has been difficult for evolutionary biologists to document reciprocal altruism—difficult enough, in fact, to make many biologists suspect that this type of natural selection is rare. Here we will examine one of the most robust studies done to date: food sharing in vampire bats. In this system, the altruistic act is regurgitating a blood meal. The cost of altruism can be measured as an increase in the risk of starvation, and the benefit as a lowered risk of starvation.

Blood-Sharing in Vampire Bats

Gerald Wilkinson (1984) worked on a population of about 200 vampire bats (*Desmodus rotundus*) at a study site in Costa Rica (Figure 10.17). The basic social unit in this species consists of 8–12 adult females and their dependent offspring.

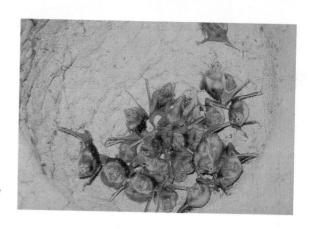

Figure 10.17   Vampire bats
This photo shows a group of vampire bats roosting in a hollow tree. (Gerald Wilkinson, University of Maryland)

Members of these groups frequently roost together in hollow trees during the day, although subgroups often move from tree to tree. (There was a total of 14 roosting trees at Wilkinson's study site.) As a result of this social structure, many individuals in the population associate with one another daily. The degree of association between individuals varies widely, however. Wilkinson quantified the degree of association between each pair of bats in the population by counting the number of times they were seen together at a roost and dividing by the total number of times they were observed roosting.

Wilkinson was able to capture and individually mark almost all of the individuals at his study site over a period of four and a half years, and estimate coefficients of relatedness through path analysis of pedigrees. In the female group for which he had the most complete data, the average r between individuals was 0.11. (Recall that cousins have an r of 0.125.)

The combination of variability in association and relatedness raises interesting questions about the evolution of altruism. Vampire bats dispense altruistic behavior by regurgitating blood meals to one another. This food sharing is important because blood meals are difficult to obtain. The bats leave their roosts at night to search for large mammals—primarily horses and cattle—that can provide a meal. Prey are wary, however, and 33% of young bats and 7% of adults fail to feed on any given night. By studying weight loss in captive bats when food was withheld, Wilkinson was able to show that bats who go three consecutive nights without a meal are likely to starve to death.

Vampire bats reciprocate by sharing blood meals. They usually share with close relatives or nonrelatives who are nestmates and may later reciprocate.

Because the degree of relatedness and degree of association varied among individuals in the population, either kin selection or reciprocal altruism could operate in this system. Wilkinson was able to show that both occur. Over the course of the study, he witnessed 110 episodes of regurgitation. Seventy-seven of these were between mother and child and are simply examples of parental care. In 21 of the remaining 33 cases, Wilkinson knew both the r and the degree of association between the actor and beneficiary and could examine the effect of both variables. Wilkinson discovered that both degree of relatedness and degree of association have a statistically significant effect in predicting the probability of regurgitation (Figure 10.18). Bats do not regurgitate blood meals to one another randomly. They are much more likely to regurgitate to relatives and to nonrelatives who are frequent roostmates.

To confirm that bats actually do reciprocate, Wilkinson held nine individuals in captivity, withheld food from a different individual each night for several weeks,

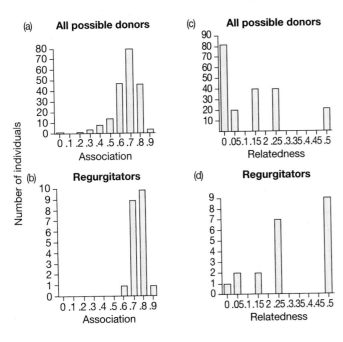

Figure 10.18 Association, relatedness, and altruism in vampire bats These histograms plot the total number of bat–bat pairs at Gerald Wilkinson's study site versus their (a) degree of association, for all potential blood donors in the roost, (b) degree of association, for blood-sharing pairs who are not related as mother–offspring, (c) coefficient of relatedness, for all potential blood donors in the roost, and (d) coefficient of relatedness, for blood-sharing pairs who were not related as mother–offspring. The visual impression in these figures is that regurgitators are more likely to be related and more likely to be roostmates than the general population. This is confirmed by a statistical procedure called a stepwise logistic regression. Both relatedness and association affect the probability of blood-sharing. From Wilkinson (1984).

and recorded who regurgitated to whom over the course of the experiment. Statistical tests rejected the null hypothesis that hungry individuals received blood randomly from cagemates. Instead, hungry individuals were much more likely to receive blood from an individual they had fed before. This confirms that vampire bats are reciprocal altruists.

Territory Defense in Lions

Lions (*Panthera leo;* Figure 10.19) are the only species of cat that lives in social groups. These groups, called prides, consist of 3–6 related females, their offspring, and a coalition of males. Males are often related to one another but are unrelated to pride females (Packer and Pusey 1982; Packer et al. 1991). Males cooperate in defending themselves against other coalitions of males that attack and try to take over the pride. If a pride takeover occurs, the incoming males often kill the young cubs present (see Section 9.2).

Females cooperate in defending their young against infanticidal attacks, in nursing young, in hunting prey that are difficult to capture (females do the vast majority

Figure 10.19 African lions When female lions hear roars made by unfamiliar females, they move across their territory toward the source. Females that lead the movement frequently glance back at female pride members that are lagging behind. (Mitsuaki Iwago/Minden Pictures)

of hunting in lions), and in defending the pride's territory against incursions by females in neighboring prides (Packer and Pusey 1983, 1997). Battles with intruding females are dangerous, especially if pride females do not cooperate in defense. Solitary lions are often killed in same-sex encounters.

To study cooperation during incursions by strange females who threaten the territory, Robert Heinsohn and Craig Packer (1995) placed speakers near the edge of pride territories and played tape recordings of roars given by unfamiliar females. Pride females respond to these roars by approaching the speakers; they even attack if a stuffed female lion is placed near the speaker. They also do not habituate to this stimulus—they continue responding when the experiment is repeated. As a result, Heinsohn and Packer were able to quantify how females responded to threats over multiple trials. In addition to recording how long it took an individual to reach the midpoint between the pride's original position and the speaker, they also calculated the difference between each individual's time-to-midpoint and the leader's time, documented the order within the group that each female reached the midpoint, and counted the number of glances a female made back at lagging pride members. They collected data on female responses in eight different prides.

Statistical analyses showed significant differences in the strength of responses among females within prides. Some females in each pride always led; others always lagged behind. Other females adopted conditional strategies: They would assist the lead female(s) more frequently when Heinsohn and Packer played tapes of more than one female roaring (that is, when the threat to the pride was greater). Still others would lag behind more when multiple roars were played. These differences were not correlated with the age or body size of females or with their coefficient of relationship with other pride members.

The dynamics of group defense in lions have yet to be explained by kin selection or reciprocal altruism.

These results are paradoxical in the context of both inclusive fitness and reciprocity theory. Why do the leaders tolerate the laggards? According to the theory we developed earlier, they should be punished. But leaders were never observed to threaten laggards or to withhold benefits. For example, they did not stop leading until laggards caught up. They glanced back and appeared to recognize that laggards were lagging, but continued approaching the speaker.

The simple answer is that we do not know why this combination of altruist and non-reciprocator strategies exists among lions. The leading hypothesis, which is still to be tested, is that laggard females make fitness benefits up to the leaders in other ways: through exceptional hunting prowess or milk production, for example. But clearly, social interactions among lions are substantially more complex than current theory would suggest.

Summary

When individuals interact, four outcomes are possible with respect to fitness: cooperation, altruism, selfishness, and spite. The evolution of altruism was one of the great paradoxes of evolutionary biology until it was resolved by two important advances:

1. William Hamilton showed mathematically that a gene for altruism will spread when $Br - C > 0$

where B is the benefit to the recipient in units of surviving offspring, r is the coefficient of relatedness between actor and recipient, and C is the cost to the actor. When Hamilton's rule holds, kin selection results in altruistic behavior.

2. Robert Trivers developed the theory of reciprocal altruism. Altruism among unrelated individuals can evolve if the benefits of an altruistic act to the re-

cipient are large and the cost to the actor is small, and the benefits are later returned to the actor by the recipient.

Kin selection explains phenomena such as alarm calling in ground squirrels and helping behavior in birds. In Belding's ground squirrels, individuals are more willing to risk giving an alarm call if close relatives are nearby. In white-fronted bee-eaters, 1-year-old individuals preferentially help at the nests of closely related individuals (often their parents).

Kin selection has also been important in explaining the evolution of eusociality in Hymenoptera and in naked mole-rats. Phylogenetic analyses show that nest-building and extensive care of young was a precondition for the evolution of reproductive altruism in ants, wasps, and bees. In these groups, individuals are unlikely to reproduce on their own successfully, so reproductive altruism is favored by kin selection. In obligately eusocial groups like ants and bees, asymmetries in relatedness between egg-laying queens and nonreproductive workers result from the haplodiploid system of sex determination and produce sharp conflicts over the sex ratio of offspring. Helping behavior is facultative in *Polistes* wasps, however. In this group, females may or may not help at the nest depending on their body size and their coefficient of relatedness relative to nestmates. In naked mole-rats, eusociality is supported by the queen's physical dominance and by extensive inbreeding that leads to high coefficients of relatedness among individuals.

Parent–offspring conflict and sibling conflict occur when the fitness interests of individuals within families clash. Parents are equally related to each of their offspring, but offspring are more closely related to themselves than to their siblings. Weaning conflict occurs because young mammals demand more resources for themselves than for their siblings; siblicide occurs if perpetrators gain enough direct fitness benefits by removing competition for food to outweigh the indirect fitness cost of killing a sibling. Parents may acquiesce to siblicide if it increases the probability that at least one offspring will survive.

Reciprocal altruism has been successful as an explanation for food-sharing between vampire bats, and may be involved in interactions among females in lion prides. It is often difficult, however, to distinguish when cooperation is due to reciprocal altruism and when it results from kin selection or simple mutualism.

Questions

1. Suppose adult bee-eaters could raise only 0.3 more offspring with a helper than without a helper. Would you still expect male bee-eaters to "give in" to the harassment of their fathers, or would male bee-eaters tend to fight off their fathers? Explain your reasoning.

2. When a Thomson's gazelle detects a nearby stalking cheetah, the gazelle often begins bouncing up and down with a stiff-legged gait called "stotting" (see Figure 10.20). One hypothesis is that stotting has evolved because it may help alert the gazelle's kin to the presence of a predator, analogous to the alarm calls of ground squirrels. Caro (1986) reports that stotting does not seem to increase the gazelle's risk of being attacked. In fact, once a gazelle begins to stott, the cheetah often gives up the hunt. How is C (the cost of stotting) different for a gazelle, compared to C (the cost of alarm calls) for a ground squirrel? Do you

Figure 10.20 A Thomson's gazelle stotting. (R. D'Estes/ Photo Researchers, Inc.)

think it is likely that stotting is an altruistic behavior? With this in mind, make a prediction about whether a gazelle will stott when there are no other gazelles around, and then look up Caro's papers to see if you are right.

Caro, T. M. 1986. The function of stotting in Thomson's gazelles: Some tests of the hypotheses. *Animal Behaviour.* 34: 663–684.

Caro, T. M. 1994. Ungulate antipredator behaviour: Preliminary and comparative data from African bovids. *Behaviour* 128: 189–228.

3. The cubs of spotted hyenas often begin fighting within moments of birth, and often one hyena cub dies. The mother hyena does not interfere. How could such a behavior have evolved? For instance, from the winning sibling's point of view, what must B (benefit of siblicide) be, relative to C (cost of siblicide), to favor the evolution of siblicide? From the parent's point of view, what must B be, relative to C, for the parent to watch calmly rather than to interfere? [See Frank (1997) for more about the unusual social system of spotted hyenas, and Golla et al. (1999) for new information from studies of wild hyenas.]

Frank, Laurence G. 1997. Evolution of genital masculinization: Why do female hyaenas have such a large 'penis'? *Trends in Ecology and Evolution* 12: 58–62.

Golla, W., H. Hofer, and M. L. East. 1999. Within-litter sibling aggression in spotted hyaenas: Effect of maternal nursing, sex and age. *Animal Behaviour* 58: 715–726.

4. Blue jays (*Cyanocitta cristata*) seem to be better than American robins (*Turdus migratorius*) at recognizing individuals. In one study, blue jays raised with American robins could distinguish strange from familiar robins better than the robins themselves (Schimmel and Wasserman 1994). Do you think these species differ in occurrence of kin selection or reciprocal altruism (or both)? Why?

Schimmel, K. L. and F. E. Wasserman. 1994. Individual and species preference in two passerine birds: Auditory and visual cues. *Auk* 111: 634–642.

5. The first paragraph of this chapter refers to crows who cooperate in chasing a predator away (a behavior known as mobbing) and who help their parents raise their siblings. Which behavior is mutualistic, and which behavior is favored by kin selection? Suggest a hypothesis to explain why young crows in some populations might help at the nest, while in other populations they nest on their own.

6. The biologist J. B. S. Haldane was once explaining kin selection to some friends in a pub. As the story goes, he scribbled some calculations on an envelope and announced that he would be willing to die for two brothers or eight cousins. Explain his reasoning.

7. Look at Figure 10.14 on parent–offspring conflict. Explain, in general terms, why the behavior of females should evolve so that mothers start weaning when B/C falls below 1. (*Hint:* Consider the reproductive success of mothers who wean very early, and of mothers who wean very late.) If a mother could have only one litter of young in her lifetime, how would the period of weaning conflict change?

8. The text claims that eusociality has evolved several times independently within the hymenoptera. What is the evidence for this statement? If it is true, in what sense is eusociality in ants, bees, and wasps an example of convergent evolution (see Chapter 9)?

9. How would you go about testing the hypothesis that female lions who do not participate in territory defense reciprocate by providing milk to the offspring of territory defenders? List the predictions made by the hypothesis and the types of data you would have to collect.

10. House sparrows often produce two successive broods of young. Males feed their first brood only briefly, but feed their second brood for much longer [see Hegner & Wingfield (1986) for further information]. Why do males feed first broods less than second broods? (*Hint:* Consider how C, the cost of feeding the current brood, changes). How could you test your hypothesis? How is this situation analogous to weaning conflict in mammals?

Hegner, R. E. and J. C. Wingfield. 1986. Behavioral and endocrine correlates of multiple brooding in the semicolonial house sparrow *Passer domesticus*. I. Males. *Hormones and Behavior* 20: 294–312.

11. Which is more common in human cultures—eusociality (look back at the three requirements of eusociality; can you think of any human cultures that fit?), or a helper-at-the-nest social system? Which do you think is generally more common in social animals? Why?

12. Human siblings often show intense sibling rivalry that typically declines during the teenage years. Suggest an evolutionary explanation for this pattern.

Exploring the Literature

13. Throughout this chapter, we concentrated on the fitness consequences of social interactions and paid little attention to the issue of why organisms live in groups in the first place. To learn how social living has been favored by

factors such as a requirement for group defense against predators, benefits from group foraging, and a need for long-term care of dependent young, see

Alexander, R. D. 1974. The evolution of social behavior. *Annual Review of Ecology and Systematics* 5: 325–383.

Packer, C., D. Scheel, and A. E. Pusey. 1990. Why lions form groups: Food is not enough. *American Naturalist* 136: 1–19.

14. Because this chapter emphasizes theories that explain why cooperative behavior can evolve when a fitness cost is involved, we spent little time on the evolution of mutualism. For examples of cooperative behavior that are not caused by kin selection or reciprocal altruism, see

McDonald, D. B., and W. K. Potts. 1994. Cooperative display and relatedness among males in a lek-breeding bird. *Science* 266: 1030–1032.

Watts, D. P. 1998. Coalitionary mate guarding by male chimpanzees at Ngogo, Kibale National Park, Uganda. *Behavioral Ecology and Sociobiology* 44: 43–55.

15. A variety of models and experiments (some using college students as experimental subjects) have shown that certain variations on the tit-for-tat strategy are extremely successful in interactions among individuals. To begin reviewing this literature, see

Wedekind, C., and M. Milinski. 1996. Human cooperation in the simultaneous and the alternating Prisoner's Dilemma: Pavlov versus generous tit-for-tat. *Proceedings of the National Academy of Sciences, USA* 93: 2686–2689.

Roberts, G., and T. N. Sherratt. 1998. Development of cooperative relationships through increasing investment. *Nature* 394: 175–179.

Citations

Alexander, R. D., K. M. Noonan, and B. J. Crespi. 1991. The evolution of eusociality. In P. W. Sherman, J. U. M. Jarvis, and R. D. Alexander. *The Biology of the Naked Mole Rat.* Princeton, NJ: Princeton University Press, 3–44.

Anderson, D. J., and R. E. Ricklefs. 1995. Evidence of kin-selected tolerance by nestlings in a siblicidal bird. *Behavioral Ecology and Sociobiology* 37: 163–168.

Axelrod, R., and W. D. Hamilton. 1981. The evolution of cooperation. *Science* 211:1390–1396.

Bartz, S. H. 1979. Evolution of eusociality in termites. *Proceedings of the National Academy of Sciences, USA* 76:5764–5768.

Betzig, L. L., and P. W. Turke. 1986. Parental investment by sex on Ifaluk. *Ethology and Sociobiology* 7:29–37.

Bourke, A. F. G., and N. R. Franks. 1995. *Social Evolution in Ants.* Princeton, NJ: Princeton University Press.

Brown, J. L. 1987. *Helping and Communal Breeding in Birds.* Princeton, NJ: Princeton University Press.

Brown, J. L., and A. Eklund. 1994. Kin recognition and the major histocompatibility complex: An integrative review. *American Naturalist* 143: 435–461.

Charnov, E. L. 1982. *The Theory of Sex Allocation.* Princeton, NJ: Princeton University Press.

Clutton-Brock, T. H., S. D. Albon, and F. E. Guinness. 1984. Maternal dominance, breeding success and birth sex ratios in red deer. *Nature* 308: 358–360.

Crozier, R. H., and P. Pamilo. 1996. *Evolution of Social Insect Colonies.* Oxford: Oxford University Press.

Darwin, C. 1859. *The Origin of Species.* London: John Murray.

Duffy, J. E. 1996. Eusociality in a coral-reef shrimp. *Nature* 381: 512–514.

Dugatkin, A. L. 1998. *Cooperation among animals.* Oxford: Oxford University Press.

Emlen, S. T., and P. H. Wrege. 1988. The role of kinship in helping decisions among white-fronted bee-eaters. *Behavioral Ecology and Sociobiology* 23: 305–315.

Emlen, S. T., and P. H. Wrege. 1991. Breeding biology of white-fronted bee-eaters at Nakuru: The influence of helpers on breeder fitness. *Journal of Animal Ecology* 60: 309–326.

Emlen, S. T., and P. H. Wrege. 1992. Parent–offspring conflict and the recruitment of helpers among bee-eaters. *Nature* 356:331-333.

Emlen, S. T., P. H. Wrege, and N. J. Demong. 1995. Making decisions in the family: An evolutionary perspective. *American Scientist* 83: 148–157.

Fisher, R. A. 1930. *The Genetical Theory of Natural Selection.* Oxford: Clarendon Press.

Godfrey, H. C. J. 1995. Evolutionary theory of parent–offspring conflict. *Nature* 376: 133–138.

Hamilton, W. D. 1964. The genetical evolution of social behaviour. I. *Journal of Theoretical Biology* 7: 1–16.

Hamilton, W. D. 1964. The genetical evolution of social behaviour. II. *Journal of Theoretical Biology* 7: 17–52.

Hamilton, W. D. 1967. Extraordinary sex ratios. *Science* 156: 477–488.

Hamilton, W. D. 1972. Altruism and related phenomena, mainly in the social insects. *Annual Review of Ecology and Systematics* 3: 193–232.

Hammerstein, P., and S. E. Riechert. 1988. Payoffs and strategies in territorial contests: ESS analyses of two ecotypes of the spider *Agelenopsis aperta*. *Evolutionary Ecology* 2: 115–138.

Hegner, R. E., S. T. Emlen, and N. J. Demong. 1982. Spatial organization of the white-fronted bee-eater. *Nature* 298: 264–266.

Heinsohn, R., and C. Packer. 1995. Complex cooperative strategies in group-territorial African lions. *Science* 269: 1260–1262.

Honeycutt, R. L. 1992. Naked mole-rats. *American Scientist* 80: 43–53.

Hunt, J. H. 1999. Trait mapping and salience in the evolution of eusocial vespid wasps. *Evolution* 53: 225–237.

Keller, L., M. Milinski, M. Frischknecht, N. Perrin, H. Richner, and F. Tripet. 1994. Spiteful animals still to be discovered. *Trends in Ecology and Evolution* 9: 103.

Lougheed, L. W., and D. J. Anderson. 1999. Parent blue-footed boobies suppress siblicidal behavior of offspring. *Behavioral Ecology and Sociobiology* 45: 11–18.

Manning, C. J., E. K. Wakeland, and W. K. Potts. 1992. Communal nesting patterns in mice implicate MHC genes in kin recognition. *Nature* 360: 581–583.

Maynard Smith, J. 1974. The theory of games and the evolution of animal conflicts. *Journal of Theoretical Biology* 47: 209–221.

Maynard Smith, J. 1982. *Evolution and the Theory of Games.* Cambridge: Cambridge University Press.

Michener, C. D. 1969. Comparative social behavior of bees. *Annual Review of Entomology* 14: 299–342.

Milinski, M. 1996. By-product mutualism, tit-for-tat reciprocity and cooperative predator inspection: A reply to Connor. *Animal Behaviour* 51: 458–461.

Mock, D. W., and G. A. Parker. 1997. *The evolution of sibling rivalry.* Oxford: Oxford University Press.

Nonacs, P., and H. K. Reeve. 1995. The ecology of cooperation in wasps: Causes and consequences of alternative reproductive decisions. *Ecology* 76: 953–967.

Oldroyd, B. P., M. J. Clifton, S. Wongsiri, T. E. Rinderer, H. A. Sylvester, and R. H. Crozier. 1997. Polyandry in the genus *Apis,* particulary *Apis andreniformis. Behavioral Ecology and Sociobiology* 40: 17–26.

Oldroyd, B. P., M. J. Clifton, K. Parker, S. Wongsiri, T. E. Rinderer, and R. H. Crozier. 1998. Evolution of mating behavior in the genus *Apis* and an estimate of mating frequency in *Apis cerana* (Hymenoptera: Apidae). *Annals of the Entomological Society of America* 91: 700–709.

Packer, C. 1977. Reciprocal altruism in *Papio anubis. Nature* 265: 441–443.

Packer, C., and A. E. Pusey. 1982. Cooperation and competition within coalitions of male lions: Kin selection or game theory? *Nature* 296: 740–742.

Packer, C., and A. E. Pusey. 1983. Adaptations of female lions to infanticide by incoming males. *American Naturalist* 121: 716–728.

Packer, C., and A. E. Pusey. 1997. Divided we fall: Cooperation among lions. *Scientific American* 276 (May): 52–59.

Packer, C., D. A. Gilbert, A. E. Pusey, and S. J. O'Brien. 1991. A molecular genetic analysis of kinship and cooperation in African lions. *Nature* 351: 562–565.

Page, R. E. Jr., and R. A. Metcalf. 1982. Multiple mating, sperm utilization, and social evolution. *American Naturalist* 119: 263–281.

Pamilo, P. 1984. Genetic relatedness and evolution of insect sociality. *Behavioral Ecology and Sociobiology* 15: 241–248.

Peters, J. M., D. C. Queller, V. L. Imperatriz-Fonseca, D. W. Roubik, and J. E. Strassmann. 1999. Mate number, kin selection and social conflicts in stingless bees and honeybees. *Proceedings of the Royal Society of London,* Series B 266: 379–384.

Pfennig, D. W., and P. W. Sherman. 1995. Kin recognition. *Scientific American* 272: 98–103.

Queller, D. C. 1989. The evolution of eusociality: Reproductive head starts of workers. *Proceedings of the National Academy of Sciences, USA* 86: 3224–3226.

Queller, D. C., and K. F. Goodnight. 1989. Estimating relatedness using genetic markers. *Evolution* 43: 258–275.

Queller, D. C., and J. E. Strassmann. 1998. Kin selection and social insects. *BioScience* 48: 165–175.

Reeve, H. K. 1992. Queen activation of lazy workers in colonies of the eusocial naked mole-rat. *Nature* 358: 147–149.

Reeve, H. K., D. F. Westneat, W. A. Noon, P. W. Sherman, and C. F. Aquadro. 1990. DNA "fingerprinting" reveals high levels of inbreeding in colonies of the eusocial naked mole-rat. *Proceedings of the National Academy of Sciences, USA* 87: 2496–2500.

Reeve, H. K., J. M. Peters, P. Nonacs, and P. T. Starks. 1998. Dispersal of first "workers" in social wasps: Causes and implications of an alternative reproductive strategy. *Proceedings of the National Academy of Sciences, USA* 95: 13737–13742.

Reeve, H. K., and P. W. Sherman. 1991. Intracolonial aggression and nepotism by the breeding female naked mole-rat. In P. W. Sherman, J. U. M. Jarvis, and R. D. Alexander, eds. *The Biology of the Naked Mole Rat.* Princeton, NJ: Princeton University Press, 337–357.

Roisin, Y. 1994. Intragroup conflicts and the evolution of sterile castes in termites. *American Naturalist* 143: 751–765.

Sherman, P. W. 1977. Nepotism and the evolution of alarm calls. *Science* 197:1246–1253.

Sherman, P. W. 1980. The limits of ground squirrel nepotism. In George W. Barlow and J. Silverberg, eds. *Sociobiology: Beyond Nature/Nurture?* Washington, DC: AAAS; and Boulder, CO: Westview Press, 505–544.

Sherman, P. W. 1981. Kinship, demography, and Belding's ground squirrel nepotism. *Behavioral Ecology and Sociobiology* 8:251–259.

Sherman, P. W., J. U. M. Jarvis, and S. H. Braude. 1992. Naked mole rats. *Scientific American* 267: 72–78.

Sigurjónsdóttir, H., and G. A. Parker. 1981. Dung fly struggles: Evidence for assessment strategy. *Behavioral Ecology and Sociobiology* 8: 219–230.

Stacey, P. B., and W. D. Koenig, eds. 1990. *Cooperative Breeding in Birds: Long-term Studies of Ecology and Behaviour.* Cambridge: Cambridge University Press.

Sundström, L., M. Chapuisat, and L. Keller. 1996. Conditional manipulation of sex ratios by ant workers: A test of kin selection theory. *Science* 274: 993–995.

Thorne, B. L. 1997. Evolution of eusociality in termites. *Annual Review of Ecology and Systematics* 28: 27–54.

Trivers, R. L. 1971. The evolution of reciprocal altruism. *Quarterly Review of Biology* 46: 35–57.

Trivers, R. L. 1974. Parent–offspring conflict. *American Zoologist* 14: 249–264.

Trivers, R. L. 1985. *Social Evolution.* Menlo Park, CA: Benjamin Cummings.

Trivers, R. L., and D. E. Willard. 1973. Natural selection of parental ability to vary the sex ratio of offspring. *Science* 179: 90–92.

Trivers, R. L., and H. Hare. 1976. Haplodiploidy and the evolution of the social insects. *Science* 191: 249–263.

Werren, J. H. 1984. A model for sex ratio selection in parasitic wasps: Local mate competition and host quality effects. *Netherlands Journal of Zoology* 34: 81–96.

Wilkinson, G. S. 1984. Reciprocal food sharing in the vampire bat. *Nature* 308: 181–184.

Wilson, E. O. 1971. *The Insect Societies.* Cambridge, MA: Harvard University Press.

CHAPTER 12

Mechanisms of Speciation

These flowers are from different species of monkeyflowers and their hybrid offspring. Researchers produced the hybrids to investigate the loci and alleles responsible for the differences between monkeyflower species. (Douglas W. Schemske, University of Washington, Seattle)

ALL ORGANISMS ALIVE TODAY TRACE THEIR ANCESTRY BACK THROUGH TIME TO the origin of life some 3.8 billion years ago. Between then and now, millions—if not billions—of branching events have occurred as populations split and diverged to become separate species. In this chapter we examine how these branching events happened. In Chapters 5-7 we investigated how mutation, natural selection, migration, and drift act to change allele frequencies within populations; now we ask how these four processes can lead to genetic differences between populations.

In addition to providing a foundation for studying the history of life, studying speciation has important practical applications. Much of the material we explore focuses on the extent and causes of gene flow (or lack of gene flow) among differentiated groups of organisms. Understanding these topics is fundamental to creating effective strategies for preserving biodiversity, and to managing genetically engineered organisms that are released into the environment.

Along with considering these applied issues and the general problem of how evolutionary processes can isolate populations, we need to examine two additional questions: What happens when recently diverged populations come into contact and interbreed? What genetic changes take place during differentiation? To begin our analysis we start with the field's most fundamental question: What is a species?

403

12.1 Species Concepts

All human cultures recognize different types of organisms in nature and name them. These taxonomic systems are based on judgments about the degrees of similarity among organisms. People intuitively group like with like. The challenge to biologists has been to move beyond these informal judgments to a definition of species that is mechanistic and testable, and to a classification system that accurately reflects the evolutionary history of organisms. This has been difficult to do. In the past 30 years alone, there have been at least half a dozen species concepts proposed, recurrent controversies about which definition is best, and even philosophical debates about whether the unit we call the species actually exists in nature or whether it is merely a linguistic and cultural construct (for example see Donoghue 1985; Templeton 1989).

Species consist of interbreeding populations that evolve independently of other populations.

In this section, we describe the pros and cons of three major species concepts and review how they are applied. Although they differ in detail, these definitions agree that species share a distinguishing characteristic, which is evolutionary independence. Evolutionary independence occurs when mutation, selection, migration, and drift operate on each species separately. This means that species form a boundary for the spread of alleles. Consequently, different species follow independent evolutionary trajectories.

The differences among species concepts center on the problem of establishing practical criteria for identifying evolutionary independence. This is a challenge because the data available to define species vary between sexual and asexual organisms and between fossil and extant groups. The following three examples illustrate this point.

The Biological Species Concept

Under the biological species concept (BSC), the criterion for identifying evolutionary independence is reproductive isolation. Specifically, if populations of organisms do not hybridize, or fail to produce fertile offspring when they do, then they are reproductively isolated and considered good species. The BSC has been the textbook definition of a species since Ernst Mayr proposed it in 1942. It is used in practice by many zoologists and is the legal definition employed in the Endangered Species Act, which is the flagship biodiversity legislation in the United States.

Reproductive isolation is clearly an appropriate criterion for identifying species because it confirms lack of gene flow. This is the litmus test of evolutionary independence. But although the BSC is compelling in concept and useful in some situations, it is often difficult to apply. For example, if nearby populations do not actually overlap, we have no way of knowing whether they are reproductively isolated. Instead, biologists have to make subjective judgments to the effect that, "If these populations were to meet in the future, we believe that they are divergent enough already that they would not interbreed, so we will name them different species." In these cases, species designations cannot be tested with data. Further, the biological species concept can never be tested in fossil forms, is irrelevant to asexual populations (see Box 12.1), and is difficult to apply in the many plant groups where hybridization between strongly divergent populations is routine.

The Phylogenetic Species Concept

Systematists are the people responsible for classifying the diversity of life, and a growing number are promoting an alternative to the BSC called the phylogenetic or evolutionary species concept. This approach focuses on a criterion called

BOX 12.1 Species concepts in bacteria

Much of the research reviewed in this chapter focuses on evolutionary processes that lead to reproductive isolation. Indeed, the biological species concept treats this property as *the* criterion of speciation. But in bacteria and many other asexual forms, reproduction takes place via mitosis—without an exchange of genetic material. When gene exchange does occur between bacteria, it is limited to small segments of the genome and is unidirectional (Figure 12.1). Just as important, recombination can occur between members of widely diverged taxa. In bacteria, gene flow can occur between cells whose genomes have diverged up to 16% (Cohan 1995). Bacteria that are classified as members of different phyla can and do exchange genes, such as the alleles responsible for antibiotic resistance, via the extra-chromosomal loops of DNA called plasmids (Cohan 1994). In contrast, genetic exchange between eukaryotes is generally limited to organisms whose genomes have diverged a total of 2% or less. As a result, eukaryotic species that hybridize are almost always classified in the same genus.

In short, what most of us consider "normal" sex—meaning meiosis followed by the reciprocal exchange of homologous halves of genomes, among members of the same species—is unheard of in enormous numbers of organisms. As a result, gene flow in bacteria plays a relatively minor role in homogenizing allele frequencies among populations (Cohan 1994, 1995). The primary consequence of gene exchange in bacteria is that certain populations acquire alleles with high fitness advantages, such as sequences that confer antibiotic resistance.

Based on these data, Lawrence and Ochman (1998) have proposed that acquiring novel alleles through gene exchange is the primary mechanism for speciation in bacteria. Their hypothesis is that gene flow triggers divergence among bacteria populations, even though it prevents divergence among eukaryotes.

Work continues on the task of creating a workable species concept for bacteria and on measuring the rate of recombination in natural populations of these organisms. Exploring the mechanisms of speciation in bacteria is an exciting frontier in speciation research.

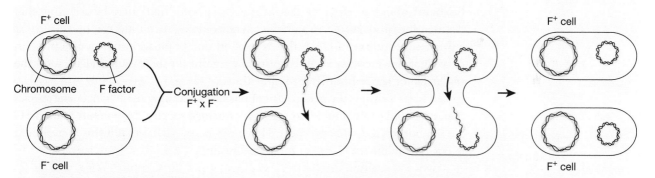

FIGURE 12.1 Genetic recombination in bacteria *Escherichia coli* cells with an extrachromosomal loop of DNA called an F (for fertility) factor can engage in recombination. The process starts when cells with F factors form conjugation tubes with F⁻ cells. A copy of the F factor migrates through the conjugation tube, converting the recipient cell from F⁻ to F⁺. Occasionally F factors will integrate into the chromosome. These integrated sequences can later leave the chromosome. When they do, they frequently take chromosomal sequences (that is, new genes) with them. In this way, F factors can transfer alleles between bacterial chromosomes.

monophyly. Monophyletic groups are defined as taxa or suites of taxa that contain all of the known descendants of a single common ancestor (Figure 12.2).

Under the phylogenetic species concept (PSC), species are identified by estimating the phylogeny of closely related populations and finding the smallest monophyletic groups. On a tree like this, species form the tips. For example, the taxa labeled A–J in Figure 12.2 are the smallest monophyletic groups on the tree and represent distinct species.

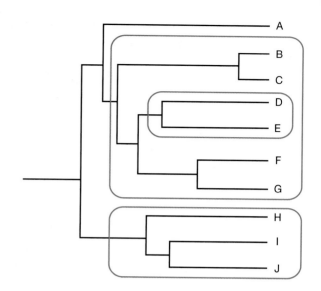

Figure 12.2   Monophyletic groups   The taxa labeled A–J on the tips of this phylogeny may represent any taxonomic level ranging from populations to phyla. The groups that are circled on this phylogenetic tree are all monophyletic. Note that monophyletic groups can be nested—one inside another—and that there are many other monophyletic subgroups in this clade besides the ones that are circled.

The rationale behind the PSC is that traits can only distinguish populations on a phylogeny if the populations have diverged from one another in isolation. Put another way, to be called separate species under the PSC, populations must have been evolutionarily independent long enough for diagnostic traits to emerge. The appeal of this approach is that it is testable: Species are named on the basis of statistically significant differences in the traits used to estimate the phylogeny.

The problem comes with putting this criterion into practice. Carefully constructed phylogenies are available for only a handful of groups thus far. Also, many biologists object to the idea that a "species-specific trait" may be anything that distinguishes populations in a phylogenetic context. Such traits can be as trivial as a single substitution in DNA that is fixed in one population but not in another, or a slight but measurable and statistically significant increase in hairiness on the underside of leaves in different populations.

Each species concept has advantages and disadvantages.

Estimates vary, but the general opinion is that instituting the phylogenetic species concept could easily double the number of named species. Proponents of the PSC are not bothered by that prospect. They respond by saying that if this increase did occur, it would merely reflect biological reality.

The Morphospecies Concept

Paleontologists define species on the basis of morphological differences among fossils. When rigorous tests of reproductive isolation or well-estimated phylogenies are lacking, as they usually are, botanists and zoologists working on extant species do the same. The great advantage of the morphospecies concept is that it is so widely applicable. But when it is not applied carefully, species definitions can become arbitrary and idiosyncratic. In the worst-case scenario, species designations made by different investigators are not comparable.

Paleontologists have to work around other restrictions when identifying species. Fossil species that differed in color or the anatomy of soft tissues cannot be distinguished. Neither can populations that are similar in morphology but were strongly divergent in traits like songs, temperature or drought tolerance, habitat use, or courtship displays. These are called **cryptic species**.

Given these limitations, is the morphospecies concept still useful? Specifically, are the species we identify in the fossil record analogous to those we recognize today, using much larger suites of characters?

Jeremy Jackson and Alan Cheetham (1990, 1994) have performed the most careful analysis to date of the morphological species concept. Jackson and Cheetham study speciation in fossil forms of the colonial, marine-dwelling invertebrates called cheilostome Bryozoa. (The Cheilostomata is an order in the animal phylum Bryozoa.) Accordingly, they set out to check a critical assumption in their work: that the fossil morphospecies they have named conform to genetically differentiated species of bryozoans living today (Figure 12.3).

Jackson and Cheetham's first task was to establish that the skeletal measurements used to distinguish fossil morphospecies have a genetic basis. It is possible that these skeletal characteristics vary among bryozoan species simply because of environmental differences. To test this hypothesis, the researchers collected embryos from several extant cheilostomes and raised them in the same environment: a shallow-water habitat in the Caribbean. When they measured skeletal characters in the full-grown individuals, all but nine of the 507 offspring they raised were assigned to the correct morphospecies (that of their parents). This confirmed that the species-specific characters have a genetic basis. Then, in the critical experiment, Jackson and Cheetham surveyed variation in proteins isolated from eight species in three different genera. They found unique types of proteins in each of the named morphospecies. This result indicates that strong genetic divergence has occurred, and that no gene flow is occurring between the populations. Jackson and Cheetham interpreted these experiments as evidence that morphospecies, at least in Bryozoa, correspond to independent evolutionary units.

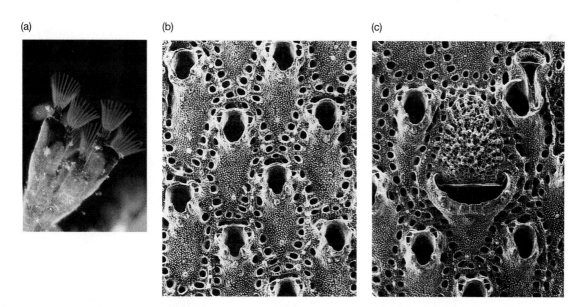

(a) (b) (c)

FIGURE 12.3 Morphological characters used to distinguish morphospecies in cheilostome Bryozoa Living colony members are shown in photo (a). (Kjell B. Sandved/Butterfly Alphabet, Inc.) The enlarged photos show the skeletons of *Stylopoma spongites* (b) and *Metrarabdotos tenue* (c). Each colony member occupies one of the long chambers that have an orifice near the top. To distinguish morphospecies in these genera, Jackson and Cheetham (1994) measured traits like orifice length and width and the number of pores present per 0.2mm square. (b, c: Smithsonian Institution Photo Services)

Applying Species Concepts: The Case of the Red Wolf

Although it is probably unrealistic to insist on a single, all-purpose criterion for identifying species (Endler 1989), the major species concepts that have been proposed are productive when applied in appropriate situations. Consider, for example, how different species definitions have informed the controversy over the red wolf (Wayne and Gittleman 1995).

The red wolf, *Canis rufus,* is a member of the dog family native to the southeastern United States (Figure 12.4). Due to widespread hunting and clearing of forest habitats, its population had dwindled to a mere handful of individuals by the early 1970s. Many of the animals that were left showed characteristics typical of coyotes (*Canis latrans*), which started to become abundant in the wolf's range in the 1930s. This morphological similarity suggested that wolves and coyotes were hybridizing extensively. Fortunately, biologists from the U.S. Fish and Wildlife Service were able to capture 14 red wolves that apparently had no coyote traits before the population went extinct in the wild. These animals bred readily in captivity, and now several hundred red wolves await reintroduction to protected habitats in the wild.

Under the BSC, however, the extensive hybridization with coyotes made the species status of the red wolf questionable. Are red wolves reproductively isolated, evolutionarily independent units? Or are they actually a population of hybrids between the gray wolf (*Canis lupus*) and coyote? Ronald Nowak (1979, 1992) studied a large series of skull and dental characters and showed that red wolves collected before 1930 were a clearly identifiable morphospecies. These individuals had characteristics intermediate between gray wolves and coyotes. Because his data showed that animals collected after 1930 were much more similar to coyotes, Nowak suggested that hybridization was a recent phenomenon caused by the expansion of the coyote population, and the inability of wolves to find mates when their population dwindled. His conclusion was that red wolves clearly qualify as a species.

Genetic studies using DNA extracted from the captive population and from wolf pelts collected before 1930 told a different story, however. Surveys of mitochondrial DNA variation and alleles at 10 microsatellite loci showed no diagnostic (that is, no species-specific) differences between red wolves and coyotes (Wayne and Jenks 1991; Roy et al. 1994; Reich et al. 1999). Instead, the genetic data strongly supported the

Figure 12.4 **The red wolf** (Barbara von Hoffman/ Animals Animals/Earth Scenes)

hypothesis that red wolves are a hybrid between gray wolves and coyotes, and have no unique genetic characteristics of their own. This analysis implies that morphological data are simply not informative in this case, and that the red wolf's intermediate characteristics are the result of hybridization and not independent evolution. Under the PSC as well as the BSC, red wolves are not a distinct species.

Reliable criteria for identifying species are essential for preserving biodiversity.

The fate of the red wolf remains to be decided. The genetic research suggests that other species may be a higher priority for public monies committed to preserving biodiversity, and that the reintroduction program's greatest value may lie in bringing a top predator back into the ecosystem of North America's southern woodlands. Employing several criteria for identifying species can be a productive approach in clarifying conservation and evolutionary issues.

12.2   Mechanisms of Isolation

Having explored different criteria for identifying species, we now consider how species form. Speciation can be analyzed as a three-stage process: an initial step that isolates populations, a second step that results in divergence in traits such as mating tactics or habitat use, and a final step that produces reproductive isolation. In this section, we consider how physical separation or changes in chromosome complements can reduce gene flow. Once gene flow is dramatically reduced or ceases, evolutionary isolation occurs and speciation is initiated. In Section 12.3, we ask how genetic drift and natural selection, in combination with mutation, can cause populations to diverge; in Section 12.4, we consider how natural selection can complete the speciation process by causing reproductive isolation.

Physical Isolation as a Barrier to Gene Flow

In Chapter 6, we introduced migration as gene flow between populations and developed models showing that migration tends to homogenize gene frequencies and reduce the differentiation of populations. Using the example of water snakes from mainland and island habitats in Lake Erie, we also introduced the idea of a balance between migration and natural selection. Recall that experiments had shown a selective advantage for unbanded snakes on island habitats. But because migration of banded forms from the mainland occurs regularly, and because banded and unbanded forms subsequently interbreed, the island populations did not completely diverge from mainland forms. Migration continually introduced alleles for bandedness, even though selection tended to eliminate them from the island populations.

Now consider a thought experiment: What would happen if changes in shoreline habitats or lake currents effectively stopped the migration of banded forms from the mainland to the islands? The island populations would then be isolated from the mainland population. Gene flow would stop and the migration–selection balance would tip. The island population would be free to differentiate as a consequence of mutation, natural selection, and drift. These forces would act on them independently of the forces acting on mainland forms.

The speciation process begins when gene flow is disrupted and populations become genetically isolated.

This scenario illustrates a classical theory for how speciation begins, called the **allopatric model**. This theory was developed by Ernst Mayr (1942, 1963). One of Mayr's most important hypotheses is that speciation is especially likely to occur in small populations that become isolated on the periphery of a species' range, such as the island forms of water snakes. Population genetic models have shown

Geographic isolation produces genetic isolation.

that speciation in peripheral populations can occur rapidly when selection for divergence is strong and gene flow is low (García-Ramos and Kirkpatrick 1997).

Physical isolation is obviously an effective barrier to gene flow, and undoubtedly has been an important trigger for the second stage in the speciation process: genetic and ecological divergence. Geographic isolation can come about through dispersal and colonization of new habitats or through vicariance events, where an existing range is split by a new physical barrier (Figure 12.5).

Geographic Isolation Through Dispersal and Colonization

One of the most spectacular radiations in the class Insecta is also a superb example of geographic isolation through dispersal. The Hawaiian drosophilids, close relatives of the fruit flies we have encountered before, number over 500 named species in two genera and an estimated 350 species yet to be formally described and named.

The ecological diversification in this group is also unprecedented. Hawaiian flies can be found from sea level to montane habitats and from dry scrub to rainforests. Food sources, especially the plant material used as the medium for egg laying and larval development, vary widely among species. One of the Hawaiian flies even lays its eggs in spiders, while another has aquatic larvae. In addition, many species have elaborate traits, such as patterning on their wings or modified head shapes, that are used in combat or courtship displays (Figure 12.6).

Populations can become geographically isolated when individuals colonize a new habitat.

How did this enormous diversity come to be? The leading explanation is called the **founder hypothesis**. Many of the Hawaiian flies are island endemics, meaning that their range is restricted to a single island in the archipelago. The founder hypothesis maintains that this endemism results when small populations of flies, or perhaps even single gravid females, disperse to new habitats or islands. As a result, the colonists found new populations that are cut off from the ancestral species. Divergence begins after the founding event, resulting from drift and selection on the genes involved in courtship displays and habitat use.

The logic of the founder hypothesis is compelling, but do we have evidence, other than endemism, that these events actually occurred? Because the geology of

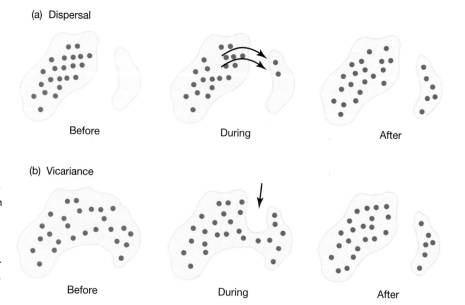

(a) Dispersal

Before   During   After

(b) Vicariance

Before   During   After

Figure 12.5 Isolation by dispersal and vicariance In the diagram of dispersal (a), the arrows indicate movement of individuals. In the diagram of vicariance (b), the arrows indicate an encroaching physical feature such as a river, glacier, lava flow, or new habitat.

Figure 12.6   Hawaiian *Drosophila*   As these photos of *Drosophila nigribasis, D. macrothrix,* and *D. suzukii* (left to right) show, the *Drosophila* found in Hawaii are remarkably diverse in body size, wing coloration, and other traits. (Kenneth Y. Kaneshiro, University of Hawaii)

the Hawaiian islands is well known, the hypothesis makes a strong prediction about speciation patterns in flies. The Hawaiian islands are produced by a volcanic hot spot under the Pacific Ocean. The hot spot is stationary, but periodically spews magma up and out onto the Pacific plate. After islands form, continental drift carries them to the north and west (see Figure 12.7a). As time passes, the volcanic cones gradually erode down to atolls and submarine mountains.

The founder hypothesis makes two predictions based on these facts: (1) Closely related species should almost always be found on adjacent islands, and (2) at

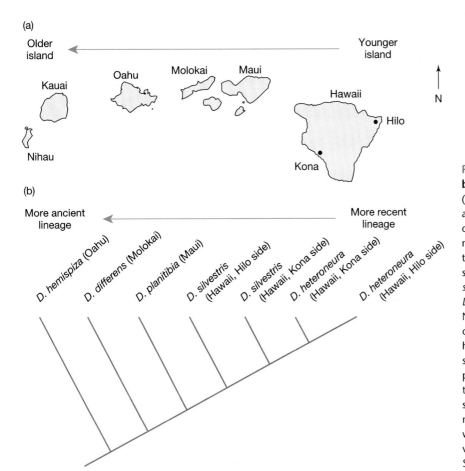

Figure 12.7   Evidence for speciation by dispersal and colonization events (a) The Hawaiian islands are part of an archipelago that stretches from the island of Hawaii to the Emperor Seamounts near Siberia. The youngest landform in the chain is the island of Hawaii, which still has active volcanoes. (b) *Drosophila silvestris, D. heteroneura, D. planitibia,* and *D. differens* are a closely related group. Note that the older-to-younger sequence of branches on the phylogeny shown here corresponds to the older-younger sequence of island formation shown in part (a). This pattern is consistent with the hypothesis that at least some of the speciation events in this group were the result of island hopping. (The phylogeny was estimated from data on sequence divergence in mitochondrial DNA; see De-Salle and Giddings 1986.)

least some sequences of branching events should correspond to the sequence in which islands were formed. Rob DeSalle and Val Giddings (1986) used sequence differences in mitochondrial DNA to estimate the phylogeny of four closely related species, and found exactly these patterns. The most recent species are found on the youngest islands, and several of the branching events correspond to the order of island formation (Figure 12.7b). This is strong evidence that dispersal to new habitats can trigger speciation.

As a mechanism for producing physical isolation and triggering speciation, the founder hypothesis is relevant to a wide variety of habitats in addition to oceanic islands. Hot springs, deep sea vents, fens, bogs, caves, mountaintops, and lakes or ponds with restricted drainage also represent habitat islands. Dispersal to novel environments is a general mechanism for initiating speciation.

Geographic Isolation Through Vicariance

Populations can also become geographically isolated when a species' former range is split into two or more distinct areas.

Vicariance events split a species' distribution into two or more isolated ranges and discourage or prevent gene flow between them. There are many possible mechanisms of vicariance, ranging from slow processes such as the rise of a mountain range or a long-term drying trend that fragments forests, to rapid events such as a mile-wide lava flow that bisects a snail population.

Nancy Knowlton and colleagues have been studying a classical vicariance event: the recent separation of marine organisms on either side of Central America. We know from geological evidence that the Isthmus of Panama closed (and the land bridge between South and North America opened) about 3 million years ago. Is this enough time for speciation to occur?

Knowlton et al. (1993) recently looked at a series of snapping shrimp (*Altheus*) populations from either side of the isthmus (Figure 12.8a). The populations they sampled appeared to represent seven pairs of closely related morphospecies, with one member of each pair found on each side of the land bridge. The phylogeny of these shrimp, estimated from differences in their mitochondrial DNA sequences, confirms this hypothesis (Figure 12.8b). The species pairs from either side of the isth-

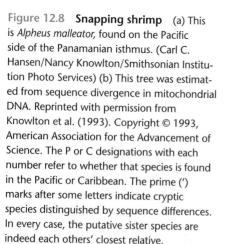

Figure 12.8 Snapping shrimp (a) This is *Alpheus malleator,* found on the Pacific side of the Panamanian isthmus. (Carl C. Hansen/Nancy Knowlton/Smithsonian Institution Photo Services) (b) This tree was estimated from sequence divergence in mitochondrial DNA. Reprinted with permission from Knowlton et al. (1993). Copyright © 1993, American Association for the Advancement of Science. The P or C designations with each number refer to whether that species is found in the Pacific or Caribbean. The prime (') marks after some letters indicate cryptic species distinguished by sequence differences. In every case, the putative sister species are indeed each others' closest relative.

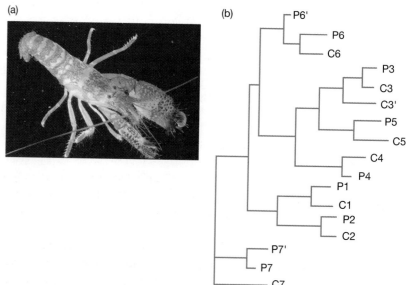

mus, reputed to be sisters on the basis of morphology, are indeed each others' closest relatives. This is consistent with the prediction from the vicariance hypothesis.

Further, when Knowlton et al. put males and females of various species pairs together in aquaria and watched for aggressive or pairing interactions, the researchers found a strong correlation between the degree of genetic distance between species pairs and how interested the shrimp were in courting. Males and females from species with greater genetic divergence, indicative of longer isolation times, were less interested in one another. Finally, almost none of the pairs that formed during the courtship experiments produced fertile clutches. This last observation confirms that the Pacific and Caribbean populations are indeed separate species under all three of the species concepts we have reviewed.

One of the most interesting aspects of the study, though, was that the data contradicted a prediction made by the vicariance hypothesis. If the land bridge had formed rapidly, we would expect that genetic distances and degrees of reproductive isolation would be identical in all seven species pairs. This is not the case. For example, DNA sequence divergence between species pairs varied from about 6.5% to over 19%.

What is going on? Because it is unlikely that the land bridge popped up all at once, a prediction of identical divergence would be naïve. Instead, as the land rose and the ocean gradually split and retreated on either side, different shrimp populations would become isolated in a staggered fashion, depending on the depth of water each species occupied and how efficiently their larvae dispersed. The ranges of deeper-water species, or those with less-motile larvae, would be cut in two first. Consistent with this idea, the species numbered 6 and 7 in Figure 12.8b inhabit deep water, while the species numbered 1–4 live in shallower water (see Knowlton and Weigt 1998). Note also that the degree of genetic divergence in the species pairs numbered 1–4 is very similar. These are the lowest values observed, perhaps indicating "the final break" between the two oceans.

Changes in Chromosomes as a Barrier to Gene Flow

If a mutation results in a large-scale change in an individual's chromosomes, the event may cause rapid or even instantaneous isolation between the individual's descendants and the parental population. In Chapter 4, for example, we pointed out that polyploidization can result in instant reproductive isolation because of incompatibilities between gametes with different chromosome numbers. Purely on the basis of its distribution in plants, polyploidization has to be considered an important mechanism for initiating speciation.

Changes in chromosome number isolate populations genetically.

We need to introduce a distinction, however, between two types of polyploidy. Polyploids whose chromosomes originate from the same ancestral species are called autopolyploids. Polyploids that result from hybridization events between different species are called allopolyploids. Although no exact figures are available, allopolyploids are thought to be significantly more common than autopolyploids (Soltis and Soltis 1993). We examine allopolyploids in more detail in Section 12.4, when we consider gene flow between closely related populations and the third stage in the speciation process.

How important is polyploidization as a mechanism of speciation's first stage? Unfortunately, estimates for the frequency of auto- and allopolyploid species are rarely done in a phylogenetic context, where we can infer which ploidy is ancestral and get precise counts for the number of times that polyploidization has occurred. But under the assumption that any plant with a haploid number of chromosomes (symbolized n) greater than 14 is polyploid, Verne Grant (1981) estimated that 43% of species in the flowering plant class Dicotyledonae and 58% of species in the flowering plant class Monocotyledonae are the descendants of ancestors that underwent polyploidy. Jane Masterson (1994) came up with an even higher estimate. She showed that cell size correlates strongly with chromosome number in extant plants, and then measured the size of cells in plant fossils that lived early in the radiation of flowering plants. Her data support the hypothesis that $n = 7$ or 9 or lower is the ancestral haploid number in angiosperms. If so, then 70% of flowering plants have polyploidy in their history. Polyploidy is also common in mosses and almost the rule in ferns, where 95% of species occur in clades with an ancestral polyploidization event. Grant goes so far as to say that polyploidy "is a characteristic of the plant kingdom" (1981: 289).

Speciation triggered by changes in chromosome number has been especially important in plants.

Changes in chromosome number less drastic than polyploidization may also be important in speciation. For example, Oliver Ryder and colleagues (1989) studied chromosome complements in a series of small African antelopes—called dik-diks—that were being displayed in North American zoos. Although zookeepers traditionally recognized just two species, Ryder's team distinguished three on the basis of chromosome number and form. Further, they were able to show that hybrid offspring between unlike karyotypes are infertile. Their research revealed a cryptic species. Two of the dik-dik species have apparently differentiated on the basis of karyotype.

It is extremely common to find small-scale chromosomal changes like these when the karyotypes of closely related species are compared. Although these mutations could be important in causing genetic divergence between populations (White 1978), much of the extensive work on chromosomal differentiation done to date is merely correlative. That is, many studies have measured chromosome differences in related species and claimed that chromosomal incompatibilities are responsible for genetic isolation. But in many cases, it is likely that the chromosome differences arose after speciation had occurred due to other causes (Patton and Sherwood 1983). Until more causative links are established, we have to be cautious in interpreting the importance of small-scale karyotype differences in speciation.

12.3 Mechanisms of Divergence

Polyploidization, dispersal, and vicariance only create the conditions for speciation. For the event to continue, genetic drift and natural selection have to act on mutations in a way that creates divergence in the isolated populations. In this section we review how drift and selection act on closely related populations once gene flow between them has been reduced or eliminated.

Genetic Drift

In Chapter 6, we introduced population genetic models that quantified the major effects of genetic drift within populations: random fixation of alleles and random loss of alleles. We also reviewed data from a founder event observed by Peter Grant and Rosemary Grant during a study of Darwin's finches in the Galápagos. Their measurements of body size in a flock of colonizing birds confirmed that the founding population was a nonrandom sample of the source population.

Because genetic drift is a sampling process, its effects are most pronounced in small populations. This is important because most species are thought to have originated with low population sizes. Normally, only tiny numbers of individuals are involved in colonization events, and peripheral populations tend to be small. As a consequence, genetic drift has long been hypothesized as the key to speciation's second stage.

Drift can produce rapid genetic divergence in small, isolated populations.

A variety of genetic models have examined how drift might lead to rapid genetic differentiation in small populations (for a recent review, see Templeton 1996). The general message of these models is that small populations that become isolated start out as a nonrandom sample of the ancestral population. Subsequently, other effects of drift—including random loss of alleles and random fixation of existing and new alleles—encourage rapid divergence in the isolated population. In general, though, the overall genetic diversity of the founding populations is not necessarily lower than the source population. Lande (1980, 1981) has shown that when a population is reduced to a small size for a short period of time—the phenomenon known as **bottlenecking**—only very rare alleles tend to be lost due to drift. For genetic diversity to be reduced dramatically, the founding population has to be extremely small.

The role of drift in speciation events is controversial, however. Peter Grant and Rosemary Grant (1996) point out that hundreds of small populations have been introduced to new habitats around the world in the last 150 years due to the action of humans, but that few, if any, dramatic changes in genotypes have resulted because of genetic drift. Although genetic drift once dominated discussions of speciation mechanisms, most evolutionary biologists now take a much more balanced view. Natural selection has also been shown to be an important force promoting the divergence of isolated populations.

Natural Selection

Marked genetic differences have to emerge between closely related populations for speciation to proceed beyond the first stage. Drift almost always plays a role when at least one of the populations is small. But natural selection can also lead to divergence if one of the populations occupies a novel environment.

Selection's role in the second stage of speciation is clearly illustrated by recent research on apple and hawthorn flies. These closely related insect populations are diverging because of natural selection on preferences for a crucial resource: food.

The apple maggot fly, *Rhagoletis pomonella,* is found throughout the northeastern and north central United States (Figure 12.9). The species is a major agricultural pest, causing millions of dollars of damage to apple crops each year. The flies also parasitize the fruits of trees in the hawthorn group (species of *Crataegus*), which are closely related to apples.

Male and female *Rhagoletis* identify their host trees by sight, touch, and smell. Courtship and mating occur on or near the fruits. Females lay eggs in the fruit while it is still on the tree; the eggs hatch within two days and then develop through three larval stages in the same fruit. This takes about a month. After the fruit falls to the ground, the larvae leave and burrow a few inches into the soil. There they pupate after 3–4 days and spend the winter in a resting state called diapause. Most leave this resting stage and emerge as adults the next summer, starting the cycle anew.

Figure 12.9 Apple and hawthorn maggot flies
Apple and hawthorn races of *Rhagoletis pomonella* are indistinguishable to the eye. This is an apple fly. (Guy Bush, Michigan State University, and Jeff Feder, University of Notre Dame)

Apple trees clearly represent a novel food source for *Rhagoletis*. Hawthorn trees and *Rhagoletis* are native to North America, but apple trees were introduced from Europe less than 300 years ago. Our question is this: Are the flies that parasitize apple fruits and hawthorn fruits distinct populations? This hypothesis implies that natural selection, based on a preference for different food sources, has created two distinct races of flies. The contrasting hypothesis is that flies parasitizing hawthorns and apples are members of the same population. This hypothesis predicts that flies on hawthorns and apples interbreed freely, and that selection for exploiting different hosts has not occurred.

The hypothesis of no differentiation actually appears much more likely, because the first stage in speciation has not occurred. The two host trees and fly populations occur together throughout their ranges. Far from being isolated, at some sites hawthorn and apple trees are almost in physical contact. Marked flies have been captured over a mile from the site where they were originally captured, proving that individuals do search widely for appropriate fruit to parasitize. Thus, flies from the same population might simply switch from apple to hawthorn trees and back, based on fruit availability.

To test these two hypotheses, Jeff Feder and colleagues looked at the genetic make-up of flies collected from hawthorns versus apples, using the technique called protein electrophoresis introduced in Chapter 4. Remarkably, they found a clear distinction in the two samples: Flies collected from hawthorns versus apples have statistically significant differences in the frequencies of alleles for six different enzymes (Feder et al. 1988, 1990). This is strong support for the hypothesis that hawthorn and apple flies have diverged and now form distinct populations. Even though the two races look indistinguishable, they are easily differentiated on the basis of their genotypes.

How could this have occurred? Have these flies skipped the first stage in speciation (Box 12.2)? The key is that instead of being isolated by geography or by chromosomal incompatibilities, apple and hawthorn flies are isolated on different host species. In experiments where individuals are given a choice of host plants, apple and hawthorn flies show a strong preference for their own fruit type (Prokopy et al. 1988). Because mating takes place on the fruit, this habitat preference should result in strong nonrandom mating. Feder and colleagues (1994) confirmed this prediction by following marked individuals in the field. They found that matings between hawthorn and apple flies accounted for just 6% of the total observed.

Natural selection can cause populations to diverge even when a small amount of gene flow occurs.

Although host plant fidelity serves as an important barrier to mating, the two populations continue to exchange alleles. To cause the genetic divergence that has been observed, natural selection must overwhelm this gene flow in some way. Feder and co-workers (1997) hypothesized that natural selection for divergence is triggered by a marked difference in when apple and hawthorn fruits ripen. Because hawthorn fruits ripen about three weeks after apples, Feder and colleagues suggested that hawthorn fly larvae are selected to develop rapidly so they can pupate and enter diapause before the ground freezes. In contrast, they predicted that apple fly larvae are selected to develop slowly, so that they avoid emerging from diapause, as adults, before the onset of winter.

To test this hypothesis the researchers collected a large number of pupae from hawthorn fruits, split them into groups, and exposed each sample to 1–5 weeks of warm weather. In each group of pupae, the warm period was followed by a period of cold to simulate winter and then a period of warm temperatures to simulate

Omit

BOX 12.2 **Parapatric and sympatric speciation**

An enduring debate in speciation research has been whether physical isolation is an absolute requirement for populations to diverge, or whether natural selection for divergence can overwhelm gene flow and trigger speciation. Careful genetic modeling suggests that it is possible for populations to diverge even when they remain in physical contact. Joseph Felsenstein (1981) and William Rice (1987) were the first to show that populations can diverge even with low to moderate degrees of gene flow if two important conditions are met: Selection for divergence must be strong, and mate choice must be correlated with the factor that is promoting divergence. Exactly these conditions are met by apple and hawthorn flies, because mating takes place on different host plants.

Parapatric speciation is the other major mode of divergence that does not require physical isolation of populations. In parapatric speciation, strong selection for divergence causes gene frequencies in a continuous population to diverge along a gradient (Figure 12.10). Although theory demonstrates that parapatric divergence is possible (Endler 1977), we still lack well-documented examples in natural populations.

Original range

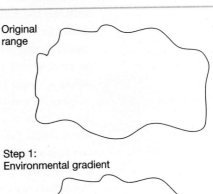

Step 1:
Environmental gradient

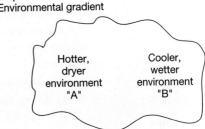

Step 2:
Natural selection favors divergent genotypes

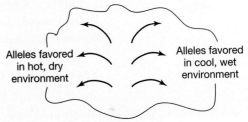

Step 3:
Formation of hybrid zone

Step 4:
Speciation

Figure 12.10 **Parapatric speciation** This diagram illustrates the series of steps involved in a mode of divergence called parapatric ("beside place") speciation.

spring. The last step in the experiment was to collect the individuals that emerged as adults in the "spring" and assay the frequencies of the six allozymes that differ between the hawthorn and apple races. The results for the allele called *Acon-2 95,* shown in Figure 12.11, are typical. This graph shows that the hawthorn race individuals that were exposed to a month of warm days as pupae, and that survived to develop into adults during the spring, had allozyme frequencies similar to those found in apple flies.

This is a remarkable result. It confirms the hypothesis that hawthorn flies making the switch to apples have to develop slowly to stay in diapause through the warm days of late fall and emerge at the correct time in the spring. The experiment also suggests that the six alleles surveyed, or closely linked loci, are responsible for the change in development time. In a single generation, then, the researchers succeeded in replicating the selection events that have produced divergence between the apple race and the hawthorn race in nature over the past 300 years.

The diapause experiment demonstrates that natural selection is responsible for strong divergence between *R. pomonella* populations even in the face of gene flow. Many biologists now consider hawthorn and apple flies to be incipient species. This means that the populations have clearly diverged and are largely, but not completely, isolated in terms of gene flow.

Finally, it is important to recognize that apple maggot flies are by no means an isolated case. As Table 12.1 shows, many other examples of divergence due to selection on food or habitat choice, primarily in insects and fish, are being documented.

Sexual Selection

Sexual selection acts on characters involved in mate choice. Changes in sexual selection may isolate populations and cause rapid divergence.

Sexual selection results from differences among individuals in their ability to obtain mates. This is considered a form of selection distinct from natural selection and was the focus of Chapter 9. Population genetic models have shown that changes in the way that a population of sexual organisms chooses or acquires mates can lead to rapid differentiation from ancestral populations (Fisher 1958; Lande 1981, 1982). For example, if a new mutation led females in a certain population of barn swallows to prefer males with iridescent feathers instead of preferring males with long tails, then sexual selection would trigger rapid divergence. The key point is that sexual selection promotes divergence efficiently because it affects gene flow directly.

In the Hawaiian *Drosophila,* for example, sexual selection is thought to have been a key factor in promoting divergence among isolated populations. Many of

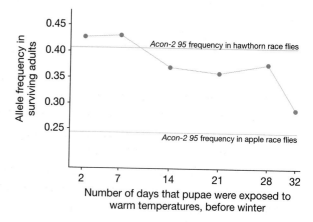

Figure 12.11 **Allele frequency changes caused by differences in temperatures experienced by apple maggot flies** This graph plots the frequencies of an allele called *Acon-2 95* in populations of hawthorn maggot fly pupae that survived to emerge as adults, as a function of the number of days of warm temperatures the pupae experienced. In the population that experienced an extended period of warm days—similar to the regime experienced by apple flies in nature—allele frequencies approximated those observed in natural populations of apple flies. From Feder et al. (1997). Copyright © 1997, National Academy of Sciences, USA.

Table 12.1   **Speciation in action**

The right-most column in this table furnishes citations for recent studies on populations that are diverging due to differences in habitat use or resource use.

Species	Type of divergence that is underway	Citation
Lake whitefish	Populations of dwarf versus normal-sized individuals	Lu, G. and L. Bernatchez. 1999. *Evolution* 53: 1491–1505.
Three-spine sticklebacks (freshwater fish)	Benthic (bottom-dwelling) versus limnetic (open-water dwelling) populations	Hatfield, T. and D. Schluter. 1999. *Evolution* 53: 866–873.
Sockeye salmon	Sea-run versus lake-dwelling populations	Wood, C. C., and C. J. Foote. 1996. *Evolution* 50: 1265–1279.
Pea aphids	Different host plants	Via, S. 1999. *Evolution* 53: 1446-1457.
Army worms	Different host plants	Pashley, D. P. 1988. *Evolution* 42: 93–102.
Soapberry bugs	Different host plants	Carroll, S., H. Dingle, and S. P. Klassen. 1997. *Evolution* 51: 1182–1188.
Goldenrod ball gallmakers	Different host plants	Brown, J. M., W. G. Abrahamson, and P. A. Way. 1996. *Evolution* 50: 777–786.
Blueberry and apple maggot flies	Different host plants	Feder, J. L., C. A. Chilcote, and G.L. Bush. 1989. *Entomological Experiments and Applications* 51: 113–123.
Heliconius butterflies	Different habitats and types of warning coloration	McMillan, W. O., C. D. Jiggins, and J. Mallet. 1997. *Proceedings of the National Academy of Sciences, USA* 94: 8628–8633.

these flies court and copulate in aggregations called leks. In this mating system, males fight for small display territories and dance or sing for females, who visit the lek to select mates. Lek breeding systems are often associated with elaborate male characters, which vary widely among Hawaiian flies. Does this imply that sexual selection has been important in speciation?

The evidence in favor of the hypothesis is tantalizing, though not yet conclusive. For example, males of *Drosophila heteroneura* have wide, hammer-shaped heads (Figure 12.12a). Because males butt heads when fighting to stake out a courting arena on the lek, the unusual head shape appears to be a product of sexual selection (Kaneshiro and Boake, 1987). In contrast, males and females of *D. heteroneura*'s closest relative, *Drosophila silvestris,* have heads that are similar in size and shape to female *D. heteroneura* (Figure 12.12b). Instead of head-butting, *D. silvestris* males fight on the lek by rearing up and grappling with one another. Both species are endemic to the island of Hawaii.

These facts are consistent with the following scenario:

1. In the ancestor to *silvestris* and *heteroneura,* males had normal heads, courted on leks, and fought for display territories by rearing up and grappling. Females chose the males who were most successful in combat.

2. A mutation occurred in an isolated subpopulation, which led to males with a new fighting behavior: head-butting.

3. The mutant males were more efficient in combat on leks and experienced increased reproductive success, because females still preferred to mate with males who won the most contests.

(a)   (b)

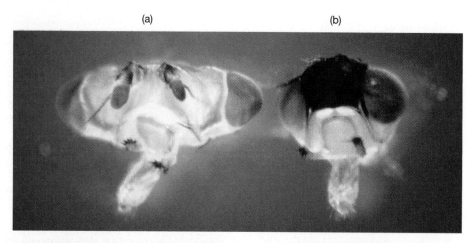

Figure 12.12 **Contrasting head shapes and fighting strategies in Hawaiian *Drosophila*** (a) Male *Drosophila heteroneura* have wide heads. As the photo at the bottom left shows, they butt heads to establish display territories on a lek. (b) Male *Drosophila silvestris* have normally shaped heads. They fight over display territories by rearing up and grappling with one another. (Kenneth Y. Kaneshiro, University of Hawaii)

4. The mutation increased to fixation, and additional mutations led to the elaboration of the trait over time. For example, it is possible that mutations leading to widely spaced eyes were favored because they made them less prone to damage during head-butting fights.

As a result of this sequence of events, strong divergence among the populations would occur due to sexual selection. The differentiation between populations would be based on the strategies and weaponry employed in male–male combat and female choice.

Formulating this type of plausible sequence is a productive way to generate testable hypotheses, but it does not substitute for genetic models, experiments, or other types of evidence. For example, consider recent work by Christine Boake and associates (1997) that tested two assumptions of the sexual selection scenario outlined above. These researchers staged a series of tests in the laboratory to assess whether female *D. heteroneura* prefer to mate with especially wide-headed males. They also staged male–male contests, to test the prediction that males with wider heads are more likely to win fights. As Figure 12.13 shows, both patterns were strongly supported by their data. The results increase our confidence that sexual selection has been a prominent cause of divergence in these populations.

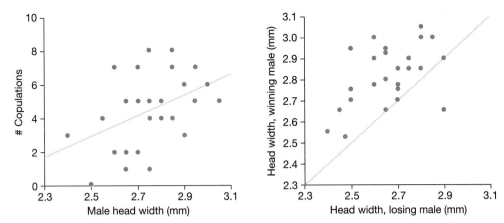

Figure 12.13 **Evidence for sexual selection on head width in *Drosophila heteroneura***
The graph on the left shows the number of copulations achieved by male *Drosophila heteroneura* when paired with a series of different females, as a function of their head width. The best-fit line indicates that there is a positive relationship between copulation success and head width. The graph on the right compares the head width of winning versus losing males in staged contests. The straight line divides the plot into sections indicating that the wider-headed male won (upper left half) or the narrower-headed male won (lower right half). From Boake et al. (1997). Copyright © 1997, National Academy of Sciences, USA.

12.4 Secondary Contact *real*

We have portrayed speciation as a three-step process that begins with the isolation of populations and continues when selection, mutation, and drift create divergence. A third step may occur if recently diverged populations come back into contact and have the opportunity to interbreed. Hybridization events between recently diverged species are especially common in plants. For example, over 700 of the plant species that have been introduced to the British Isles in the recent past have hybridized with native species at least occasionally, and about half of these native/non-native matings produce fertile offspring (Abbott 1992). Ten percent of all bird species also hybridize regularly and produce fertile offspring (Grant and Grant 1992).

    In at least some cases, the fate of these hybrid offspring determines the outcome of the speciation event. Will the hybrids thrive, interbreed with each of the parental populations, and eventually erase the divergence between them? Or will hybrids have new characteristics and create a distinct population of their own? And what happens if hybrid offspring have reduced fitness relative to the parental populations?

Hybridization occurs when recently diverged populations interbreed.

Reinforcement

The geneticist Theodosius Dobzhansky (1937) formulated an important hypothesis about speciation's third stage. Dobzhanzky reasoned that if populations have diverged sufficiently in allopatry, their hybrid offspring should have markedly reduced fitness relative to individuals in the parental population. Because producing hybrid offspring reduces a parent's fitness in this case, there should be strong natural selection favoring assortative mating. That is, selection should favor individuals that choose mates only from the same population. Selection that reduces the frequency of hybrids in this way is called **reinforcement**. If reinforcement occurs, it would finalize the speciation process by producing complete reproductive isolation.

The reinforcement hypothesis predicts that some sort of mechanism of pre-mating isolation will evolve in closely related species that come into contact and hybridize. Selection might favor mutations that alter aspects of mate choice, genetic compatibility, or life history (such as the timing of breeding). Divergence in these traits prevents fertilization from occurring and results in **prezygotic isolation** of the two species. But populations can also remain genetically isolated in the absence of reinforcement if hybrid offspring are sterile or infertile. This possibility is known as **postzygotic isolation**.

Reinforcement is a type of selection that leads to assortative mating and the prezygotic isolation of populations.

Some of the best data on prezygotic isolation and the reinforcement hypothesis have been assembled and analyzed by Jerry Coyne and Allen Orr (1997). Coyne and Orr examined data from a large series of sister-species pairs in the genus *Drosophila*. Some of these species pairs live in allopatry and others in sympatry. Coyne and Orr's data set included estimates of genetic distance, calculated from differences in allozyme frequencies, along with measurements of the degree of pre- and postzygotic isolation. When they plotted the degree of prezygotic isolation against genetic distance, which they assumed correlates at least roughly with time of divergence, they found a striking result: Prezygotic isolation evolves much faster in sympatric species pairs than it does in allopatric species pairs (Figure 12.14). This is exactly the prediction made by the reinforcement hypothesis.

These laboratory experiments with *Drosophila* are some of the best evidence we have in support of the reinforcement hypothesis. In contrast, field studies that have looked for evidence of reinforcement in hybridizing populations have produced mixed results. Genetic models exploring reinforcement's effectiveness have generally been unconvincing as well (see Butlin 1987). Although Dobzhansky considered reinforcement as a universal stage in speciation, this view is probably overstated. A new consensus is emerging, based on a series of recent studies like

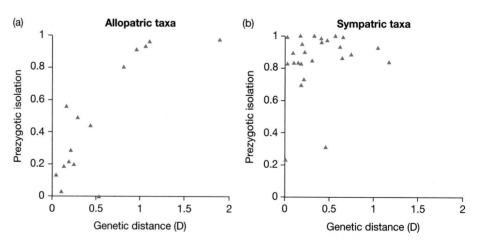

Figure 12.14 Prezygotic isolation in allopatric versus sympatric species pairs of *Drosophila* These graphs (Coyne and Orr 1997) plot degree of prezygotic isolation versus genetic distance in a variety of sister-species pairs from the genus *Drosophila*. Prezygotic isolation is estimated from mate-choice tests performed in the laboratory. A value of 0 indicates that different populations freely interbreed (0% prezygotic isolation) and 1 indicates no interbreeding (100% prezygotic isolation). Genetic distance is estimated from differences in allele frequencies found in allozyme surveys. Sibling species with the same degree of overall genetic divergence show much more prezygotic isolation if they live in sympatry.

Coyne and Orr's: Reinforcement can and does occur, but it is not essential to completing speciation (Butlin 1995; Noor 1995).

Hybridization

Reinforcement should occur when hybrid offspring have reduced fitness. But what happens to hybrid offspring that survive and reproduce well? Their fate has important consequences for speciation, and practical applications as well. For example, because several crop plants have close relatives that are serious weeds, evolutionary biologists have expressed concern about the release of genetically engineered crop plants to the wild. What benefit comes from introducing a gene for herbicide resistance into a crop species if hybridization quickly carries the allele into a closely related weed population?

Using an experimental system featuring crop sorghum (*Sorghum bicolor*) and johnsongrass (*S. halepense*), Paul Arriola and Norman Ellstrand (1996) recently confirmed that this scenario could occur. Sorghum is one of the world's most important crops; johnsongrass is a serious weed. Arriola and Ellstrand sowed a field with crop sorghum seeds that carried a distinctive allozyme marker and planted seedlings of johnsongrass at various distances nearby (Figure 12.15a). After the johnsongrass plants had set seed, Arriola and Ellstrand harvested them and raised the progeny. Gel electrophoresis of proteins isolated from these first-generation (F_1) plants confirmed that the allozyme marker had been carried by crop sorghum

Biologists are concerned about gene flow between genetically modified crops and closely related weeds.

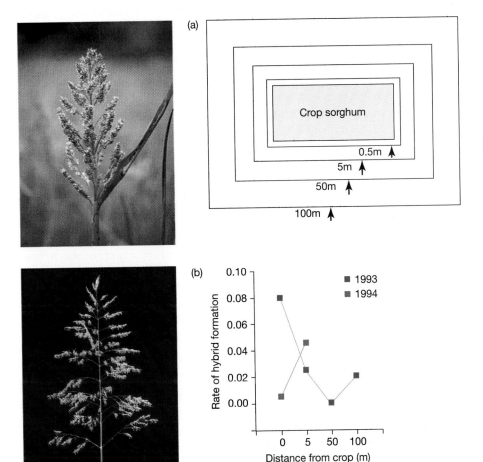

Figure 12.15 **Gene flow from crops to weeds through hybridization** The photographs show the flowering heads of crop sorghum (top) and johnsongrass (bottom). (a) This diagram shows the planting scheme employed by Arriola and Ellstrand (1996). Potted seedlings of johnsongrass were placed along each of four rectangles, as shown in the diagram. (The diagram is not to scale.) (b) In this graph, the percentage of johnsongrass plants that produced at least one hybrid offspring is plotted versus the distance that johnsongrass seedlings were growing from the edge of the crop. [Photos: (top) Michael P. Gadomski/Photo Researchers, Inc.; (bottom) Nigel Cattlin/Holt Studios International/ Photo Researchers, Inc.]

pollen to johnsongrass plants. Significant gene flow had taken place in the crop-to-weed direction (Figure 12.15b).

Creation of New Species Through Hybridization

The concern about sorghum–johnsongrass hybrids illustrates a general point: Hybrid offspring do not necessarily have lower fitness than their parents. If crop sorghum plants were transformed with a gene for herbicide resistance and these individuals hybridized with johnsongrass, it is conceivable that a few of the offspring would end up with a favorable combination of traits from each parent. The hybrids might receive the allele for herbicide resistance from the crop parent, but a suite of genes that cause rapid growth from the weedy parent. This is the basis for concern about "superweeds." And this concern is not idle. Both classical and recent studies have confirmed that interspecific hybridization is a major source of evolutionary novelty in plants (Stebbins 1950; Grant 1981; Abbott 1992; Rieseberg 1997). In newly colonized environments or in certain novel habitats, hybrid offspring may have higher fitness than either of the parental species. Will these hybrid populations occupy the new environment and become distinct species?

A recent experimental study of plant hybridization, conducted in Loren Rieseberg's lab (1996), has actually duplicated a natural hybridization event that led to speciation. These researchers worked with three annual sunflower species native to the American southwest: *Helianthus annuus, H. petiolaris,* and *H. anomalous.* Based on morphological and chromosome studies, it had long been thought that *H. anomalous* originated in a hybridization event between *H. annuus* and *H. petiolaris.*

To test this hypothesis rigorously, Rieseberg and co-workers crossed individuals of *H. annuus* and *H. petiolaris* to produce three lines of F_1 hybrids. They then either mated each line back to *H. annuus* (this is called a backcross) or sib-mated the individuals for four additional generations. As a result, each experiment line underwent a different sequence and combination of backcrossing and sib-mating. This protocol simulated different types of matings that may have occurred when populations of *H. annuus* and *H. petiolaris* hybridized naturally.

At the end of the experiment, Rieseberg and colleagues surveyed the three hybrid populations genetically. Their goal was to determine how similar the hybrids were to each other and to *H. anomalous* individuals. To make this comparison possible, the researchers mapped a large series of species-specific DNA sequences, called randomly amplified polymorphic DNA (RAPD) markers, in the two parental species. These markers allowed the researchers to determine which alleles from the two parental species were present in the three experimental hybrid populations and compare them to alleles present in *H. anomalous.* The results were striking: The three independently derived experimental hybrids and the natural hybrid shared an overwhelming majority of markers. The experimental and natural hybrids were almost identical.

Researchers have experimentally recreated a speciation event that occurred naturally via hybridization.

To interpret this result, Rieseberg and co-workers contend that only certain alleles from *H. petiolis* and *H. anuus* work in combination, and that other hybrid types are inviable or have reduced fitness. The genetic composition of the hybrids quickly sorted out into a very similar, favorable combination. Even more remarkable, this combination of alleles was nearly the same as that produced by a natural hybridization event that occurred thousands of years ago. This puts an interesting twist on speciation's third stage: Secondary contact and gene flow between recently diverged species can result in the formation of a new, third, species.

Hybrid Zones

A **hybrid zone** is a region where interbreeding between diverged populations occurs and hybrid offspring are frequent. Hybrid zones are produced by two distinct situations (Hewitt 1988): (1) After secondary contact between species that have diverged in allopatry, a hybrid zone can form where they meet and interbreed, and (2) during parapatric speciation, a hybrid zone can develop between populations that are diverging (see Box 12.2).

We have already seen that it is possible for hybrid offspring to have lower or higher fitness than purebred offspring, with very different consequences (reinforcement of parental forms or the formation of a new species). Research on hybrid zones has confirmed that a third outcome is also possible. Frequently no measurable differences can be found between the fitnesses of hybrid and pure offspring. The following three possibilities dictate the size, shape, and longevity of hybrid zones (Endler 1977; Barton and Hewitt 1985; see Table 12.2):

- When hybrid and parental forms are equally fit, the hybrid zone is wide. Individuals with hybrid traits are found at high frequency at the center of the zone and progressively lower frequencies with increasing distance. In this type of hybrid zone, the dynamics of gene-frequency change are dominated by drift. The width of the zone is a function of two factors: how far individuals from each population disperse each generation, and how long the zone has existed. The farther the individuals move each generation and the longer the populations are in contact, the wider the zone.

- When hybrids are less fit than purebred individuals, the fate of the hybrid zone depends on the strength of selection against them. If selection is very strong and reinforcement occurs, then the hybrid zone is narrow and short lived. If selection is weak, then the region of hybridization is wider and longer lived. These types of hybrid zones are an example of a selection–migration balance, analogous to the situation with water snakes in Lake Erie.

- When hybrids are more fit than purebreds, the fate of the hybrid zone depends on the extent of environments in which hybrids have an advantage. If hybrids achieve higher fitness in environments outside the ranges of the parental species, then a new species may form (as reviewed earlier). If hybrids have an advantage at the boundary of each parental population's range, then a stable hybrid zone may form. For example, many hybrid zones are found in regions called ecotones, where markedly different plant and animal communities meet. In this case, two

Table 12.2 Outcomes of secondary contact and hybridization

When populations hybridize after diverging in allopatry, several different outcomes are possible. The type of hybrid zone formed and the eventual outcome depend on the relative fitness of hybrid individuals.

Fitness of hybrids	Hybrid zone	Eventual outcome
Lower than parental forms	Relatively narrow and short lived	Reinforcement (differentiation between parental populations increases)
Equal to parental forms	Relatively wide and long lived	Parental populations coalesce (differentiation between parental populations decreases)
Higher than parental forms	Depends on whether fitness advantage occurs in ecotone or new habitat	Stable hybrid zone or formation of new species

closely related species or populations (often called subspecies or varieties) are found on either side of the ecotone, with a hybrid zone between them. To explain this pattern, researchers hypothesize that hybrid individuals with intermediate characteristics have a fitness advantage in these transitional habitats.

To illustrate how biologists go about distinguishing between these possibilities, we review recent work on what may be the most widespread and economically important plant in the American west: big sagebrush (*Artemesia tridentata*). A total of four subspecies of big sagebrush have been described, including two that hybridize in the Wasatch Mountains of Utah (Freeman et al. 1995). Basin big sagebrush (*A.t. tridentata*) is found at low elevations in river flats, while mountain sagebrush (*A.t. vaseyana*) grows at higher elevations in upland habitats. The two subspecies hybridize where they make contact at intermediate elevations.

The first task in analyzing a hybrid zone is to describe the distribution and morphology of hybrids relative to parental populations. Previous work had shown that hybrid zones between sagebrush populations are narrow—often less than the length of a football field—and Carl Freeman and colleagues (1991) found that hybrids are intermediate in form between basin and mountain subspecies (Figure 12.16). Historical records indicate that the size and distribution of hybrid zones have been stable in extent for at least 2–3 sagebrush generations.

To assess the relative fitness of hybrid offspring versus pure forms, John Graham et al. (1995) compared a variety of fitness components in individuals sampled along an elevation gradient. These fitness components included seed and flower production, seed germination, and extent of browsing by mule deer and grasshoppers. Table 12.3 shows some data representative of their results. In general, hybrids show equal or even superior production of flowers and seeds, and resistance to herbivores that is equal to the mountain forms. Thus, hybrid offspring do not appear to be less fit than offspring of the parental populations.

In intermediate or transitional habitats, hybrid populations may be more fit than either parental population.

This leaves two possibilities: The hybrid zone could be maintained by selection–mutation balance, or by positive selection on hybrids in the ecotone. To test these alternative hypotheses, the research group studied growth rates and other components of fitness in basin, hybrid, and mountain seedlings that were transplanted to habitats at low, intermediate, and high elevation (Wang et al. 1997). These reciprocal transplant experiments showed that each form performed best in its native habitat (Figure 12.17). These data suggest that the hybrid zone is maintained because hybrid offspring have superior fitness in a transitional habitat.

Figure 12.16 Hybrid sagebrush are intermediate in form between parental subspecies On this graph, a quantity called the principal component score is plotted against the elevation where sagebrush plants were sampled. Principal component analysis (PCA) is a statistical procedure for distilling information from many correlated variables into one or two quantities that summarize the variation measured among individuals in the study. In this case, Carl Freeman and colleagues (1991) measured a large series of morphological traits in sagebrush such as height, circumference, crown diameter, and branch length. The PCA was performed to combine these many variables into a single quantity, the PCA score, that summarizes overall size and shape. Each data point represents an individual.

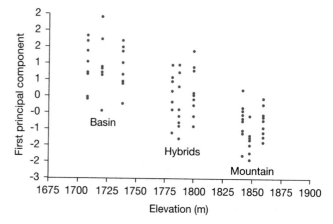

Table 12.3 Fitness of sagebrush hybrids

The rows in this table, listing basin through mountain populations, represent big sagebrush plants sampled along a lower-to-higher elevational gradient. N is the sample size and the numbers in parentheses are standard deviations—a measure of variation around the average value. Differences among these populations in the number of inflorescences (flowering stalks) are not statistically significant. But hybrids have significantly more flowering heads per unit inflorescence length—a measure of flower density ($P < 0.05$).

Population	N	Number of inflorescences		Number of flowering heads	
Basin	25	19.92	(6.16)	175.1	(124.9)
Near basin	25	17.72	(6.59)	174.4	(92.5)
Hybrid	27	20.11	(6.75)	372.7	(375.9)
Near mountain	25	17.04	(6.50)	153.7	(75.2)
Mountain	25	16.80	(6.34)	102.0	(59.4)

Source: Adapted from Table 2 in Graham et al. (1995).

Having reviewed isolation, divergence, and secondary contact, we can move on to consider the genetic mechanisms responsible for these events. Understanding the genetic basis of speciation is our focus in Section 12.5.

12.5 The Genetics of Differentiation and Isolation

What degree of genetic differentiation is required to isolate populations and produce new species? The traditional view was that some sort of radical reorganization of the genome, called a genetic revolution, was necessary (Mayr 1963). This hypothesis was inspired by a strict interpretation of the biological species concept. The logic went as follows: Under the biological species concept (BSC), species are reproductively isolated if and only if hybrids are inviable or experience dramatic reductions in fitness. For this to happen, sister species would have to be genetically incompatible. Combining their alleles would produce dysfunctional development, morphology, or behavior.

Genetic models have shown that these types of large-scale changes in the genome are not only unlikely, but unnecessary for divergence and speciation to occur (Lande 1980; Barton and Charlesworth 1984). These theoretical results have

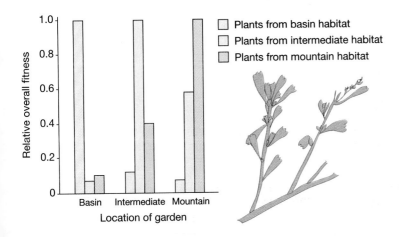

Figure 12.17 Relative fitness of big sagebrush taxa The vertical axis on this graph plots an overall measure of fitness that combines data on survivorship, flowering, seed production, and seed germination rate. The data are expressed as relative fitness by assigning a value of 1.0 to the group that had the highest fitness in each of the three experimental gardens, and then expressing the fitness of the other groups as a percentage of that group's fitness. The horizontal axis indicates whether the data come from gardens at the basin, intermediate, or mountain elevations. From Wang et al. (1997). Copyright © 1997 Evolution. Reprinted by permission of Evolution.

been verified by the work we reviewed in Section 12.3, which demonstrates that marked differentiation can occur between populations of sunflowers and sagebrush that still produce fertile hybrid offspring. As a result, the questions that motivate current research in the genetics of speciation are focused on the number, location, and nature of genes that distinguish closely related species.

Insights from Classical Genetics

When experimenters make crosses between sister species, it is not unusual to find that one sex in the F_1 generation is absent or sterile. Although premating isolation does not occur in these cases, postzygotic isolation is pronounced. The offspring that survive are incapable of mating further among themselves. This postzygotic isolation confirms that the populations are reproductively isolated and that the speciation process is complete.

Postzygotic isolation occurs when populations have diverged so thoroughly that hybrid offspring are inviable or sterile.

An important idea here is that populations that are physically isolated from one another can diverge so thoroughly in their genetic makeup over time that hybrid offspring simply do not develop normally and are sterile or inviable as a result. Allen Orr and Lynne Orr captured this point when they pointed out that reproductive isolation by postzygotic incompatibilities "is almost certainly an 'epiphenomenon' of divergence by ordinary population genetic processes ..." (Orr and Orr 1996: 1748).

Identifying the genes responsible for postzygotic isolation might tell us something interesting about this aspect of speciation. One of our best clues in this gene hunt comes from a striking observation made in experimental crosses between recently diverged taxa: If one sex in the hybrid offspring is sterile or inviable, it is almost always the one heterozygous for the sex chromosomes (Coyne and Orr 1989). This is referred to as the heterogametic sex. In species with X and Y sex chromosomes, such as insects and mammals, males are the heterogametic sex. But in species with Z and W sex chromosomes (birds and butterflies), females are the heterogametic sex. The pattern of sterility or inviability in the heterogametic sex holds, irrespective of how sex is specified genetically (Table 12.4). The generalization is so pervasive that it has been called Haldane's rule in honor of population geneticist J.B.S. Haldane, who first published on the phenomenon in 1922.

Table 12.4 Haldane's rule

In this table, the "Hybridizations with asymmetry" column indicates the number of closely related populations that have been crossed and that exhibit asymmetries in the fertility or viability of males and females in the F_1 hybrids. The "Number obeying Haldane's rule" column reports how many of these crosses showed greater fertility or viability loss in the heterogametic sex.

Group	Trait	Hybridizations with asymmetry	Number obeying Haldane's rule
Mammals	Fertility	20	19
Birds	Fertility	43	40
	Viability	18	18
Drosophila	Fertility and viability	145	141

Source: Coyne and Orr 1989.

The question is why? What is it about having one of each sex chromosome that contributes to sterility or inviability when hybrids are formed between divergent populations? Recently, a consensus has emerged that a hypothesis put forth by H. J. Muller in the early 1940s is probably correct (see Orr 1997). Muller started out by considering an autosomal locus, A, and an X-linked locus, B, in a species where males are the heterogametic sex. Then he supposed that individuals from one species are fixed for alleles A_1 and B_1, while individuals from a sister species are fixed for alleles A_2 and B_2. Further, he supposed that alleles A_1 and B_2 interact to cause inviability. Muller pointed out that if females from the first species mate with males of the second, male hybrid offspring have the genotype $A_1A_2B_1$. As a result, they are inviable. Female hybrid offspring, in contrast, have the genotype $A_1A_2B_1B_2$. They are viable because they have copies of A_2 and B_1 which interact to give a normal phenotype.

By mapping loci associated with hybrid incompatibility in crosses between *Drosophila simulans* and *D. seychellia*, Jerry Coyne and Marty Kreitman (1986) confirmed that at least one—and possibly two—loci on the X chromosome are involved in postzygotic isolation, as Muller's hypothesis predicts. More recent studies of offspring from crosses between sister species of fruit flies have shown that in hybrid males, pronounced defects occur in mitosis or sperm formation (Orr et al. 1997; Kulathinal and Singh 1998). The loci responsible for postzygotic isolation appear to be associated with basic cell functions.

In Drosophila, the genes responsible for postzygotic isolation are located on the X chromosome.

Analyzing Quantitative Trait Loci

An innovative experimental approach called quantitative trait loci (QTL) mapping is offering an additional way to locate genes involved in divergence and measure their effects. As Chapter 7 showed, many or most of the morphological and behavioral differences we observe between closely related species are quantitative traits. Characteristics like body size, body shape, songs, and flower shape result from the combined effects of many loci. QTL mapping is a technology for locating genes with small, but significant, effects on these types of traits.

H. D. Bradshaw and co-workers (1995) recently used QTL mapping to investigate divergence between sister species of monkeyflowers called *Mimulus cardinalis* and *M. lewisii* (Figure 12.18a). These two species hybridize readily in the lab and produce fertile offspring. They also have overlapping ranges in the Sierra Nevada of California. But no hybrids have ever been found in the field. The reason is that they attract different pollinators. *M. cardinalis* is hummingbird pollinated and *M. lewisii* is bee pollinated.

Flower morphology in these species correlates with the differences in the pollinators. Bees do not see well in the red part of the visible spectrum and need a platform to land on before walking into a flower and foraging. Hummingbirds, in contrast, see red well, have long, narrow beaks, and hover while harvesting nectar. *M. lewisii* has a prominent landing spot, while *M. cardinalis* has an elongated tube with a nectar reward at the end. The flower characteristics of *M. lewisii* and *M. cardinalis* conform to classical bee- and bird-pollinated colors and shapes.

Although a formal phylogenetic analysis has not been done, most species in the genus *Mimulus* are bee pollinated. This implies that the flatter, purple, bee pollinated flower is ancestral and the more tubular, reddish, hummingbird-pollinated form derived. The question is, what genes are responsible for the radical make

(a)

(b)

FIGURE 12.18 Contrasting floral traits in monkeyflowers (a) *Mimulus cardinalis* (left) is hummingbird pollinated while *M. lewisii* (right) is bee pollinated. The table below summarizes contrasts in eight floral traits. (Courtesy of Toby Bradshaw and Douglas Schemske, University of Washington. Photo by Jordan Rehm.) (b) These individuals are the products of self-fertilization of F_1 interspecific hybrids, and show a wide variety of floral characters. (Douglas W. Schemske, University of Washington, Seattle)

Characteristic	*M. cardinalis*	*M. lewisii*
Purple pigment (anthocyanins) in petals	high	low
Yellow pigment (carotenoids) in petals	low	high
Corolla width	low	high
Petal width	low	high
Nectar volume	high	low
Nectar concentration	low	high
Stamen (male structure) length	high	low
Pistil (female structure) length	high	low

Notes:

• The yellow pigment in *M. lewisii* petals is arranged in stripes called nectar guides, which are interpreted as a "runway" for bees as they land on the wide petals.

• Nectar volume and concentration are thought to contrast in bird- and bee-flowers simply because of the enormous difference in body size (hummingbirds can drink a lot more).

• The difference in stamen and pistil length is important: In *M. cardinalis* these structures extend beyond the flower and make contact with the hummingbird's forehead as it feeds.

over in flower shape? Can we pinpoint the loci that have responded to selection for hummingbird pollination? QTL mapping gives researchers a way to answer these questions.

In a QTL study, the hunt for the targeted genes takes place in hybrids between the two populations or species that have diverged. For example, Bradshaw et al. first created a large population of hybrids between *M. cardinalis* and *lewisii*. These F_1 individuals tend to be intermediate in flower type and not especially variable. This is because they are all heterozygous for flower size, shape, and color alleles from *M. cardinalis* and *M. lewisii*. But when these F_1 individuals are self-pollinated, their alleles for flower morphology segregate into many different combinations. Accordingly, the F_2 offspring have an astonishing variety of flower colors, shapes, and nectar rewards (Figure 12.18b).

In QTL mapping, researchers try to find correlations between the size or color or shape of these F_2 individuals and genetic markers that they carry (Box 12.3). If a statistically significant association is found between the trait and the marker that has been mapped, it implies that a QTL near that marker contributes to that trait. In the study done by Bradshaw et al., the researchers found that each of the eight floral traits listed in Figure 12.18a was associated with at least one QTL. In fact, in every case there was one QTL that accounted for 25% or more of the total variation in the trait. Because this is high for a polygenic trait, Bradshaw et al. refer to these loci as genes with major effects.

To confirm that these were the loci that underwent selection during the diversification of the two species, Douglas Schemske and Bradshaw (1999) reared a large series of F_2 individuals in the greenhouse and recorded the amount of purple pigment, yellow pigment, and nectar in their flowers, along with overall flower size. Then they planted the individuals out in a habitat where both species coexist and recorded which pollinators visited which flowers. Their data showed that there was a strong trend for bees to prefer large flowers and avoid flowers with a high concentration of yellow pigments. Hummingbirds, in contrast, tended to visit the most nectar-rich flowers and those with the highest amounts of purple pigment.

QTL studies can map the loci responsible for divergence between closely related species.

BOX 12.3 **QTL mapping**

The goal of QTL mapping is to find statistical associations between genetic markers that are unique to each parental species and the value of the trait in the hybrid offspring. Whenever an association between a marker and a trait is confirmed, we know that a locus at the marker, or tightly linked to it, contributes to the trait in question. By quantifying the degree of association between the QTL and the phenotype, we can also estimate how much of the observed variation is due to the alleles at each locus. That is, we can distinguish between genes that have major or minor effects on the traits we are interested in. (For a superb overview of QTL mapping, see Tanksley 1993.)

There are several tricks that increase the efficiency of a QTL analysis. First, it helps to have a very large series of species-specific genetic markers scattered among all of the chromosomes in the species being studied. In the monkeyflower study, Bradshaw et al. (1995) mapped 153 RAPD markers, five allozymes, and one visible trait (a change in the distribution of yellow color due to the *yup* locus). Second, it is easiest to identify statistically significant associations between the markers and the trait in question if the trait varies dramatically. As Figure 12.18b shows, the phenotypic variation that Bradshaw et al. could measure in F_2 hybrids was remarkable. Third, it is crucial to measure these effects in a very large number of hybrid offspring in order to find statistically significant associations. Bradshaw et al. measured flower phenotypes and mapped genetic markers in 93 hybrid offspring.

By collecting tissues from each F_2 individual planted in the field and determining which QTL markers they contained, the researchers were able to calculate that an allele associated with increased concentration of yellow pigments reduced bee visitation by 80%, while an allele responsible for increasing nectar production doubled hummingbird visitation. It is reasonable to conclude that changes in the frequencies of these alleles, driven by differential success in attracting hummingbirds as pollinators, was the mechanism behind speciation. Studies like these promise to identify and characterize "speciation genes" in a diverse array of organisms.

Summary

Although a wide variety of species concepts have been proposed, all agree that the distinguishing characteristic of a species is evolutionary independence. The various species concepts differ in the criteria that are employed for recognizing evolutionary independence.

Speciation can be analyzed as a three-step process: (1) Isolation of populations caused by dispersal, vicariance, or large-scale chromosome changes such as polyploidization, (2) divergence based on drift or selection, and (3) completion or elimination of divergence upon secondary contact. There are numerous exceptions to this sequence, however. In some cases, selection for divergence is strong enough that populations can differentiate without physical isolation, as research on apple and hawthorn maggot flies illustrates. Further, a variety of outcomes are possible after secondary contact. These include formation of stable hybrid zones and creation of a new species containing genes from each of the parental forms.

The primary strategy employed in genetic analyses of speciation is to look for correlations between mapped phenotypic or molecular markers and the distribution of traits in F_2 offspring of recently diverged species. These strategies have confirmed that loci on the X chromosome are particularly important in postzygotic isolation in *Drosophila* and have identified several loci responsible for changes in flower shape during speciation in monkeyflowers.

Speciation is the event that produces new branches on the tree of life. Understanding how biologists estimate the size, shape, and growth of this tree is the focus of Chapter 13.

Questions

1. Different species definitions tend to be advocated by people working in different disciplines. Consider the needs of a botanist studying the ecology of oak trees, a zoologist studying bird distributions, a conservation biologist studying endangered marine turtle populations, and a paleontologist studying extinction events using fossils from planktonic organisms. Which species definition would be most useful to each type of scientist?

2. Global travel and the shipping industry are causing widespread interchange of some "weedy" species across oceans and continents, while many "nonweedy" species (less tolerant of human activity) are losing many small fringe populations and subspecies. What are the implications for speciation rates for weedy and nonweedy species, and for the current global speciation rate?

3. When the Panama land bridge between North and South America was uncovered, some North American mammal lineages crossed to South America and underwent dramatic radiations. For terrestrial species, did the completion of the land bridge represent a vicariance or dispersal event? Does the recent building of the Panama Canal represent a vicariance or dispersal event for terrestrial organisms? For marine organisms? Briefly outline one experiment that would test whether the Panama Canal is affecting speciation in a terrestrial or marine species.

4. Would the recent glaciation events in northern Europe and North America have created vicariance events? If so, how? Which organisms might have been affected? For example, consider the different effects glaciation might have on small mammals, migratory birds, and trees.

5. Apple maggot flies are not the only insects that may be evolving to exploit new host plants. Within the past 50 years, soapberry bug populations in the U.S. have diversified into host race populations distinguished by markedly different beak lengths (Carroll and Boyd 1992).

These bugs eat the seeds at the center of soapberry fruits (Family Sapindaceae). Native and introduced varieties of soapberries differ greatly in fruit size. Describe the experiments or observations you would make to launch an in-depth study of host race formation in these bugs. What data would tell you whether they are separate populations evolving independently, or a single interbreeding population? Many museums contain insect specimens from decades ago. What would you examine in these old specimens? What information about the host plants would be useful?

6. Red crossbills are small finches specialized for eating seeds out of the cones of conifer trees. They fly thousands of kilometers each year in search of productive cone crops. Despite their mobility, crossbills have diverged into several "types" that differ in bill shape, body size, and vocalizations. Each type prefers to feed on a different species of conifer, and each species of conifer is only found in certain forests. Bill size and shape affects how efficiently a bird can open cones of a certain conifer species.

   Explain how a highly mobile animal such as the red crossbill could have diverged into different types in the absence of any geographic barrier. How could you test your ideas? If crossbills could not fly, do you think speciation would occur more quickly or more slowly? If conifer species were not patchily distributed (i.e. in different forests), do you think crossbill speciation would occur more quickly or more slowly? In general, how do habitat patchiness and dispersal ability interact to affect divergence?

7. The monkeyflowers studied by Bradshaw et al. tend to be found at different altitudes. The hummingbird-pollinated *M. cardinalis* occurs at higher elevations, and the bee-pollinated *M. lewisii* at lower elevations. In addition to the QTLs responsible for the differences in flower color and shape, it is likely that loci affecting physiological traits, such as the ability to photosynthesize and grow at colder temperatures, have also diverged between the two species. Write a protocol describing how you would go about mapping these traits.

8. Ellen Censky and coworkers (1998) recently documented the arrival of a small group of iguanas to the Caribbean island of Anguilla, which previously had no iguanas. The animals were carried there on a raft of fallen trees and other debris during a hurricane. Outline a long-term study that would document whether this newly isolated population diverges from iguanas on nearby islands to form a new species.

9. Despite intensive fieldwork by several hundred evolutionary biologists, very few speciation events have been observed first-hand. Comment on why this is so.

Exploring the Literature

10. Biologists frequently use the word spectacular to describe the species numbers and ecological and morphological diversity of cichlid fish found in east Africa's Lakes Malawi, Tanganyika, and Victoria. Males are brightly colored in many of the 1,000 species and recent work has shown that sexual selection may be intense. Phylogenies and geologic data indicate that the 300 species found in Lake Victoria are derived from a single founding population that arrived just 12,000 years ago. Further, each lake contains species that eat fish, mollusks, insect larvae, algae, zooplankton, or phytoplankton. To learn more about this dramatic adaptive radiation, see

Galis, R. and J. A. J. Metz. 1998. Why are there so many cichlid species? *Trends in Ecology and Evolution* 13: 1–2.

Knight, M. E., G. F. Turner, C. Rico, M. J. H. van Oppen, and G. M. Hewitt. 1998. Microsatellite paternity analysis on captive Lake Malawi cichlids supports reproductive isolation by direct mate choice. *Molecular Ecology* 7: 1605–1610.

Johnson, T. C., C. A. Scholz, M. R. Talbot, K. Kelts, R. D. Ricketts, G. Ngobi, K. Beuning, I. Ssemmanda, and J. W. McGill. 1996. Late Pleistocene desiccation of Lake Victoria and rapid evolution of cichlid fishes. *Science* 273:1091–1093.

Citations

Abbott, R. J. 1992. Plant invasions, interspecific hybridization and the evolution of new plant taxa. *Trends in Ecology and Evolution* 7: 401–405.

Arriola, P. E., and N. C. Ellstrand. 1996. Crop-to-weed gene flow in the genus *Sorghum* (Poaceae): Spontaneous interspecific hybridization between johnsongrass, *Sorghum halepense,* and crop sorguhm, *S. bicolor. American Journal of Botany* 83: 1153–1160.

Barton, N. H., and B. Charlesworth. 1984. Genetic revolutions, founder effects, and speciation. *Annual Review of Ecology and Systematics* 15: 133–164.

Barton, N. H., and G. M. Hewitt. 1985. Analysis of hybrid zones. *Annual Review of Ecology and Systematics* 15: 133–164.

Boake, C. R. B., M. P. DeAngelis, and D. K. Andreadis. 1997. Is sexual selection and species recognition a continuum? Mating behavior of the stalk-eyed fly *Drosophila heteroneura. Proceedings of the National Academy of Sciences, USA* 94: 12442-12445.

Bradshaw, H. D. Jr., S. M. Wilbert, K. G. Otto, and D.W. Schemske. 1995. Genetic mapping of floral traits associated with reproductive isolation in monkeyflowers (*Mimulus*). *Nature* 376: 762–765.

Butlin, R. 1987. Speciation by reinforcement. *Trends in Ecology and Evolution* 2: 8–13.

Butlin, R. 1995. Reinforcement: An idea evolving. *Trends in Ecology and Evolution* 10: 432–434.

Carroll, S. P., and C. Boyd. 1992. Host race radiation in the soapberry bug: Natural history with the history. *Evolution* 46: 1052–1069.

Censky, E. J., K. Hodge, and J. Dudley. 1998. Over-water dispersal of lizards due to hurricanes. *Nature* 395: 556.

Cohan, F. M. 1994. Genetic exhange and evolutionary divergence in prokaryotes. *Trends in Ecology and Evolution* 9: 175–180.

Cohan, F. M. 1995. Does recombination constrain neutral divergence among bacterial taxa? *Evolution* 49:164–175.

Coyne, J. A., and M. Kreitman. 1986. Evolutionary genetics of two sibling species, *Drosophila simulans* and *D. sechellia. Evolution* 40:673–691.

Coyne, J. A., and H. A. Orr. 1989. Two rules of speciation. In D. Otte and J. A. Endler, eds. *Speciation and Its Consequences.* Sunderland, MA: Sinauer, 180–207.

Coyne, J. A., and H. A. Orr. 1997. "Patterns of speciation in *Drosophila*" revisited. *Evolution* 51: 295–303.

DeSalle, R., and L. V. Giddings. 1986. Discordance of nuclear and mitochondrial DNA phylogenies in Hawaiian *Drosophila. Proceedings of the National Academy of Sciences, USA* 83: 6902–6906.

Dobzhansky, T. 1937. *Genetics and the Origin of Species.* New York: Columbia University Press.

Donoghue, M. J. 1985. A critique of the biological species concept and recommendations for a phylogenetic alternative. *Bryologist* 88: 172–181.

Endler, J. A. 1977. *Geographic Variation, Speciation, and Clines.* Princeton, NJ: Princeton University Press.

Endler, J. A. 1989. Conceptual and other problems in speciation. In D. Otte and J. A. Endler, eds. *Speciation and Its Consequences.* Sunderland, MA: Sinauer, 625–648.

Feder, J. L., C. A. Chilcote, and G. L. Bush. 1988. Genetic differentiation between sympatric host races of the apple maggot fly *Rhagoletis pomonella. Nature* 336: 61–64.

Feder, J. L., C. A. Chilcote, and G. L. Bush. 1990. The geographic pattern of genetic differentiation beween host associated populations of *Rhagoletis pomonella* (Diptera: Tephritidae) in the eastern United States and Canada. *Evolution* 44: 570–594.

Feder, J. L., S. B. Opp, B. Wlazlo, K. Reynolds, W. Go, and S. Spisak. 1994. Host fidelity is an effective premating barrier between sympatric races of the apple maggot fly, *Rhagoletis pomonella. Proceedings of the National Academy of Sciences, USA* 91: 7990–7994.

Feder, J. L., J. B. Roethele, B. Wlazlo, and S. H. Berlocher. 1997. Selective maintenance of allozyme differences among sympatric host races of the apple maggot fly. *Proceedings of the National Academy of Sciences, USA* 94: 11417–11421.

Felsenstein, J. 1981. Skepticism towards Santa Rosalia, or why are there so few kinds of animals? *Evolution* 35:124–138.

Fisher, R. A. 1958. *The Genetical Theory of Natural Selection.* New York: Dover.

Freeman, D. C., W. A. Turner, E. D. McArthur, and J. H. Graham. 1991. Characterization of a narrow hybrid zone between two subspecies of big sagebrush (*Artemisia tridentata*: Asteraceae). *American Journal of Botany* 78:805–815.

Freeman, D. C., J. H. Graham, D. W. Byrd, E. D. McArthur, and W. A. Turner. 1995. Narrow hybrid zone between two subspecies of big sagebrush *Artemisia tridentata* (Asteraceae). III. Developmental instability. *American Journal of Botany* 82: 1144–1152.

García-Ramos, G., and M. Kirkpatrick. 1997. Genetic models of adaptation and gene flow in peripheral populations. *Evolution* 51: 21–28.

Graham, J. H., D. C. Freeman, and E. D. McArthur. 1995. Narrow hybrid zone between two subspecies of big sagebrush. II. Selection gradients and hybrid fitness. *American Journal of Botany* 82: 709–716.

Grant, P. R., and B. R. Grant. 1992. Hybridization of bird species. *Science* 256: 193–197.

Grant, P. R., and B. R. Grant. 1996. Speciation and hybridization in island birds. *Philosophical Transactions of the Royal Society of London,* Series B 351: 765–772.

Grant, V. 1981. *Plant Speciation.* New York: Columbia University Press.

Hewitt, G. M. 1988. Hybrid zones—natural laboratories for evolutionary studies. *Trends in Ecology and Evolution* 3: 158–166.

Jackson, J. B. C., and A. H. Cheetham. 1990. Evolutionary significance of morphospecies: A test with cheilostome Bryozoa. *Science* 248: 579–583.

Jackson, J. B. C., and A. H. Cheetham. 1994. Phylogeny reconstruction and the tempo of speciation in the cheilostome Bryozoa. *Paleobiology* 20: 407–423.

Kaneshiro, K. Y., and C. R. B. Boake. 1987. Sexual selection and speciation: Issues raised by Hawaiian *Drosophila. Trends in Ecology and Evolution* 2: 207–213.

Knowlton, N., L. A. Weigt, L. A. Solórzano, D. K. Mills, and E. Bermingham. 1993. Divergence in proteins, mitochondrial DNA, and reproductive incompatibility across the isthmus of Panama. *Science* 260: 1629–1632.

Knowlton, N. and L. A. Weigt. 1998. New dates and new rates for divergence across the Isthmus of Panama. *Proceedings of the Royal Society of London,* Series B 265: 2257–2263.

Kulathinal, R. and R. S. Singh. 1998. Cytological characterization of premeiotic versus postmeiotic defects producing hybrid male sterility among sibling species of the *Drosophila melanogaster* complex. *Evolution* 52: 1067–1079.

Lande, R. 1980. Genetic variation and phenotypic evolution during allopatric speciation. *American Naturalist* 116: 463–479.

Lande, R. 1981. Models of speciation by sexual selection on polygenic traits. *Proceedings of the National Academy of Sciences, USA* 78: 3721–3725.

Lande, R. 1982. Rapid origin of sexual isolation and character divergence in a cline. *Evolution* 36: 213–223.

Lawrence, J. G. and H. Ochman. 1998. Molecular archaeology of the *Escherichia coli* genome. *Proceedings of the National Academy of Sciences, USA* 95: 9413-9417.

Masterson, J. 1994. Stomatal size in fossil plants: Evidence for polyploidy in majority of angiosperms. *Science* 264:421–424.

Mayr, E. 1942. *Systematics and the Origin of Species.* New York: Columbia University Press.

Mayr, E. 1963. *Animal Species and Evolution.* Cambridge, MA: Harvard University Press.

Noor, A. M. 1995. Speciation driven by natural selection in *Drosophila. Nature* 375:674–675.

Nowak, R. M. 1979. North American Quaternary *Canis.* Monograph 6, Museum of Natural History, University of Kansas, Lawrence.

Nowak, R. M. 1992. The red wolf is not a hybrid. *Conservation Biology* 6:593–595.

Orr, H. A. 1997. Haldane's rule. *Annual Review of Ecology and Systematics* 28: 195–218.

Orr, H. A. and L. H. Orr. 1996. Waiting for speciation: The effect of population subdivision on the time to speciation. *Evolution* 50: 1742–1749.

Orr, H. A., L. D. Madden, J. A. Coyne, R. Goodwin, and R. S. Hawley. 1997. The developmental genetics of hybrid inviability: A mitotic defect in *Drosophila* hybrids. *Genetics* 145: 1031–1040.

Patton, J. L., and S. W. Sherwood. 1983. Chromosome evolution and speciation in rodents. *Annual Review of Ecology and Systematics* 14: 139–158.

Prokopy, R. J., S. R. Diehl, and S. S. Cooley. 1988. Behavioral evidence for host races in *Rhagoletis pomonella* flies. *Oecologia* 76: 138–147.

Reich, D. E., R. K. Wayne, and D. B. Goldstein. 1999. Genetic evidence for a recent origin by hybridization of red wolves. *Molecular Ecology* 8: 139-144.

Rice, W. R. 1987. Speciation via habitat specialization: The evolution of reproductive isolation as a correlated character. *Evolutionary Ecology* 1: 301–314.

Rieseberg, L. H. 1997. Hybrid origins of plant species. *Annual Review of Ecology and Systematics* 28: 359–389.

Rieseberg, L. H., B. Sinervo, C. R. Linder, M. C. Ungerer, and D. M. Arias. 1996. Role of gene interactions in hybrid speciation: Evidence from ancient and experimental hybrids. *Science* 272: 741–745.

Roy, M. S., E. Geffen, D. Smith, E. A. Ostrander, and R. K. Wayne. 1994. Patterns of differentiation and hybridization in North American wolflike canids, revealed by analysis of microsatellite loci. *Molecule Biology and Evolution* 11: 553–570.

Ryder, O. A., A. T. Kumamoto, B. S. Durrant, and K. Benirschke. 1989. Chromosomal divergence and reproductive isolation in dik-diks. In D. Otte and J.A. Endler. *Speciation and its Consequences.* Sunderland, MA: Sinauer, 180–207.

Schemske, D. W. and H. D. Bradshaw, Jr. 1999. Pollinator preference and the evolution of floral traits in monkeyflowers (*Mimulus*). *Proceedings of the National Academy of Sciences, USA* 96: 11910–11915.

Soltis, D. E., and P. S. Soltis. 1993. Molecular data and the dynamic nature of polyploidy. *Critical Reviews in the Plant Sciences* 12: 243–273.

Stebbins, G. L. 1950. *Variation and Evolution in Plants.* New York: Columbia University Press.

Tanksley, S. D. 1993. Mapping polygenes. *Annual Review of Genetics* 27: 205–233.

Templeton, A. R. 1989. The meaning of species and speciation: A genetic perspective. In D. Otte and J.A. Endler. *Speciation and its Consequences.* Sunderland, MA: Sinauer, 3–27.

Templeton, A. R. 1996. Experimental evidence for the genetic-transilience model of speciation. *Evolution* 50: 909–915.

Wang, H., E. D. McArthur, S. C. Sanderson, J. H. Graham, and D. C. Freeman. 1997. Narrow hybrid zone between two subspecies of big sagebrush (*Artemisia tridentata:* Asteraceae). IV. Reciprocal transplant experiments. *Evolution* 51: 95–102.

Wayne, R. K., and J. L. Gittleman. 1995. The problematic red wolf. *Scientific American* 273: 36–39.

Wayne, R. K., and S. M. Jenks. 1991. Mitochondrial DNA analysis implying extensive hybridizaton of the endangered red wolf *Canis rufus. Nature* 351: 565–568.

White, M. J. D. 1978. *Modes of Speciation.* San Francisco: W. H. Freeman.

CHAPTER 13

Reconstructing Evolutionary Trees

This chapter uses research on the dolphins, porpoises, and whales as an example of how evolutionary biologists estimate phylogenies. (Flip Nicklin/Minden Pictures)

THE EVOLUTIONARY HISTORY OF A GROUP IS CALLED ITS **PHYLOGENY**. A **phylogenetic tree** is a graphical summary of this history. The tree describes the pattern, and in some cases the timing, of branching events. It records the sequence of speciation and documents which taxa are more closely or distantly related.

In Chapter 1, we introduced the use of phylogenetic thinking by using a parsimony analysis to determine whether HIV was transmitted from humans to monkeys or from monkeys to humans. In Chapter 2, we introduced the idea of tree thinking more formally and explored how to use a phylogenetic tree to determine whether the swim bladders found in fish evolved from lungs, or vice versa. But in these and other instances, we have been using trees without asking how they were put together.

The task before us now is to understand how phylogenies are estimated, so we can interpret them critically and make independent judgments about their quality. The goal of this chapter is to explain and illustrate the logic of inferring a phylogeny from data.

Because we do not have direct knowledge of evolutionary history, a phylogeny must be inferred indirectly from data. In the cases we have already discussed, many different trees could possibly represent the evolutionary history of a group. In any particular case, what data should we use, and how do we know that we have inferred the true tree?

We illustrate these issues with a controversial and surprising example: the phylogenetic relationships between whales and dolphins (the order Cetacea) and other mammals. We use this case study to show how the principle of parsimony is used in phylogeny estimation, how researchers choose data for a phylogenetic problem, and how the reliability of a particular phylogeny can be tested. This presentation parallels the sequence of decisions that face researchers when estimating phylogenies (Swofford et al. 1996).

Finally, we explore the various ways that phylogenies can be used to answer questions about evolutionary patterns and processes. The chapter closes with examples illustrating how phylogenetic thinking is applied in contemporary research. Topics in this last section range widely, from how we should classify the diversity of life to the evolution of ants that farm fungi.

13.1 Parsimony and Phylogeny

At its most basic level, the logic of estimating evolutionary relationships is simple: The most closely related taxa should have the most traits in common. Naively, we would say that any traits or characters that are independent of one another, heritable, and variable among the taxa in the study can help us reconstruct who evolved from whom. These characters might be things like DNA sequences, the presence or absence of certain skeletal elements or flower parts, or the mode of embryonic or larval development. The only requirements are that different characters be independent of each other and that each one can be scored as a homologous character state in all of the species to be studied. (We reviewed the criteria for making a statement about homology in Chapter 2.)

In choosing characters to study, however, it is essential to realize that evolutionary relationships are only revealed by traits that are similar because they were derived from a common ancestor. (Box 13.1 explains why this is so.) These shared

---

BOX 13.1   Cladistic methods

Techniques that identify monophyletic groups on the basis of shared derived characters are called cladistic methods. Traits that are shared because they were modified in a common ancestor are called synapomorphies. Mammals, for example, share fur and lactation as traits that were derived from their common ancestor (a population from a long-extinct group called the synapsids). Synapomorphies can be identified at whatever taxonomic level a researcher might be interested in: populations, species, genera, families, orders, or classes.

Two ideas are key to understanding why this approach to phylogeny inference is valid. The first is that synapomorphies identify evolutionary branch points. Why? After a species splits into two lineages that begin evolving independently, some of their homologous traits undergo changes due to mutation, selection, and drift. These changed traits are synapomorphies that identify

populations in the two independent lineages. The second key idea is that synapomorphies are nested. That is, as you move back in time and trace an evolutionary tree backward from its tips to its root, each branching event adds one or more synapomorphies. As a result, the hierarchy described by synapomorphies replicates the hierarchy of branching events. The source of these insights is the German entomologist Willi Hennig, who began writing on cladistic approaches in the 1950s.

The cornerstone of tree building with cladistic methods is to identify these shared, derived traits accurately. Identifying and evaluating synapomorphies requires judgments about the homology of traits and the direction, or polarity, of change through time. There are several ways to determine which states of a trait are ancestral and which are derived. One of the most basic and reliable ways is called outgroup analysis. In outgroup analy-

BOX 13.1 Continued

sis, the character state in the group of interest (the ingroup) is compared to the state in a close relative that clearly branched off earlier (the outgroup). The outgroup is assumed to represent the ancestral state. Finding an appropriate outgroup, in turn, involves borrowing conclusions from other phylogenetic analyses or confirming an earlier appearance in the fossil record. Most investigators prefer to examine several outgroups so they can corroborate that the characters used in the analysis were not present in the "derived" state earlier in evolution.

When no convergence, parallelism, or reversal occurs, all the similarities observed in a data set are due to modifications that took place in common ancestors. A researcher would say that all synapomorphies identified are congruent. In this case, inferring the phylogeny is straightforward: The investigator simply groups the taxa according to their synapomorphies. Each branch on the tree corresponds to one or more

synapomorphies that distinguish the derived groups. A phylogenetic tree inferred in this manner is called a cladogram. By convention, the location of these synapomorphies is indicated on published trees with bars across the branches. The synapomorphies are described in a key or labels that accompany the diagram. Figure 13.1 presents an example cladogram.

When homoplasy is present, synapomorphies are not completely congruent and the strategy for inferring phylogenies changes slightly. The goal now is to find the branching pattern that minimizes homoplasy. Many or all of the possible branching patterns have to be examined and evaluated, and a best tree chosen. How the evaluation and selection are done is the subject of Sections 13.2 through 13.5.

For further background on cladistic approaches, see Hennig (1979), Eldredge and Cracraft (1980), Nelson and Platnick (1981), and Mayden and Wiley (1992).

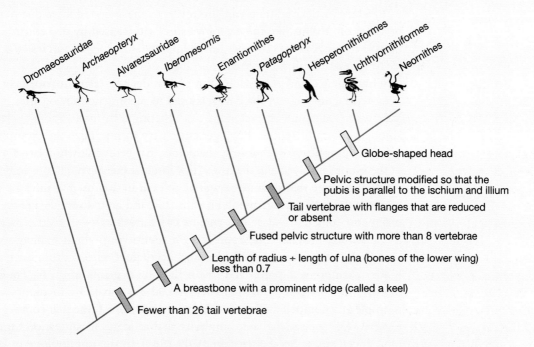

Figure 13.1 Phylogeny of bird groups from the Mesozoic era Luis Chiappe (1995) used skeletal characters to infer the phylogeny of early bird lineages. *Archaeopteryx, Iberomesornis,* and *Patagopteryx* are genera; all the rest of the taxa indicated are families or higher-level groupings. The synapomorphies listed on this cladogram identify trends in changes to the forelimbs, hindlimbs, breastbone, tail, and pelvis of birds. The fusions, reductions in bone number, and other modifications were undoubtedly favored as adaptations for flight.

Shared traits that are derived from a common ancestor are called synapomorphies.

derived character states are similarities that arose due to a change from the character state in the common ancestor of all members of the group. For example, Figure 13.1 shows that a series of these shared derived character states, or **synapomorphies**, defines phylogenetic relationships among groups of birds that lived during the Mesozoic Era. These synapomorphies identify trends in changes to the forelimbs, hindlimbs, breastbone, tail, and pelvis of birds. The fusions, reductions in bone number, and other modifications were undoubtedly favored as adaptations for flight.

If similarities among organisms occurred only because of descent from a common ancestor, then inferring a phylogeny for any group of species would be a simple problem of combining progressively larger sets of species together based on their synapomorphies, as in Figure 13.1.

Unfortunately, things are not nearly this simple in practice. For example, species can have similar traits because those traits evolved independently in each of the lineages leading to those species. Flippers are a derived trait found in both penguins and seals, but they did not evolve through modification in the common ancestor of penguins and seals. Instead, the similarity we observe in the forelimbs of penguins and seals results from natural selection that favored the same type of structure in ancestors from very different lineages (birds and mammals). This is called **convergent evolution**. We can be fairly sure that this similarity is due to convergence because many other traits (other than the shape of the forelimbs) unite penguins with other birds and seals with other mammals. From this point of view, the phylogenetic information from the forelimb characteristics of penguins and seals disagrees with information from many other characters.

In addition, derived traits can also revert to the ancestral form due to mutation or selection. Events like these remove similarity caused by descent from a common ancestor. A **reversal** wipes out the phylogenetic signal and restricts our ability to estimate evolutionary relationships.

Convergence and reversal are lumped under the term **homoplasy**. Homoplasy represents noise in the data sets used to reconstruct phylogenies, and it will arise whenever some characters give conflicting information about relationships among a group of species. Phylogeneticists try to minimize the confusing influence of homoplasy by choosing characters that evolve slowly relative to the age of the groups involved and that show few instances of apparent convergence or reversal. But given that such noise will be present in data used to infer a phylogeny, how can the true phylogeny still be estimated, and how do we decide the strength of support for a particular phylogenetic conclusion?

Parsimony provides one approach for identifying which branching pattern, among the many that are possible, most accurately reflects evolutionary history. Under parsimony, the preferred tree is the one that minimizes the total amount of evolutionary change that has occurred. The rationale for invoking parsimony is simple and compelling. In many instances, we can assume that convergence and reversal will be rare relative to similarity that is due to modification from a common ancestor (but see Felsenstein 1978, 1983). In the terminology of Box 13.1, synapomorphies are usually more common than convergence and reversals. It makes sense, then, that the most parsimonious tree will minimize the amount of homoplasy inferred for the data, and this will be the best estimate of the true phylogenetic relationships among the species being studied. In the following sections, we use recent analyses of whale phylogeny to illustrate the process of inferring this best phylogeny by parsimony.

13.2 The Phylogeny of Whales

The whales, dolphins, and porpoises (called Cetacea) share a set of features that are unusual among the mammals, such as loss of the posterior limbs. The relationships between the cetaceans and other mammal groups are difficult to discern because whales are highly evolved for aquatic life. Several studies, however, have placed cetaceans as a relative of the ungulates (including horses, rhinoceroses, deer, pigs, antelope, and camels) as in Figure 13.2a (Flower 1883; Simpson 1945; Novacek 1993). The oldest fossils that can be recognized as whales come from Eocene rocks in the Himalayas that are about 55 million years old. These archaeocete whales had some terrestrial traits, such as hind limbs (Thewissen and Hussain 1993; Bajpai and Gingerich 1998), and resembled an extinct group of amphibious mammals called the mesonychians (Thewissen et al. 1994).

Recent analyses of DNA sequences and other molecular characters have challenged this view of whale relationships. These molecular studies strongly suggest that whales are not merely related to the ungulates but are, in fact, close relatives of one particular group of ungulates: the hippopotamuses (Figure 13.2b). Notice that the two trees in Figure 13.2 differ only in the location of the whale branch, and that otherwise the relationships between the artiodactyl groups are not different.

This conclusion would upset our traditional understanding of mammalian evolution and classification. For example, it would suggest that some traits of hippos and whales, thought to be convergent adaptations for aquatic life, are perhaps shared

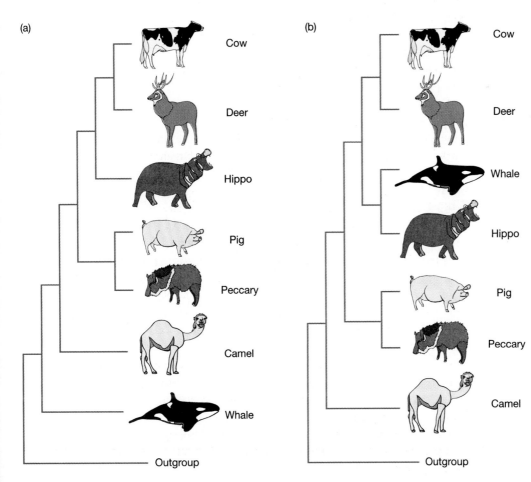

(a) Cow, Deer, Hippo, Pig, Peccary, Camel, Whale, Outgroup

(b) Cow, Deer, Whale, Hippo, Pig, Peccary, Camel, Outgroup

Figure 13.2 Phylogenetic hypotheses for whales and other mammals The tree in (a) shows the Artiodactyla hypothesis: Whales and dolphins are related to the ungulates, possibly as the sister group to the artiodactyls (represented by cows, deer, hippos, pigs, peccaries, and camels). The outgroup to these species is from the ungulate group called Perissodactyla (horses and rhinos). The tree in (b) shows the whale+hippo hypothesis. It is identical to (a) with one exception: the branch leading to whales is moved so that whales are the sister group to the hippos.

derived characters. How do we test these competing ideas about whale phylogenetic relationships?

Choosing Characters: Morphology and Molecules

The first task of any phylogenetic analysis is choosing which characters to use as data. Like many other phylogenetic problems, the phylogeny of whales has been studied using two very different types of characters: morphological traits (especially those of the skeleton) and molecular traits (including allozymes, DNA restriction sites, immunological similarity, and especially DNA sequences). Morphological traits are essential in the case of extinct species found only in museum collections or as fossils. To reduce homoplasy in the data, the homology of morphological similarities can often be assessed by looking at the embryological origins of similar structures. A disadvantage of morphological characters is that scoring a single morphological trait for a group of species may require slow, painstaking work by a highly trained taxonomic expert.

Morphological and molecular traits each have advantages and disadvantages when used to infer evolutionary relationships.

Molecular characters (especially DNA sequences) have other advantages and disadvantages. Nucleotides may be scored rapidly in nearly limitless numbers in different genes, and molecular biologists have developed sophisticated models to predict how sequences change through time. However, homoplasy in molecular similarities can be difficult to identify, and DNA sequence characters are limited to just four character states (A, C, G, and T). These different features often lead phylogeneticists to use both morphological and molecular characters whenever possible to analyze relationships.

Parsimony with a Single Morphological Character

The ungulates are traditionally divided into two monophyletic taxa: hippos, cows, deer, pigs, giraffes, antelope, and camels (called Artiodactyla) and the horses and rhinoceroses (called Perissodactyla). The Artiodactyla are grouped together on the basis of some skull and dental characteristics, but most notably by the form of a bone in the ankle called the astragalus (Prothero et al. 1988; Milinkovich and Thewissen 1997). In all artiodactyls, the astragalus has an unusual shape. Both ends of the bone are smooth and pulley-shaped (Figure 13.3). This shape allows the foot

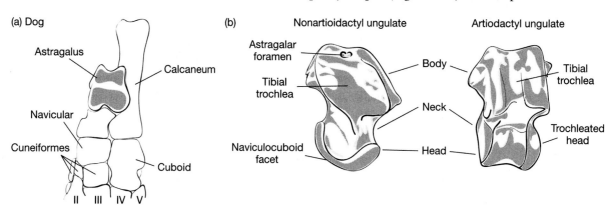

Figure 13.3   The astragalus defines artiodactyl mammals as a taxon   (a) The astragalus (in this case, of a dog) is the highest bone in the ankle, around which the foot rotates to extend forward or backward. Numbers II–V indicate the four digits. From Thewissen and Madar (1999). (b) The astragalus of an artiodactyl (right) and a nonartiodactyl (left) ungulate. In the artiodactyl, both ends of the astragalus are pulley-shaped. From Schaeffer (1948). Copyright © 1948 Evolution. Reprinted by permission of Evolution.

to rotate in a wide arc around the end of the ankle, and contributes to the long stride and excellent running ability of most artiodactyls.

This shared derived character state is one reason some morphologists have rejected the idea that hippos and whales could be sister groups (Luckett and Hong 1998). The straightforward logic is illustrated in Figure 13.4. If hippos and other Artiodactyla form a monophyletic group, then the pulley-shaped astragalus evolved just once without subsequent changes (a single change in character state), as shown in Figure 13.4a. On the other hand, if whales are a sister group to the hippos, then the origin of the pulley-shaped astragalus (one evolutionary event or step) was followed by the loss of this synapomorphy in the lineage leading to whales (a second step), as seen in Figure 13.4b. Based on this character, the whale + hippo hypothesis (Figure 13.2b) is less parsimonious than the Artiodactyla hypothesis (Figure 13.2a) because it implies one extra step in ankle bone evolution. This kind of inference is the heart of a phylogenetic analysis based on parsimony: comparing possible alternative trees, and concluding that the tree implying the fewest evolutionary changes is the tree most likely given the available data.

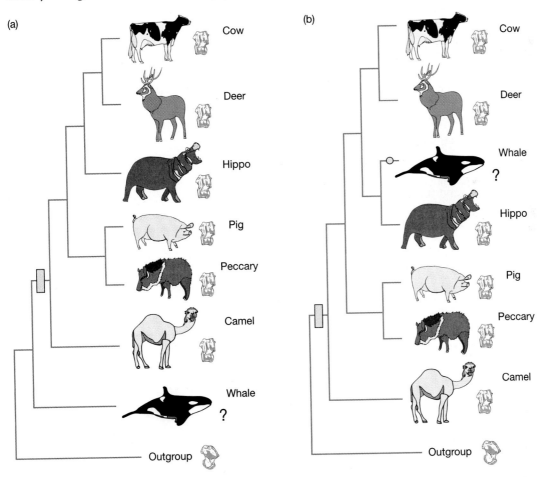

Figure 13.4 Using the astragalus as a phylogenetic character   The evolution of a pulley-shaped astragalus can be reconstructed by finding the smallest number of changes implied by each possible phylogenetic tree. In the Artiodactyla hypothesis (a), the fewest changes are implied if the pulley-shaped astragalus evolved once, at the point marked by the pink bar. In the whale + hippo hypothesis (b), the simplest reconstruction is that the pulley-shaped astragalus evolved once and was lost in the lineage leading to modern whales (marked by the blue dot), implying at least two changes in ankle morphology. There is a question mark by the whales because they do not have ankles.

Morphological traits that link whales and hippos are controversial.

Living whales have no ankles, so the shape of the whale astragalus as a possible artiodactyl trait cannot be assessed. However, some fossil whales have hindlimbs (Gingerich et al. 1990). Johannes Thewissen and Sandra Madar (1999) found fossil ankle bones in the same deposits containing the oldest archaeocete whales and compared these to the ankles of living and extinct artiodactyls. They concluded that some features of the pulley-shaped astragalus are, in fact, found in the archaeocete whales. This conclusion confirms that the whales are descended from an artiodactyl ancestor. However, this conclusion is vigorously disputed by some morphological systematists (Luckett and Hong 1998; O'Leary and Geisler 1999), who question the origin of these bones and suggest that they may belong to some other artiodactyl and not to a whale. In general, morphological traits tend to support the Artiodactyla hypothesis (Luckett and Hong 1998; O'Leary and Geisler 1999).

Parsimony with Multiple Molecular Characters

How do we extend this parsimony method to the analysis of multiple characters, especially when homoplasy is likely to appear among the data? The answer is deceptively simple. Each character is treated independently, mapped onto each of the possible trees, and the most parsimonious pattern of character change is noted for each character on each tree. Then, the number of changes is summed across characters for each tree, and the total number of changes is assessed. Under parsimony, the best tree is the one that implies the fewest character state changes across all characters.

John Gatesy and his colleagues (1999) summarized the available molecular evidence on whale relationships to other mammals. They assembled all of the DNA sequence data relevant to this question into a single data set for four whales and eight artiodactyls, including a hippo, and an outgroup from the Perissodactyla. Their analyses of this data set strongly supported the whale + hippo hypothesis, and they dubbed this collection of molecular characters the WHIPPO-1 data set (for WHale-hIPPO).

Sixty of those characters for a subset of the taxa in the WHIPPO-1 data set are shown in Figure 13.5. They correspond to nucleotide sites 141-200 in Gatesy's alignment of DNA sequences for a milk protein gene called beta-casein. We use these eight taxa and 60 characters in the following sections, in order to illustrate the way that multiple characters (in this case, nucleotides) are used to infer a phylogeny.

Of the 60 characters in Figure 13.5, 15 group 2 or more taxa. As a result, these sites contain phylogenetic information. The others are invariant (like site 142, for which all taxa have G) or variable but uninformative (like site 192, for which all taxa, including the outgroup, have C, except the camel, which has G).

The parsimony informative characters provide support for clades among the whales and artiodactyls. For example, site 162 provides a synapomorphy for a clade including the cow, deer, whale, and hippo sequences (all with T, a shared difference from the outgroup and all other artiodactyl sequences which have C). Site 166 provides a synapomorphy (the only one in this example) for a clade consisting of hippos and whales (the only sequences with C at this site). However, not all informative characters support the same groupings. Site 177 provides a synapomorphy for a clade of whales, hippos, pigs, and peccaries, excluding the cow and deer sequences. This synapomorphy conflicts with site 162, and indicates that reversal or convergence has resulted in homoplasy at one of these sites that does not reflect the evolutionary history of artiodactyls. In most cases, this is the only way that

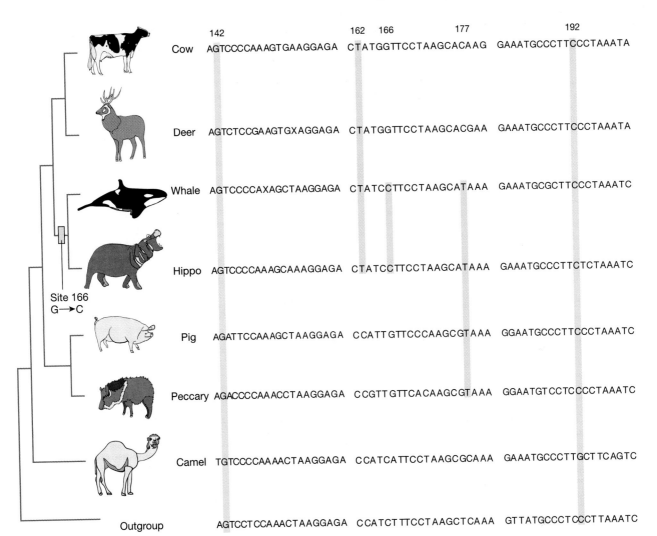

Figure 13.5 Sequence data for parsimony analysis Sixty nucleotides of aligned sequence from the beta-casein gene (which encodes a milk protein) of six artiodactyls, a whale (the dolphin *Lagenorhynchus obscurus*), and a perissodactyl. A, C, G, and T denote the nucleotides at homologous sites from 141 to 200 in the alignment of Gatesy et al. (1999). X indicates an ambiguously identified nucleotide. Some sites are invariant or uninformative (shaded blue), while others provide synapomorphies that define clades (shaded red). The phylogeny is based on a parsimony analysis of these nucleotide synapomorphies. One synapomorphy (at site 166) defines a clade of whales and hippos. Notice that not all synapomorphies agree with each other, indicating that some homoplasy has occurred in the evolution of these nucleotides.

homoplasy in molecular characters can be discovered: by comparison to other characters and the phylogeny that is implied by them.

We use the information from these characters to choose between alternative phylogenies by, first, finding the most parsimonious reconstruction of character change for each character on each tree. Then we add the total number of character changes. For the Artiodactyla hypothesis (Figure 13.2a), 47 nucleotide changes are implied by this tree for the data shown in Figure 13.5; for the same data, the whale + hippo hypothesis implies only 41 changes. This difference between the two trees can be traced back to six characters in Figure 13.5: nucleotide sites 151, 162, 166, 176, 177, and 194. For each of these characters, the whale + hippo hypothesis implies one fewer change than does the Artiodactyla hypothesis. As an exercise, try to find the most parsimonious reconstruction for each of these six characters on both trees (as we did for the astragalus in Figure 13.4), and satisfy yourself that Figure 13.2a is, in fact, six steps longer than Figure 13.2b. For these 60 characters and eight taxa, the whale +hippo hypothesis is more parsimonious than the Artiodactyla hypothesis and is, therefore, the preferred tree.

Searching Among Possible Trees

So far, we have restricted ourselves to comparing two specific phylogenetic hypotheses. However, the true number of possible trees is actually much larger, and the task is to evaluate the many possible tree topologies and find the best one. This is difficult, because the number of tree topologies that are possible becomes astonishingly large, even in a moderately sized study. When four species are included, only three different branching patterns are possible. Adding a fifth species to the data set makes the number of possible topologies jump from 3 to 15. A sixth taxon leads to 105, a seventh to 945, and for the eight taxa in Figure 13.2, there are 10,395 possible trees. However, it is fairly routine now for studies to include 50 taxa. In this case, an incomprehensibly large number of different trees is possible. Obviously, so many alternative trees cannot be evaluated manually as we have done so far. Fast computers are required to automate the task. Three different approaches can be used to search among all of these possible trees in order to find the most parsimonious one.

When the number of taxa in a study is relatively low—typically fewer than 11—it is feasible to employ computer programs that evaluate all of the possible trees. This strategy is called an exhaustive search. Because it guarantees that the optimal tree implied by a particular data set will be found, the approach is called an exact method. An exhaustive search of all 10,395 trees for the data in Figure 13.5 produced a single shortest phylogeny of 41 steps identical to the tree in Figure 13.2b. This is the same branching pattern among these eight sequences as that found by Gatesy et al. (1999), and it supports the whale + hippo hypothesis.

However, the original WHIPPO-1 data set consists of 13 taxa (including three other whale sequences) and about 8,000 molecular characters. Exhaustive searching of this data set is prohibitively slow, so Gatesy et al. (1999) used two other methods for searching among the possible trees. These methods take advantage of some logical or computational shortcuts. They search only some parts of the landscape of all possible trees, while maximizing the probability of finding the most parsimonious tree.

Analyses of DNA sequence data support a close relationship between whales and hippos.

In this case, both methods produced two most-parsimonious trees, both of which are consistent with the phylogeny in Figure 13.2b. This consistency among search methods indicates that the close relationship between whales and hippos is not an artifact of incomplete searching or of the inability of search methods to find the most parsimonious solutions.

Evaluating the Trees ˢᵒᵐⁱᵗ

Having compared several (or all) possible trees, we now need to ask: How good is the most parsimonious tree? In particular, how sure can we be that the node joining whales with hippos is reliably supported by the data? Is this tree really substantially better than one in which whales are not a sister group to the hippos?

Many investigators examine the topologies of trees close to the optimal tree visually, and make an informed judgment about how different they are from it. If the nearly optimal trees differ from the optimal tree in only minor ways, we can be more confident in using the most optimal tree to draw conclusions about the group's evolution. In addition, computer programs can evaluate multiple trees and create a consensus representing the topology supported by all of the nearly optimal trees.

The reliability of most-parsimonious trees can also be evaluated statistically (see Bremer 1994; Swofford et al. 1996; Huelsenbeck and Rannala 1997). One approach to this problem is called **bootstrapping** (Felsenstein 1985). In bootstrapping, a computer creates a new data set from the existing one by repeated sampling. For example, if there are 300 base pairs of sequence in a study, the computer begins the bootstrapping process by randomly selecting one of the sites and using it as the first entry in a new data set. Then, it randomly selects another site, which becomes the second data point in the new data set. (There is a 1/300 chance that this second point will be the same site as the first.) The computer keeps resampling like this until the new data set has 300 base-pairs of data, representing a random selection of the original data. This new data set is then used to estimate the phylogeny. By repeating this process many times, the investigator can say that particular branches occur in 50%, 80%, or 100% of the trees estimated from the resampled data sets. The more times a branch occurs in the bootstrapped estimates, the more confidence we have that the branch actually exists. If bootstrap support for a particular branch is low, say under 50%, an investigator will usually conclude that she cannot determine the branching pattern in that part of the tree, and will therefore collapse that particular branch into a polytomy (a point of uncertainty) in the published tree.

Resampling the data in Figure 13.5 through bootstrapping indicates strong support for the whale-hippo clade. Of 1000 resampled data sets, 71% included a whale-hippo clade (more than any other branching arrangement). When all taxa and all molecular characters in the WHIPPO-1 data set were analyzed, bootstrap support for this node approached 100% (Hillis 1999). In some analyses of known phylogenies (where investigators bred laboratory organisms and split their populations to create lineages of known relatedness), bootstrap support of around 70% or greater was usually associated with the identification of the true phylogeny (Hillis and Bull 1993). From this perspective as well, the close relationship between whales and hippos seems sound.

A second approach is to use a phylogenetic method other than simple parsimony. Two such alternatives, called **maximum likelihood** and **genetic distances**, are described in Box 13.2. These methods use different assumptions about how characters evolve and different methods for joining similar taxa together in the search for the best phylogeny. When these very different methods agree on the same best phylogeny, this gives some degree of confidence that the best tree has actually been found (Huelsenbeck and Hillis 1993; Hillis et al. 1994). When they conflict, we are left to make a judgment about which criterion for choosing among trees is most valid in the case being analyzed. We face a similar situation when comparing trees inferred from entirely different data sets. Trees produced by different studies are treated as competing estimates. When they conflict, researchers have more confidence in trees estimated with larger data sets and from characters thought to be less subject to homoplasy.

Bootstrapping is a technique for evaluating which branches on a particular tree are more well-supported than others.

BOX 13.2 Alternatives to parsimony: Maximum likelihood and genetic distances

One drawback of parsimony methods is that they do not use all of the information available to an investigator. Recall, from the whale example, that only 15 of 60 nucleotide sites were useful in a parsi- mony analysis. To use information more efficiently and to create the possibility of using statistical tests to choose the best tree among the many possible trees, Joseph Felsenstein (1981) introduced an inno-

	Cow	Deer	Whale	Hippo	Pig	Peccary	Camel
Deer	0.073						
Whale	0.150	0.197					
Hippo	0.148	0.197	0.053				
Pig	0.264	0.270	0.197	0.217			
Peccary	0.340	0.412	0.266	0.287	0.129		
Camel	0.284	0.347	0.216	0.236	0.291	0.340	
Outgroup	0.306	0.340	0.241	0.261	0.311	0.306	0.210

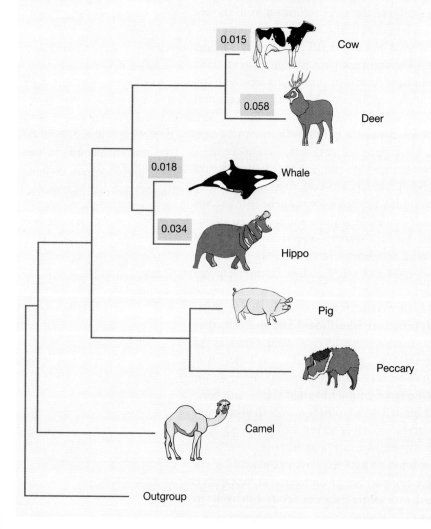

Figure 13.6 Genetic distances for cluster analysis Each entry in this table is a genetic distance between a pair of taxa, calculated from the sequence data in Figure 13.5. The phylogeny below was produced by a clustering analysis of these genetic distances. Notice that pairs of taxa, such as the cow and deer (blue), or the whale and hippo (red), with low genetic distances are grouped as sister taxa. The lengths of the branches are proportional to the expected proportion of nucleotide differences between groups (also shown numerically for several branches).

BOX 13.2   **Continued**   *read*

vative and powerful approach called maximum likelihood estimation.

The essence of the likelihood approach for molecular phylogenetics is to ask the question: Given a mathematical formula that describes the probability that different types of nucleotide substitution will occur, and given a particular phylogenetic tree with known branch lengths, how likely am I to obtain this particular set of DNA sequences? To implement this strategy, a computer program evaluates each tree topology and computes the probability of producing the observed data, given the specified model of character change. The sum of the probabilities of getting each branch represents the probability of getting the observed data, if the tree is correct. This probability is reported as the tree's likelihood. The criterion for accepting or rejecting competing tree topologies, then, is to choose the one with the highest likelihood. Unfortunately, likelihood methods are computationally slow, and very large data sets cannot be analyzed as completely by this technique as they can using much faster parsimony methods.

A radically different approach is to convert discrete character data (such as the presence or absence of a morphological trait, or the identity of a nucleotide at a homologous location in a gene) into a distance value (Swofford et al. 1996). For example, the percentage of nucleotide sites that differ between two taxa can be computed (a 10% difference means that an average of 10 nucleotides have changed per 100 bases). This conversion of discrete characters to a single distance measure results in loss of specific information, but it can capture the overall degree of similarity between taxa.

As in likelihood methods, distance analyses require the investigator to assume a model of character evolution in order to convert information from multiple characters into one composite measure of the distance between two taxa. One commonly used formula for DNA sequences corrects for multiple substitutions at the same site and for differences in the frequency of transition and transversion substitutions (Kimura 1980; Wakely 1996).

To estimate a phylogeny from distance data, computer programs are used to cluster taxa, so that the most similar forms are found close to one another on the resulting tree. This general strategy, based on clustering taxa according to their similarities, is called a phenetic approach (Sneath and Sokal 1973). The preferred tree is the one that minimizes the total distance among taxa. Several different clustering algorithms are commonly used that make more or less restrictive assumptions about the nature of the distances analyzed.

An example of this approach is shown in Figure 13.6. The top part of the figure shows the matrix of pairwise genetic distances among the sequences in Figure 13.5, calculated using a formula devised to account for multiple substitutions at the same sites (Kimura 1980). Small genetic distances should indicate recent divergence from a common ancestor and close phylogenetic relationships. Notice that the smallest genetic distances are those between the whale and hippo sequences and between the deer and cow sequences. Note also that genetic distances among these four sequences are all relatively small. The bottom part of the figure shows that a clustering analysis groups whales and hippos together as sister taxa based on these genetic distances, with cows and deer as their next nearest relatives.

Resolving Character Conflict

We began by contrasting the results of morphological and molecular character analysis for whale phylogenies. The two sets of results appear to be in strong conflict. Gatesy et al. (1999) attempted to include both morphological and molecular data in one analysis, but they could not include the wealth of morphological characters from fossils without scoring all of the molecular characters as missing for the fossil taxa. What are we to do in such a situation? The most prudent act is to wait for more data. For example, better fossil sampling may reveal character states in extinct artiodactyls and whales that would support grouping whales with hippos (or other artiodactyl lineages). On the other hand, molecular data for a larger number of artiodactyl groups might change the inferred order of character state changes and thereby support removing whales from within the artiodactyls.

A 'Perfect' Phylogenetic Character?

One way in which the passage of time tends to help resolve phylogenetic issues such as the whale-artiodactyl problem is the discovery of new kinds of phylogenetic characters. Recently, a new and potentially ideal molecular character has been applied to the problem of whale phylogeny (Milinkovitch and Thewissen 1997). SINEs and LINEs (for Short or Long INterspersed Elements) are parasitic DNA sequences that occasionally insert themselves into new locations within a host genome. The presence or absence of a particular SINE or LINE at a homologous location in two different host genomes can be used as a trait in phylogeny inference. David Hillis (1999) outlined the potential advantages of such a molecular phylogenetic character. Transposition events (in which the sequence inserts itself in a new location in the host genome) are relatively rare, so that two homologous SINEs in two independent host lineages are unlikely to insert into exactly the same place in their host genomes. This kind of convergence is possible, but it is probably extremely unusual. As a result, convergence in SINE or LINE characters should be rare. Reversal to the ancestral condition is also unlikely, because the deletion of a SINE or LINE can be detected as the loss of parts of the host genome along with the loss of the interpersed element. These features of SINE and LINE genetics allow a phylogeneticist to tell the difference between the ancestral absence of a SINE or LINE and the secondary loss of one of these elements. If convergence and reversal are rare or can be identified, then homoplasy is an unlikely source of SINE or LINE similarity. Without homoplasy, SINEs and LINEs should give excellent (though perhaps not perfect) insight into some phylogenetic relationships.

Such is the case for whales. Interspersed elements in the genomes of whales and artiodactyls were used by Masato Nikaido and colleagues (1999) in a test of the whale + hippo phylogenetic hypothesis. They analyzed 20 different SINE or LINE insertions and found no homoplasy at all! Look carefully at the matrix of SINE or LINE presence/absence data shown in Figure 13.7 for representatives of the same taxa analyzed using DNA sequences. Notice that variation in presence or absence of an element at each locus corresponds to exactly one clade in the phylogeny. This phylogeny is identical to the tree produced by sequence analysis. Four different insertions are shared by whales and hippos alone. Notice also that—unlike the DNA sequence characters in Figure 13.5—none of the SINE or LINE characters are in conflict with each other. This is similar to the pattern of synapomorphies used to define Mesozoic bird clades by Chiappe (Figure 13.1). The shared presence of SINEs or LINEs provides a perfect window into whale phylogeny and strongly corroborates the conclusion from sequence studies indicating that whales and hippos are close relatives.

13.3 Using Phylogenies to Answer Questions

The first two sections of this chapter focused on the methods of phylogeny inference. The fundamental message of this analysis is that estimating evolutionary relationships requires a series of careful decisions about which data are appropriate for the task and how they should be analyzed. Now we turn to the issue of how evolutionary trees can be used to answer interesting questions.

Locus	1	2	3	4	5	6	7	8	9	10	11	12	13	14	15	16	17	18	19	20
Cow	0	0	0	0	0	0	0	1	1	1	1	1	1	1	1	1	1	1	0	0
Deer	0	0	0	0	0	0	0	1	?	1	1	1	1	1	1	?	1	1	0	0
Whale	1	1	1	1	1	1	1	0	?	1	0	1	1	0	0	0	?	1	0	0
Hippo	0	?	0	1	1	1	1	0	1	1	0	1	1	0	0	0	?	1	0	0
Pig	0	0	0	?	0	0	0	0	?	0	0	0	?	?	0	0	0	1	1	1
Peccary	?	?	?	?	?	?	?	?	?	?	?	?	?	?	?	?	?	?	1	1
Camel	0	0	0	0	0	0	0	0	0	0	0	0	0	0	0	0	0	0	0	0

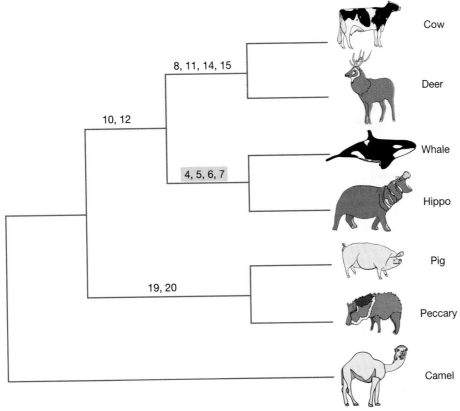

Figure 13.7 Nearly perfect phylogenetic characters? This table shows the presence (1) or absence (0) of a SINE or LINE at 20 loci in the genomes of six artiodactyls and a whale (Baird's beaked whale, *Berardius bairdii*). Question marks (?) indicate loci that could not be found in some taxa. Data from Nikaido et al. (1999). The phylogenetic tree was produced by a parsimony analysis of these 20 characters. Four retroposon insertions, at loci 4–7, define a clade of whales and hippos. No insertion events give contradictory information about the relationships among these groups. In other words, there are no homoplasies in these characters.

Research programs based on estimating and interpreting evolutionary trees are growing rapidly (Hillis 1997). In the remainder of this chapter, our goal is to sample the diversity of applications for phylogenetic thinking. This discussion will set the stage for reviewing the history of life in Chapters 14 through 16.

Rates of Change: Radiation of Hawaiian Fruit Flies

Some of our most basic questions about the history of life concern when major events occurred, and how rapidly. In Chapter 15, we introduce events that have been dated from the fossil record. Here, we look at how data on rates of divergence in a protein were used to time a major episode in evolution.

The 500-plus species of fruit flies endemic to the Hawaiian archipelago rank as one of the most spectacular of all sequences of speciation and divergence events known. The oldest island, Kauai, is 5–6 million years old, implying that speciation was extraordinarily rapid. But divergence times estimated from molecular data suggest a very different view. (Box 13.3 explains how divergence times can be estimated from molecular data—a phenomenon known as the **molecular clock**.)

To determine when flies first colonized the Hawaiian archipelago, Stephen Beverly and Allan Wilson (1985) estimated how extensively larval hemolymph

BOX 13.3 The molecular clock

Many of the uses of a phylogeny (and many questions about the evolution of organisms) have inspired evolutionary biologists to ask about the age of particular evolutionary events or taxonomic groups. Fossils give direct minimum estimates of the ages of clades in a phylogeny. However, if the characters used for phylogenetic analysis could themselves be shown to evolve with clock-like regularity, then ages of nodes in a tree could be estimated from the number or amount of character change without direct observations from the fossil record. This hypothesis, called the molecular clock, originated with Emile Zuckerkandl and Linus Pauling (1962) and was promoted and elaborated throughout the 1970s and 1980s in a series of papers from Allan Wilson's laboratory. (See Wilson 1985.) The neutral theory of molecular evolution (see Chapter 18) later provided a theoretical basis for expecting that certain nucleotide changes should accumulate at a rate equal to the mutation rate. If this mutation rate does not change much over time, and if generation times are similar, then the number of neutral molecular differences between two taxa should be proportional to the age of their most recent common ancestor. The prospect of estimating the age of nodes in a molecular phylogeny from the molecular data themselves has tremendous appeal. The idea was to calculate the rate of molecular divergence in groups where the time of divergence was known from the fossil record and then use this calibration to date divergence times in groups with no fossil record.

How fast does a particular molecular clock run? Eldredge Bermingham and Harilaos Lessios (1993), for example, estimated mitochondrial DNA (mtDNA) sequence divergence in sister species of sea urchins found on either side of the Isthmus of Panama. Because the land bridge between North and South America separated these populations about 3 million years ago, the authors were able to calibrate the amount of sequence

divergence for absolute time. The urchins provide an estimate of 1.8% to 2.2% divergence per million years for a protein-coding gene—remarkably close to the rate of mtDNA-sequence divergence of mammals (Brown et al. 1979). Similar mtDNA calibrations have been made in butterflies (Brower 1994) and geese (Shields and Wilson 1987).

Many such clocks have eventually proven to be unreliable. Nancy Knowlton and her colleagues (Knowlton et al. 1993; Knowlton and Weigt 1998) examined similar mtDNA sequence data, as well as allozyme data for pairs of sister species of snapping shrimp (genus *Alpheus*). These shrimp had also been separated from each other by the Panamian land bridge. We discussed this same example as a study of speciation through a vicariance event in Chapter 12. Knowlton and her colleagues found that pairs of sister species varied widely in their genetic divergence. Because the genetic differences for mtDNA were correlated with allozyme differences within pairs of *Alpheus* species, the variation among pairs of species probably arose because some pairs were isolated on either side of the rising land bridge up to 15 Ma before the final closure of the seaway. Knowlton concluded that many other studies using the Panamian land bridge or other biogeographic events may provide poor estimates of divergence dates based on sequence differences. This is because the ages of the biogeographic events do not correspond closely to the actual times when lineages of organisms became separate from each other and stopped interbreeding. Other departures from clock-like molecular evolution may arise from variation in mutation rate (Martin et al. 1992; Martin and Palumbi 1993) or generation time (Martin and Palumbi 1993; Hillis et al. 1996). As a result of such problems, researchers are cautious about applying molecular clocks to interpret phylogenies (Hillis et al. 1996).

protein (LHP) has diverged in a series of Hawaiian flies and outgroup species. They used these data to estimate the phylogeny of the Hawaiian flies and outgroup species (Figure 13.8). Beverly and Wilson (1984) could also estimate the *rate* of evolution of LHP, from comparisons of LHP differences between other fly groups in which the time of divergence was already known. In other words, they could calibrate a molecular clock for fly LHP (see Box 13.3). This allowed them to date each of the major nodes on the phylogenetic tree for Hawaiian flies. The analysis pointed to a startling conclusion: The amount of LHP difference among Hawaiian flies (compared to LHP differences among flies with known age of divergence) implied that Hawaiian flies first colonized the archipelago some 42 million years ago. This was long before the existing Hawaiian islands were formed.

How can this be? Recall, from our discussion of fly speciation in Chapter 12, that the Hawaiian islands originated from a hot spot under the Pacific plate. These volcanic islands drift to the north and west after they are formed and gradually erode, eventually becoming underwater mountains called seamounts. Many of the landforms in the chain have been dated using the radiometric dating techniques introduced in Chapter 2, confirming the old-to-new sequence. In Figure 13.8, this picture of island formation is matched to the fly phylogeny, the LHP divergence data, and the dates implied by the molecular clock.

Taken together, the geographical, phylogenetic, and clock data offer a logical resolution to the paradox of "young islands, old flies." *Drosophila* first colonized the Hawaiian chain when the islands that are now in the Koko seamount were over the hot spot. As these older islands eroded and new islands were formed, the flies hopped from the old landforms to new. This "ancient origin" hypothesis for Hawaiian flies has now been confirmed by investigators using different gene sequences and independent clock calibrations (see DeSalle and Hunt 1987). Hawaiian crickets, in contrast, have radiated solely on the current group of islands (Shaw 1996).

The Age of Clades

When the origin and duration of a lineage is well-documented in the fossil record, branching points on a phylogeny can be directly aligned with an absolute time scale. This combination of phylogenetic and geological information can lead to some surprising results. Luis Chiappe (1995) was able to use dates from the fossil record to scale his cladogram of Mesozoic era bird groups for time (Figure 13.9). Adding information on time enriches the interpretation of this phylogeny. It is clear that several of the major bird lineages disappeared 65 million years ago, during the mass extinction event at the Cretaceous–Tertiary boundary. Even more interesting is that the branching patterns and the chronology do not align closely in every case. Look again at the tree in Figure 13.9. Note that the early dates documented for *Archaeopteryx* and the group called Enantiornithes dictate that branches 1–4 must be placed deep in time. But fossil material that old had not been found from the derived groups called Dromaeosauridae, Alvarezsauridae, and the genus *Iberomesornis*. The placement of branches 5–7 in the early Cretaceous is also startling, because fossil material that old has not yet been found. The point is that many of the branches on this tree have to be much longer than the current fossil record indicates (that is, they have to go further back in time.) The cladogram thus makes a strong prediction: Older representatives of these three fossil taxa will eventually be

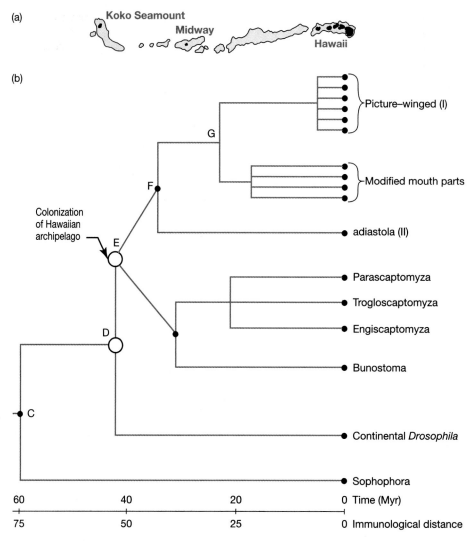

(a)

Koko Seamount

Midway

Hawaii

(b)

G

F

Picture–winged (I)

Modified mouth parts

adiastola (II)

Colonization
of Hawaiian
archipelago

E

Parascaptomyza

Trogloscaptomyza

Engiscaptomyza

D

Bunostoma

C

Continental *Drosophila*

Sophophora

60	40	20	0 Time (Myr)
75	50	25	0 Immunological distance

Figure 13.8   Young islands, old flies   Part (a) in this diagram shows the Hawaiian archipel-ago, scaled so that the age of the landforms corresponds to the absolute time scale at the bottom of the figure. Islands are shown in black and the extent of undersea structures is outlined in beige. The phylogeny of fruit flies, part (b), is based on clustering of genetic distance between larval he-molymph proteins (LHP). The branch lengths are scaled so that a molecular-clock calibration for di-vergence in LHP corresponds to the absolute time scale at the bottom of the figure. The "Picture-winged" through "Bunostoma" designations on the right refer to subgroups of Hawaiian fruit flies. The outgroup called Sophophora is represented by the common household fruit fly, *Drosophila melanogaster*. Node E, then, represents the ancestral population that first colonized the Hawaiian islands. From Beverly and Wilson (1985).

Note that several nodes are reported as polytomies (among species within the picture-winged group, for example). These branch points cannot be distinguished on the basis of LHP distance. Note also that the picture-winged group has radiated within the last 5 million years, solely within the current group of Hawaiian islands.

found. In at least one case, this prediction may have been confirmed. Xing Xu and colleagues (1999) discovered and described an early Cretaceous dro-maeosaurid from China. Their discovery extends the fossil record for dro-maeosaurids to near the predicted age of this group, based on Chiappe's estimate for the phylogeny.

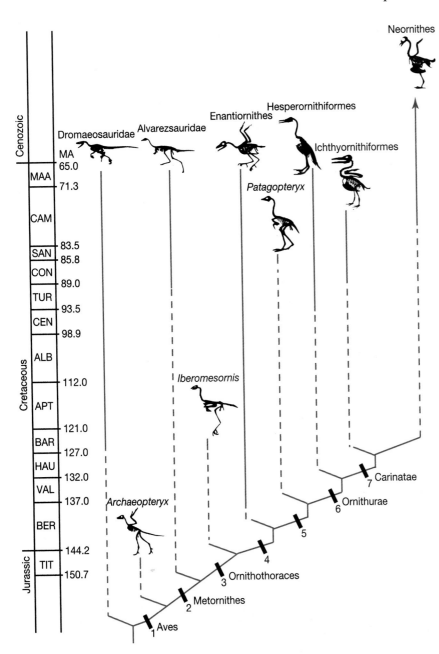

Figure 13.9 A phylogeny of fossil birds, scaled for time This is the same cladogram given in Figure 13.1, modified to reflect additional information on times of divergence and the duration of branches. The scale at the left of this diagram gives the era or period, stage, and absolute age of the events depicted in this phylogeny. The solid vertical branches leading to each taxon represent intervals where fossil representatives of a lineage have been found; the dashed bars represent intervals where fossil forms are yet to be discovered. From Chiappe (1995).

Classifying the Diversity of Life

The phylogenetic species concept, introduced in Chapter 12, considers every population that occupies a tip on an evolutionary tree as a different species. What does phylogenetic thinking have to say about how we should organize higher-order taxa such as genera, families, orders, and classes?

Traditional classifications group organisms according to similar features. This is called a **phenetic** approach. Phylogenetic schemes for classifying organisms, in contrast, are based on evolutionary relationships. Phylogenetic systematics argues that classification systems should be tree-based, with names and categories that reflect the actual sequence of branching events. According to this point of view, only

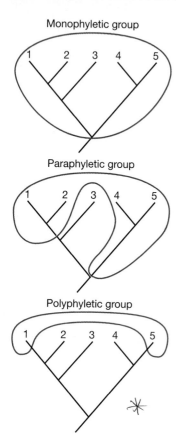

Monophyletic group

Paraphyletic group

Polyphyletic group

Figure 13.10 Monophyletic, paraphyletic, and polyphyletic groups Taxonomic groups can be monophyletic, paraphyletic, or polyphyletic. Monophyletic groups, or clades, contain all the descendants of a common ancestor. Paraphyletic groups contain some, but not all, the descendants of a common ancestor. A polyphyletic grouping does not contain the most recent common ancestor of all the taxa.

In a cladistic classification, only monophyletic groups are named. In contrast, traditional taxonomic schemes occasionally assign names to polyphyletic and paraphyletic groups.

monophyletic groups, which include all descendants of a common ancestor, are named (Figure 13.10).

Although phenetic and phylogenetic naming schemes frequently lead to the same conclusions, they can produce conflicts (see Schwenk 1994). The relationship between whales and ungulates is one of many recent examples. A cladistic classification would nest whales as a subgroup within the Artiodactyla (Figure 13.5), which in turn are a subgroup of the Mammalia. The important break from traditional mammalian classification in this case would be the reduction of the Cetacea from a high-level taxon (an order) to a low-level group (perhaps a subfamily related to hippos).

Phylogenetic systematics represents an important philosophical break from classical approaches to taxonomy (de Queiroz and Gauthier 1992; Simpson and Cracraft 1995). An increasing number of taxonomists and systematists are calling for a complete overhaul of the traditional phenetic scheme, the goal being to create a phylogenetic classification (see Pennisi 1996). A phylogenetic naming scheme is already being implemented in prominent forums like GenBank, the online database of DNA sequences. However, some organismal biologists disagree. For example, whale specialists might object that a strictly phylogenetic scheme for naming and ranking groups would ignore the many functionally and ecologically important differences between whales and other artiodactyls. Ungulate specialists might also object that classifying whales within the Artiodactyla detracts from the unity of form found among the rest of the artiodactyls (apart from whales).

Coevolution

Coevolution is an umbrella term for interactions among species that result in reciprocal adaptation. We introduced this field of research in Chapter 8, when we discussed predation, mutualism, and parasitism. Here, we introduce how phylogenetic thinking is used in coevolutionary studies. Our focal system is ants that farm fungi.

The 200 species of ants in the tribe Attini are the dominant herbivores in the New World tropics. The group includes the leaf-cutting ants, which dissect pieces from leaves and carry them to their nests. There, they use the leaf material as a substrate for growing fungi in underground gardens. The fungi are harvested and serve as the primary food source for the ant colony. This symbiosis, or mutually beneficial relationship, between ants and fungi is thought to be 50 million years old. This time estimate is based on the first appearance of attine ants in the fossil record. The relationship is also obligate: To the best of our knowledge, none of the symbiotic ant or fungal species can live without the other.

We would like to answer the following question about this association: If the symbiosis originated just once, did the ants and fungi subsequently evolve in tandem? That is, did the two groups "cospeciate"? If so, we would expect the phylogenies of the two groups to be congruent (match up branch for branch).

To answer this question, Gregory Hinkle and colleagues (1994) collected fungi from the nests of five different species of attine ants and sequenced over 1800 base pairs from the coding region for the small subunit of their ribosomal RNA. They used these data to estimate the phylogeny of the attine fungi and several outgroups, using a parsimony criterion. When they matched the fungal phylogeny to a cladogram for the attine ants, they found a close correspondence: Branching patterns were identical in four of the five species compared (Figure 13.11). This is strong support for the idea that the ants and fungi have cospeciated. The fifth fungus–farming ant species, however, posed a dilemma. The sequence data were unable to resolve the relationship of the fungus used by the ant *Apterostigma collare* relative to free-living and symbiotic forms. If this fungus branched earlier than the free-living forms in the polytomy shown in Figure 13.11, it breaks the pattern of cospeciation. If so, it means that ants acquired fungal symbionts more than once, or that some fungi have escaped from the farms to resume a free-living lifestyle.

A study performed by Ignacio Chapela et al. (1994) has helped clarify the history of mutualism. These researchers sequenced the 28S rRNA gene in 37 species of ant-associated and free-living fungi and matched the branching pattern inferred from these data to the same ant phylogeny shown in Figure 13.11. Their analysis clearly shows that the *Apterostigma* fungus split earlier than free-living forms in the polytomy we just examined (Figure 13.12). This confirms that strict cospeciation has not been universal in the coevolution of the attine ants and fungi. Early in the evolution of ant–fungi symbiosis, some ants that farmed fungi switched species, picking up new, free-living fungi to "domesticate." Cospeciation has occurred only in the most recently evolved forms.

It is noteworthy that, in at least some of these highly derived ant genera, like *Trachymyrmex* and *Atta*, queens that leave established nests to found new colonies carry a small ball of fungus with them, and use it to start a new garden. This behavior, which should lead to strict cospeciation, has not been found in the older lineages like *Apterostigma* and *Myrmicocrypta*.

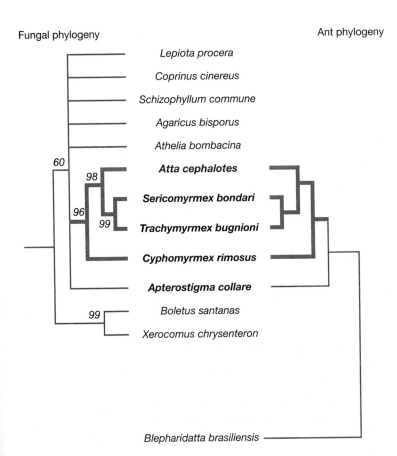

Fungal phylogeny

Ant phylogeny

Figure 13.11   Comparing phylogenies of fungi and their ant symbionts I   The left side of this figure shows the phylogeny of five species of fungi cultivated by ants, along with several free-living fungi. The free-living forms are shown in light type and the symbiotic forms in bold type. Note that the free-living forms included in the study are ancestral to the species cultivated by ants. This observation confirms that symbiosis is a derived trait. The numbers indicate the percentage of bootstrapped trees that include given branches; branches that appeared in less than 50% of the bootstrapped replicates were collapsed into polytomies.

The right side of the figure shows the phylogeny of some fungal-farming ants. The topology is based on synapomorphies identified in the morphology of prepupal worker larva. The names in bold type are the names of ants that farm fungi; *Blepharidatta* serves as an outgroup.

The thick red lines highlight the congruence between ants and the fungi they farm. From Hinkle et al. (1994).

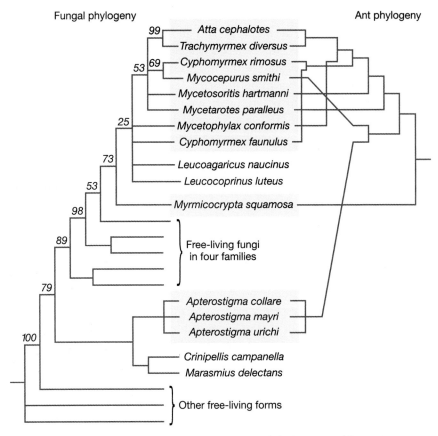

Figure 13.12　Comparing phylogenies of fungi and their ant symbionts II　The left side of this figure (Chapela et al. 1994) shows the phylogeny of fungi cultivated by ants, along with free-living fungi. The free-living forms are shown on a light background and the symbiotic forms in a shaded background. This is a strict consensus tree of the 22 equally most-parsimonious trees (meaning that only branches found in all 22 best trees are shown). The numbers indicate the percentage of bootstrapped phylogenies that include given branches. The right side of the figure shows the phylogeny of fungal-farming ants, based on the same cladistic data used in Figure 13.16.

　　To interpret this (very complicated) diagram, begin by tracing the ant tree up from the base. Note that the first lineage to branch off leads to *Myrmicocrypta squamosa*. If cospeciation were occurring, the next branch off should have led to *Leucocoprinus* or *Leucoagaricus*. Instead it leads to *Apterostigma*. This means that ants "domesticated" free-living fungal species more than once. Now read from the fungal side of the paired phylogenies. Note that *Leucocoprinus* and *Leucoagaricus* are part of an ant-associated clade. This fact suggests that these fungal species escaped domestication and again became free-living.

The Spread of AIDS

In Chapter 1, we used the biology of HIV to illustrate the kinds of questions and answers that occupy evolutionary biologists. Phylogeny inference methods are being used to understand the origins of emerging viruses like HIV and how AIDS and other diseases spread. In the early 1990s, an HIV-positive dentist in Florida was suspected of transmitting the virus to one of his patients. In response, many of his patients were tested for the presence of the virus. Several tested positive. Did they get the virus from the dentist? This was unclear, because some had other risk factors for transmission. To answer the question, investigators from the Centers for Disease Control sequenced the *gp120* gene from viruses in infected patients and

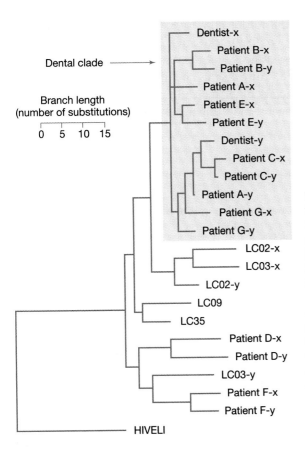

Dental clade

Branch length
(number of substitutions)

0   5   10   15

Figure 13.13 **Using a phylogeny to determine the history of HIV transmission** This tree shows the evolutionary relationships among human immunodeficiency viruses collected from a Florida dentist, a series of his patients, and HIV-positive individuals from the same geographic area (denoted as LC) in the early 1990s. The *x* and *y* designations refer to different HIV clones cultured from the same individual, at different times. The outgroup, called HIVELI, is from an African HIV-1 sequence.

Reading up the tree, the first branch-off identifies a clade that includes a local individual (LC03-*y*) who was *not* a patient of the dentist, along with patients D and F. The existence of this branch shows that these patients did not get the virus from the dentist; it happens that these individuals had other risk factors for transmission. The clade enclosed by the tan box, however, suggests that the virus that infected the dentist in the late 1980s is ancestral to those found in patients A, B, C, E, and G (and in the dentist) in the early 1990s. These five patients did not have other risk factors for the disease, suggesting that they contracted the virus while being treated by the dentist. From Hillis et al. (1994).

infected nonpatients, and estimated the viruses' evolutionary relationships (Ou et al. 1992). The resulting tree clearly demarcated a "dental clade" (Figure 13.13). This defined a group of individuals in whom the *gp120* sequences were closely related to the *gp120* sequences of the dentist, leading to the conclusion that these patients (but not others) had acquired the AIDS virus from the dentist. This conclusion was immediately controversial (DeBry et al. 1993) but has been confirmed (Hillis et al. 1994). The fact that transmission was confirmed helped promulgate extensive changes in the practice of dentistry *and* medicine. The changes were designed to decrease the risk of transmission from health care providers to patients and vice versa.

Summary

Recent conceptual and technological advances have revolutionized our ability to estimate phylogenies accurately. Research in systematics is advancing rapidly, and phylogenetic thinking is beginning to pervade evolutionary biology.

The first step in estimating a phylogeny is to select and measure characters that can be phylogenetically informative. The molecular or morphological characters employed in phylogeny inference have to be independent, homologous, variable among the taxa in the study, and resistant to homoplasy. The second step in phylogeny inference is to decide whether a parsimony, maximum likelihood, or distance method is most appropriate for analyzing the data in hand. Parsimony approaches are implemented by reconstructing the pattern of change in each character that implies the smallest number of character state changes. This process is repeated for each character on each candidate tree. Several different computer algorithms can be employed to search among the very large number of trees that are possible and evaluate them. Under parsimony, for example, the best tree is the one on which the smallest number of changes (across all characters) is implied for the data available. Then, a variety of statistical techniques can be used to evaluate the degree of support for the whole tree or for specific clades.

Phylogenetic thinking has been applied to a wide variety of problems in evolutionary biology, from the transmission of HIV to systems for classifying the diversity of life. Informative uses of phylogenies include dating events that are poorly documented in the fossil record, studying the rate and pattern of evolution in characters other than those used in constructing the phylogeny, and studying coevolution.

Questions

1. Mammals with high-crowned teeth, which are well suited for grazing, include some rodents (Rodentia), rabbits and hares (Lagomorpha), most cloven-hoofed animals (Artiodactyla), horses (Perissodactyla), and elephants (Proboscidea). Examine Figure 13.14, which shows the relationships of these and other mammalian orders. Are high-crowned teeth a synapomorphy (e.g., did the last common ancestor of mammals have high-crowned teeth) or have they arisen via convergent evolution?

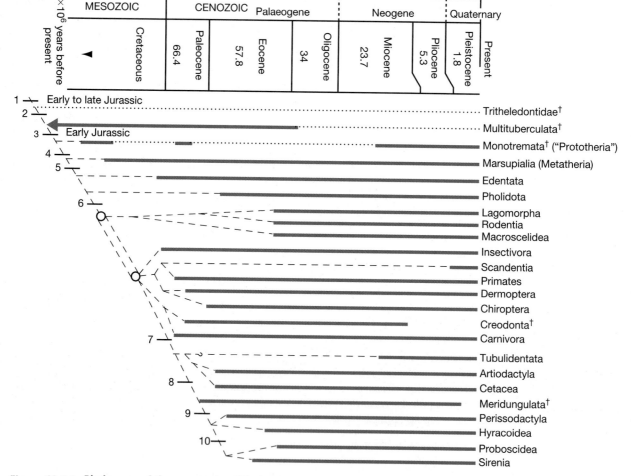

Figure 13.14 Phylogeny of the mammals This cladogram was modifed by Pough et al. (1996) based on work by Michael Novacek (1992, 1993). The names given along the right of the tree refer to mammalian orders. The numbers across branches refer to synapomorphies listed in Pough et al. The dark branches indicate the presence of fossil forms. The dashed lines indicate when the presence of an order has to be inferred.

2. The *gp120* gene of HIV evolves so quickly that clones of the virus from the HIV-positive Florida dentist (labelled Dentist-*x* and Dentist-*y* in Figure 13.13) evolved many nucleotide differences between the time that patients were infected in the late 1980s and the time that viral samples were collected from the dentist and his patients in the early 1990s. As a result, the two *gp120* sequences from the dentist are not very closely related to each other. Imagine, instead, that Ou et al. (1992) had found the Dentist-*x* and Dentist-*y* viral clones to be sister groups arising from the basal node of the dental clade (Figure 13.15 compared to Figure 13.13). How would this affect your hypothesis about the history and source of the infections of patients A, B, C, E, and G (and the dentist himself)? Would you still conclude that the den-

tist had transmitted the virus to each of these patients independently? What more parsimonious explanation could be found if this had been the result observed by Ou et al.?

3. In what sense do the HIV-positive local individuals included in Figure 10.3 serve as a control?

4. Examine the three primate phylogenies shown in Figure 13.16. Figure 13.16a shows a detailed phylogeny for most Old World primates, Figure 13.16b emphasizes relationships of great apes and humans, and Figure 13.16c emphasizes relationships of Old World monkeys. Do the three phylogenies agree with each other? (That is, do they show the same relationships and the same order of branching?) Do they give different impressions of whether there was a "goal" of primate evolution, or of what the "highest" primate is? If so, what aspects of the figures give the impression of a goal, and is this truly reflected in the complete data set? (*Sources:* data for great apes from various sources listed in Chapter 16; data for macaques from Hayasaka, K., Fujii, K., and Horai, S. 1996. Molecular phylogeny of macaques: Implications of nucleotide sequences from an 896-base pair region of mitochondrial DNA. *Molecular Biology and Evolution* 13:1044–1053.)

5. For several centuries, biologists have used the Linnaean system of classification, in which all species are assigned a spot in a hierarchy with seven major tiers (kingdom, phylum, class, order, family, genus, species). As explained in the text, some biologists have called for the abolition of the Linnaean system and the institution of new names, such as "Tetrapoda" and "Certartiodactyla," for each major evolutionary branching event. In this new system,

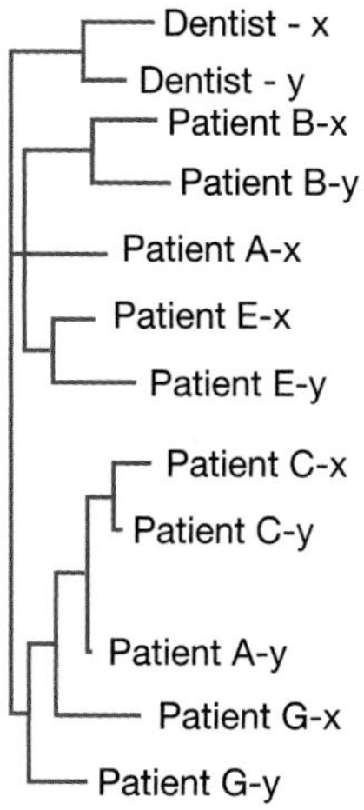

Figure 13.15   An alternative phylogeny of HIV *gp120* sequences

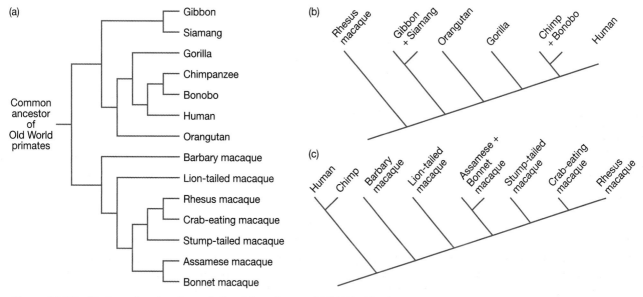

Figure 13.16   **Phylogenies showing relationships of several Old World primates**   (Branch lengths are not scaled.)

what would determine the number of tiers required to classify a species? Would different species have the same number of tiers? The Linnaean system gives extra weight to those evolutionary branching events that produced noticeable morphological innovations, such as the evolution of birds (see text). Do you think it is worthwhile to distinguish between those branching events that produced noticeable morphological innovation and those that did not?

6. In Figure 13.5, site 192 was considered "variable but uninformative." Why is it uninformative?

7. Why does a fossil provide only a minimum age for its taxon?

8. Suppose it were discovered that aquatic mammals show convergence in milk proteins—e.g., suppose a certain form of milk protein, with certain amino acids in key positions, is particularly beneficial for aquatic mammals. How would that affect your interpretation of the milk casein data shown in Figure 13.5?

9. Do base pairs from different positions in one gene represent independent information? Why do evolutionary geneticists try to include as many genes in their analysis as their computers can handle?

10. In the late 1990s, hundreds of fossils of primitive birds were discovered in northeastern China, including birds with various combinations of traits 4, 5, and 6 of Figure 13.9 (see, for example, Martin & Zhou 1997; Hou et al. 1996, 1999). Early reports dated these fossil beds as late Jurassic. Does this match the predictions of Figure 10.8? The late Jurassic date was later shown to be incorrect—do you think the corrected date is likely to be earlier or later? Look up Swisher et al.'s 1999 paper to see if you are right.

Exploring the Literature

11. Leading phylogenetic systematists are now maintaining World Wide Web sites containing finished trees for all types of life forms and/or copies of the raw data sets used to estimate phylogenies. One major effort is called The Tree of Life (http://www.phylogeny.arizona.edu/tree/phylogeny.html). For background on this effort and the addresses of some key sites, see Morell (1996) and the Web site associated with this text.

12. Phylogenetic studies of coevolution are a booming research area. For entrees to the literature on relationships between flowering plants and herbivorous insects, fungal–algal relationships in lichen, and the evolution of warning coloration in butterflies, see

> Brower, A. V. Z. 1996. Parallel race formation and the evolution of mimicry in *Heliconius* butterflies: A phylogenetic hypothesis from mitochondrial DNA sequences. *Evolution* 50: 195–221.

> Farrell, B. D. 1998. Inordinate fondness explained: Why are there so many beetles? *Science* 281: 555–559.

> Gargas, A., P. T. DePriest, M. Grube, and A. Tehler. 1995. Multiple origins of lichen symbioses in fungi suggested by SSU rDNA phylogeny. *Science* 268: 1492–1495.

13. Mapping traits onto phylogenies has confirmed or challenged several traditional views of how traits evolved. The following papers offer a test of how social behavior evolved in wasps, insight into the evolution of endothermy in fish, an analysis of the evolution of self-fertilization in a family of flowering plants, and a general review of the field.

> Block, B. A., J. R. Finnerty, A. F. R. Stewart, and J. Kidd. 1993. Evolution of endothermy in fish: Mapping physiological traits on a molecular phylogeny. *Science* 260: 210–214.

> Carpenter, J. M. 1989. Testing scenarios: Wasp social behavior. *Cladistics* 5: 131–144.

> Kohn, J. R., S. W. Graham, B. Morton, J. J. Doyle, and S. C. H. Barrett. 1996. Reconstruction of the evolution of reproductive characters in Pontederiaceae using phylogenetic evidence from chloroplast DNA restriction-site variation. *Evolution* 50: 1454–1469.

> Maddison, D. R. 1994. Phylogenetic methods for inferring the evolutionary history and processes of change in discretely valued characters. *Annual Review of Entomology* 39: 267–292.

Citations

Bajpai, S., and P. D. Gingerich. 1998. A new Eocene archaeocete (Mammalia, Cetacea) from India and the time of origin of whales. *Proceedings of the National Academy of Sciences, USA* 95: 15464–15468.

Bermingham, E., and H.A . Lessios. 1993. Rate variation of protein and mitochondrial DNA evolution as revealed by sea urchins separated by the Isthmus of Panama. *Proceedings of the National Academy of Sciences, USA* 90: 2734–2738.

Beverly, S. M., and A. C. Wilson. 1984. Molecular evolution in *Drosophila* and the higher Diptera II. A time scale for fly evolution. *Journal of Molecular Evolution* 21: 1–13.

Beverly, S. M., and A. C. Wilson. 1985. Ancient origin for Hawaiian Drosophilinae inferred from protein comparisons. *Proceedings of the National Academy of Sciences, USA* 82: 4753–4757.

Bremer, K. 1994. Branch support and tree stability. *Cladistics* 10: 295–304.

Brower, A. V. Z. 1994. Rapid morphological radiation and convergence among races of the butterfly *Heliconius erato*, inferred from patterns of mitochondrial DNA evolution. *Proceedings of the National Academy of Sciences, USA* 91: 6491–6495.

Brown, W. M., M. George, Jr., and A. C. Wilson. 1979. Rapid evolution of animal mitochondrial DNA. *Proceedings of the National Academy of Sciences, USA* 76: 1967–1971.

Chapela, I. H., S. A. Rehner, T. R. Schultz, and U. G. Mueller. 1994. Evolutionary history of the symbiosis between fungus-growing ants and their fungi. *Science* 266: 1691–1694.

Chiappe, L. M. 1995. The first 85 million years of avian evolution. *Nature* 378: 349–355.

DeBry, R. W., L. G. Abele, S. H. Weiss, M. D. Hill, M. Bouzas, E. Lorenzo, F. Graebnitz, and L. Resnick. 1993. Dental HIV transmission? *Nature* 361: 691.

DeSalle, R., and J. A. Hunt. 1987. Molecular evolution in Hawaiian drosphilids. *Trends in Ecology and Evolution* 2: 212–215.

Dixon, M. T., and D. M. Hillis. 1993. Ribosomal RNA structure: Compensatory mutations and implications for phylogenetic analysis. *Molecular Biology and Evolution* 10: 256–267.

Eldredge, N., and J. Cracraft. 1980. *Phylogenetic Patterns and the Evolutionary Process.* New York: Columbia University Press.

Felsenstein, J. 1978. Cases in which parsimony or compatibility methods will be positively misleading. *Systematic Zoology* 27: 401–410.

Felsenstein, J. 1981. Evolutionary trees from DNA sequences: A maximum likelihood approach. *Journal of Molecular Evolution* 17: 368–376.

Felsenstein, J. 1983. Parsimony in systematics: Biological and statistical issues. *Annual Review of Ecology and Systematics* 14: 313–333.

Felsenstein, J. 1985. Confidence limits on phylogenies: An approach using the bootstrap. *Evolution* 39: 783–791.

Flower, W. H. 1883. On whales, present and past and their probable origin. *Proceedings of the Zoological Society of London* 1883: 466–513.

Gatesy, J., M. Milinkovitch, V. Waddell, and M. Stanhope. 1999. Stability of cladistic relationships between Cetacea and higher-level artiodactyl taxa. *Systematic Biology* 48: 6–20.

Gingerich, P. D., B. H. Smith, and E. L. Simons. 1990. Hind limbs of Eocene *Basilosaurus*: Evidence of feet in whales. *Science* 249: 154–157.

Hennig, W. 1979. *Phylogenetic Systematics.* Urbana: University of Illinois Press.

Hillis, D. M. 1997. Biology recapitulates phylogeny. *Science* 276: 218–219.

Hillis, D. M. 1999. SINEs of the perfect character. *Proceedings of the National Academy of Sciences, USA* 96: 9979–9981.

Hillis, D. M., and J. J. Bull. 1993. An empirical test of bootstrapping as a method for assessing confidence in phylogenetic analysis. *Systematic Biology* 42: 182–192.

Hillis, D. M., J. P. Huelsenbeck, and C. W. Cunningham. 1994. Application and accuracy of molecular phylogenies. *Science* 264: 671–677.

Hillis, D. M., B. K. Mable, and C. Moritz. 1996. Applications of molecular systematics: The state of the field and a look to the future. In D. M. Hillis, C. Moritz, and B. K. Mable, eds. *Molecular Systematics.* Sunderland, MA: Sinauer, 515–543.

Hinkle, G., J. K. Wetterer, T. R. Schultz, and M. L. Sogin. 1994. Phylogeny of the attine ant fungi based on analysis of small subunit ribosomal RNA gene sequences. *Science* 266: 1695–1697.

Hou, L-H., L. D. Martin, Z-H. Zhou, and A. Feduccia. 1996. Early adaptive radiation of birds: Evidence from fossils from northeastern China. *Science* 274: 1164–1167.

Hou, L-H., L. D Martin, Z-H. Zhou, A. Feduccia, and F. Zhang. 1999. A diapsid skull in a new species of the primitive bird *Confuciusornis*. *Nature* 399: 679–682.

Huelsenbeck, J. P., and D. M. Hillis. 1993. Success of phylogenetic methods in the four-taxon case. *Systematic Biology* 42: 247–264.

Huelsenbeck, J. P., and B. Rannala. 1997. Phylogenetic methods come of age: Testing hypotheses in an evolutionary context. *Science* 276: 227–232.

Kimura, M. 1980. A simple method for estimating evolutionary rates of base substitution through comparative studies of nucleotide sequences. *Journal of Molecular Evolution* 16: 111–120.

Knowlton, N., L. A. Weigt, L. A. Solorzano, D. K. Mills, and E. Bermingham. 1993. Divergence in proteins, mitochondrial DNA, and reproductive compatibility across the Isthmus of Panama. *Science* 260: 1629–1632.

Knowlton, N., and L. A. Weigt. 1998. New dates and new rates for divergence across the Isthmus of Panama. *Proceedings of the Royal Society of London, Series B* 265: 2257–2263.

Luckett, W. P., and N. Hong. 1998. Phylogenetic relationships between the orders Artiodactyla and Cetacea: A combined assessment of morphological and molecular evidence. *Journal of Mammalian Evolution* 5: 127–182.

Maddison, W. P., M. J. Donoghue, and D. R. Maddison. 1984. Outgroup comparison and parsimony. *Systematic Zoology* 33: 83–103.

Martin, A. P., G. J. P. Naylor, and S. R. Palumbi. 1992. Rates of mitochondrial DNA evolution in sharks are slow compared with mammals. *Nature* 357: 153–155.

Martin, A. P., and S. R. Palumbi. 1993. Body size, metabolic rate, generation time, and the molecular clock. *Proceedings of the National Academy of Sciences, USA* 90: 4087–4091.

Martin, L. D., and Z. Zhou. 1997. Archaeopteryx-like skull in enantiornithine bird. *Nature* 389:556.

Mayden, R. L., and E. O. Wiley. 1992. The fundamentals of phylogenetic systematics. In R. L. Mayden, ed. *Systematics, Historical Ecology, and North American Freshwater Fishes.* Stanford, CA: Stanford University Press, 114–185.

Milinkovitch, M. C., and J. G. M. Thewissen. 1997. Even-toed fingerprints on whale ancestry. *Nature* 388: 622–624.

Morell, V. 1996. Web-crawling up the tree of life. *Science* 273: 568–570.

Nelson, G., and N. Platnick. 1981. *Systematics and Biogeography: Cladistics and Vicariance.* New York: Columbia University Press.

Nikaido, M., A. P. Rooney, and N. Okada. 1999. Phylogenetic relationships among cetartiodactyls based on insertions of short and long interspersed elements: Hippopotamuses are the closest extant relatives of whales. *Proceedings of the National Academy of Sciences, USA* 96:10261–10266.

Novacek, M. J. 1992. Mammalian phylogeny: Shaking the tree. *Nature* 356: 121–125.

Novacek, M. J. 1993. Reflections on higher mammalian phylogenetics. *Journal of Mammalian Evolution* 1: 3–30.

O'Leary, M. A., and J. H. Geisler. 1999. The position of Cetacea within Mammalia: Phylogenetic analysis of morphological data from extinct and extant taxa. *Systematic Biology* 48: 455–490.

Ou, C.-Y., Carol A. Ciesielski, G. Myers, C. I. Bandea, C.-C. Luo, B. T. M. Korber, J. I. Mullins, G. Schochetman, R. L. Berkelman, A. N. Economou, J. J. Witte, L. J. Furman, G. A. Satten, K. A. MacInnes, J. W. Curran, H. W. Jaffe, Laboratory Investigation Group, and Epidemiologic Investigation Group. 1992. Molecular epidemiology of HIV transmission in a dental practice. *Science* 256: 1165–1171.

Pennisi, E. 1996. Evolutionary and systematic biologists converge. *Science* 273: 181–182.

Pough, F. H., J. B. Heiser, and W. N. McFarland. 1996. *Vertebrate Life.* Upper Saddle River, NJ: Prentice Hall.

Prothero, D. R., E. M. Manning, and M. Fischer. 1988. The phylogeny of the ungulates. In M. J. Benton, ed. *The phylogeny and classification of the tetrapods, Volume 2—Mammals.* Oxford: Clarendon Press, 201–234.

de Queiroz, K., and J. Gauthier. 1992. Phylogenetic taxonomy. *Annual Review of Ecology and Systematics* 23: 449–480.

Schaeffer, B. 1948. The origin of a mammalian ordinal character. *Evolution* 2: 164–175.

Schwenk, K. 1994. Comparative biology and the importance of cladistic classification: A case study from the sensory biology of squamate reptiles. *Biological Journal of the Linnaean Society* 52: 69–82.

Shaw, K. L. 1996. Sequential radiations and patterns of speciation in the Hawaiian cricket genus *Laupala* inferred from DNA sequences. *Evolution* 50: 237–255.

Shields, G. F., and A. C. Wilson. 1987. Calibration of mitochondrial DNA evolution in geese. *Journal of Molecular Evolution* 24: 212–217.

Simpson, B. B., and J. Cracraft. 1995. Systematics: The science of biodiversity. *BioScience* 45: 670–672.

Simpson, G. G. 1945. The principles of classification and a classification of mammals. *Bulletin of the American Museum of Natural History* 85: 1–350

Sneath, P. H. A., and R. R. Sokal. 1973. *Numerical Taxonomy: The Principles and Practice of Numerical Classification.* San Francisco: Freeman.

Swisher, C. C., Y-Q Wang, X-L Wang, X. Xu, and Y. Wang. 1999. Cretaceous age for the feathered dinosaurs of Liaoning, China. *Nature* 400: 58–61.

Swofford, D. L., G. J. Olsen, P. J. Waddell, and D. M. Hillis. 1996. Phylogenetic Inference. In D. M. Hillis, C. Moritz, and B. K. Mable, eds. *Molecular Systematics.* Sunderland, MA: Sinauer, 407–514.

Thewissen, J. G. M., and S. T. Hussain. 1993. Origin of underwater hearing in whales. *Nature* 361: 444–445.

Thewissen, J. G. M., S. T. Hussain, and M. Arif. 1994. Fossil evidence for the origin of aquatic locomotion in archaeocete whales. *Science* 263: 210–212.

Thewissen, J. G. M., and S. I. Madar. 1999. Ankle morphology of the earliest cetaceans and its implications for the phylogenetic relations among ungulates. *Systematic Biology* 48: 21–30.

Wakely, J. 1996. The excess of transitions among nucleotide substitutions: New methods of estimating transition bias underscore its significance. *Trends in Ecology and Evolution* 11: 158–163.

Wilson, A. C. 1985. The molecular basis of evolution. *Scientific American* 253: 164–173.

Xu, X., X.-L. Wang, and X.-C. Wu. 1999. A dromaeosaurid dinosaur with a filamentous integument from the Yixian formation of China. *Nature* 401: 262–266.

Zuckerkandl, E., and L. Pauling. 1962. Molecular disease, evolution and genic heterogeneity. In M. Kash and B. Pullman, eds. *Horizons in Biochemistry.* New York: Academic Press.

CHAPTER 18

Molecular Evolution

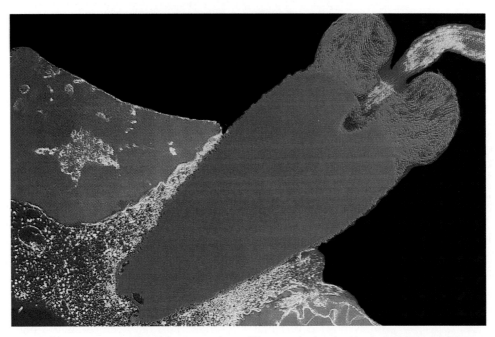

A sea urchin sperm penetrating the egg membrane. The proteins involved in the initial contact between sperm and egg evolve rapidly. (Dr. Everett Anderson/Science Photo Library/Photo Researchers, Inc.)

THE ADVENT OF TECHNIQUES FOR STUDYING PROTEIN AND DNA SEQUENCES opened up a new arena for the study of evolution. Beginning with the first large-scale amino acid sequencing studies in the 1960s and continuing to the current explosion of data on the sequences of entire genomes, researchers have addressed a wide variety of questions about how proteins and nucleic acids change through time.

Several important issues in molecular evolution were introduced in earlier chapters. In Chapter 4, we explored the origin of genetic variation by analyzing how new alleles arise by point mutation and investigating how new loci are created by gene duplication, polyploidy, and other events. The observation of steady rates of change in certain proteins and genes, noted in Chapter 13, led to the development, testing, and implementation of the molecular-clock hypothesis.

The goal of this chapter is to explore two additional questions addressed by current research on molecular evolution. The first is how the evolutionary processes of drift and selection act at the molecular level. If we compare homologous protein or DNA sequences in two organisms and observe differences, how can we discern whether the changes resulted from drift or natural selection? Sections 18.1

and 18.2 are devoted to this topic. Then we turn to the larger scale issue of how whole genomes evolve. Section 18.3 explains that genomes are not cohesive units in which all loci cooperate to maximize the fitness of the individual. Most genomes are infected with parasitic sequences that detract from the fitness of the host. What are these parasites, and what limits their spread? The chapter's final section discusses the origin and history of the chloroplast and mitochondrial genomes. Once free-living bacteria were acquired by eukaryotes via endosymbiosis (see Chapter 14), what happened to their genes? Addressing these questions will reinforce the chapter's overall objective: introducing the data, theory, and analyses that biologists are using to study evolution at the molecular level.

18.1 The Amount and Rate of Sequence Change

The field of molecular evolution was launched in the mid-1960s, when biochemists succeeded in determining the amino acid sequences of hemoglobin, cytochrome *c,* and other particularly abundant and well-studied proteins found in humans and other vertebrates. These data sets provided the first opportunity for evolutionary biologists to compare the amount and rate of molecular change among species.

Early workers in the field made several striking observations about these data sets. Foremost among these were calculations made by Motoo Kimura (1968). Kimura showed that, if the number of sequence differences observed in the well-studied proteins of humans and horses were scaled for time, using divergence dates from the fossil record, and if these rates of molecular evolution were then extrapolated to all of the protein-coding loci in the genome, it meant that a mutation leading to an amino acid substitution had increased to fixation every two years, on average, as vertebrates diverged. This rate seemed far too high to be due to natural selection, given that most mutations should be deleterious. Beneficial mutations fixed by natural selection should be extremely rare.

A second observation, contributed by Emil Zuckerkandl and Linus Pauling (1965), was that the rate of amino acid sequence change in certain proteins appeared to be constant through time, or clocklike, during the diversification of vertebrates. This result also seemed to be inconsistent with the action of natural selection, which should be episodic in nature and correlated with changes in the environment rather than correlated with of time.

Early analyses of molecular evolution suggested that rates of change were high and were constant through time.

In short, early data on molecular evolution did not gibe with the expectation that natural selection was responsible for most evolutionary change. The results raised an important question: If natural selection does not explain evolution at the molecular level, then what process *is* responsible for the observation of rapid, clocklike change?

The Neutral Theory of Molecular Evolution

Kimura (1968, 1983) formulated the Neutral Theory of Molecular Evolution to explain the observed patterns of amino acid sequence divergence. This theory claims that the vast majority of base substitutions that become fixed in populations are neutral with respect to fitness and that genetic drift dominates evolution at the level of the DNA sequence. Kimura held that natural selection on beneficial mutations is largely inconsequential as an explanation for the differences among species observed at the molecular level.

Kimura modeled the evolution of neutral mutations as follows:

- If there are N individuals in a diploid population, then there are 2N copies of each gene present in that population.
- All of the 2N copies present in the current population are descendants of a single allele that existed at some time in the past. Conversely, of the 2N copies currently in existence, only one will become the ancestor of all copies present in the population at some point in the future.
- If all 2N copies of the gene are selectively equivalent, or neutral in their effect on the bearer's fitness, then each has an equal chance of becoming the allele that becomes fixed in the population. This chance is equal to 1/2N.
- In every generation, mutation will introduce new neutral alleles to the population. If ν is the mutation rate per gene per successful gamete, then 2Nν new mutants will be introduced into the population each generation.
- Based on the preceding statements, the rate at which new neutral mutants become fixed in the population is equal to (2Nν)(1/2N), or simply ν.

This derivation means that the rate of sequence evolution, if all of the alleles are neutral, is simply equal to the mutation rate. This is an elegant result. It is also astonishing, for two reasons:

The neutral theory models the fate of alleles whose selection coefficient is zero.

1. Positive natural selection is excluded. The theory's central claim is that the vast majority of base substitutions are neutral. The overall rate of evolution will be equal to the neutral mutation rate only when this proposition is true. Proponents of the neutral theory go further, however, by pointing out that even if a small proportion of nonneutral mutations occur in a population, they are likely to be deleterious and rapidly eliminated by natural selection. Thus, ν will represent the maximum rate of evolutionary change measured.

2. The size of the population has no role. The models and experiments reviewed in Chapter 6 showed that genetic drift is far more effective at changing the frequency of alleles in small populations than in large ones. But Kimura's result shows that, for strictly neutral mutations, the rate of fixation of novel alleles due to drift does not depend on population size.

Although Kimura's theory appeared to explain why the amino acid sequences of hemoglobin, cytochrome c, and other proteins change steadily through time, the theory was inspired by fairly limited amounts of protein sequence data. How did the neutral theory hold up, once large volumes of DNA sequence data became available?

Patterns in DNA Sequence Divergence

During the late 1970s and 1980s researchers mined growing databases of DNA sequences to analyze the amounts and rates of change in different loci. To discern meaningful patterns in the data, it became routine to create categories defined by the type of sequence being considered. The most basic distinction was between coding and noncoding sequences. Coding sequences contain the instructions for tRNAs, rRNAs, or proteins; noncoding sequences include introns, regions that flank coding regions, regulatory sites, and the unusual loci called pseudogenes that were introduced in Chapter 4. What predictions does the neutral theory make about the rate and pattern of change in these different types of sequences? Have these predictions been verified or rejected?

Pseudogenes Establish a Canonical Rate of Neutral Evolution

Pseudogenes are functionless stretches of DNA that result from gene duplication events (see Chapter 4). Because they do not code for proteins, mutations in pseudogenes should be completely neutral with respect to fitness and should increase to fixation solely in response to genetic drift. For this reason, pseudogenes are considered a paradigm of neutral evolution (Li et al. 1981). As predicted by the neutral theory, the divergence rates recorded in pseudogenes—which should be equal to the neutral mutation rate v—are among the highest observed among loci and sites in nuclear genomes (Li et al. 1981, Li and Graur 1991). This finding provided strong support for the neutral theory as an explanation for evolutionary change at the molecular level. It also quantified the rate of evolution due to drift. How do rates of change in other types of sequences compare to this standard, or canonical, rate of evolution caused by drift?

The evolution of pseudogenes conforms to the assumptions and predictions of the neutral theory.

Silent Sites Change Faster than Replacement Sites in Most Coding Loci

Chapter 4 pointed out that two basic types of point mutations occur in the coding regions of genes. To review, recall that bases in DNA are read in groups of three, called codons, and that only 20 different amino acids need to be specified by the 64 codons in the genetic code. As a result, base-pair substitutions may or may not lead to amino acid sequence changes. (To capture this point, biologists say that the genetic code is redundant.) DNA sequence changes that do not result in amino acid changes are called **silent-site (or synonymous) substitutions**; sequence changes that do result in an amino-acid change are called **replacement (or nonsynonymous) substitutions**.

In most coding sequences, substitution rates are higher at silent sites than at replacement sites.

Table 18.1 presents data on the rate of replacement versus silent substitution, based on comparisons of 28 homologous loci from humans and either mice or rats. The important point in these data is that, in every locus surveyed, the rate of silent changes is far higher than the rate of replacement changes.

This pattern accords with the neutral theory in important ways. Silent changes are not exposed to natural selection on protein function because they do not alter the amino acid sequence. As a result, silent substitutions should increase or decrease in frequency through time largely as a result of drift. Replacement substitutions, in contrast, change the amino-acid sequences of proteins. If most of these alterations are deleterious, then they should be eliminated by natural selection. (This type of natural selection is called **negative** or **purifying selection**, as opposed to positive selection on beneficial mutations.) Less frequently, replacement substitutions occur that have no effect on protein function and may be fixed by drift. Because these observations are consistent with the patterns predicted if drift dominates molecular evolution, they support the central tenet of the neutral theory.

Natural selection against deleterious mutations is called negative selection. Natural selection favoring beneficial mutations is called positive selection.

Variation Among Loci: Evidence for Functional Constraints

The data in Table 18.1 contain another important pattern. When homologous coding sequences from humans and rodents are compared, some loci are found to be nearly identical, while others have undergone rapid divergence. This result turns out to be typical. Rates of molecular evolution vary widely among loci.

Table 18.1   Rates of nucleotide substitution vary among genes and among sites within genes

These data report rates of replacement and silent substitutions in a series of protein-coding genes compared between humans and either mice or rats. The data are expressed as the average number of substitutions per site per billion years, plus or minus a statistical measure of uncertainty called the standard error.

Gene	L	Replacement rate ($\times 10^9$)	Silent rate ($\times 10^9$)
Histones			
Histone 3	135	0.00 ± 0.00	6.38 ± 1.19
Histone 4	101	0.00 ± 0.00	6.12 ± 1.32
Contractile system proteins			
Actin *a*	376	0.01 ± 0.01	3.68 ± 0.43
Actin *b*	349	0.03 ± 0.02	3.13 ± 0.39
Hormones, neuropeptides, and other active peptides			
Somatostatin-28	28	0.00 ± 0.00	3.97 ± 2.66
Insulin	51	0.13 ± 0.13	4.02 ± 2.29
Thyrotropin	118	0.33 ± 0.08	4.66 ± 1.12
Insulin-like growth factor II	179	0.52 ± 0.09	2.32 ± 0.40
Erythropoietin	191	0.72 ± 0.11	4.34 ± 0.65
Insulin C-peptide	35	0.91 ± 0.30	6.77 ± 3.49
Parathyroid hormone	90	0.94 ± 0.18	4.18 ± 0.98
Luteinizing hormone	141	1.02 ± 0.16	3.29 ± 0.60
Growth hormone	189	1.23 ± 0.15	4.95 ± 0.77
Urokinase-plasminogen activator	435	1.28 ± 0.10	3.92 ± 0.44
Interleukin I	265	1.42 ± 0.14	4.60 ± 0.65
Relaxin	54	2.51 ± 0.37	7.49 ± 6.10
Hemoglobins and myoglobin			
α-globin	141	0.55 ± 0.11	5.14 ± 0.90
Myoglobin	153	0.56 ± 0.10	4.44 ± 0.82
β-globin	144	0.80 ± 0.13	3.05 ± 0.56
Apolipoproteins			
E	283	0.98 ± 0.10	4.04 ± 0.53
A-I	243	1.57 ± 0.16	4.47 ± 0.66
A-IV	371	1.58 ± 0.12	4.15 ± 0.47
Immunoglobulins			
Ig V_H	100	1.07 ± 0.19	5.66 ± 1.36
Ig γ1	321	1.46 ± 0.13	5.11 ± 0.64
Ig κ	106	1.87 ± 0.26	5.90 ± 1.27
Interferons			
α1	166	1.41 ± 0.13	3.53 ± 0.61
β1	159	2.21 ± 0.24	5.88 ± 1.08
γ	136	2.79 ± 0.31	8.59 ± 2.56

Source: Li and Graur (1991)

The key to explaining this pattern lies in the following observation: Genes that are responsible for the most vital cellular functions appear to have the lowest rates of replacement substitutions. Histone proteins, for example, interact with DNA to form structures called nucleosomes. These protein–DNA complexes are a major feature of the chromatin fibers in eukaryotic cells. Changes in the amino acid sequences of histones disrupt the structural integrity of the nucleosome, with negative consequences for DNA transcription and synthesis. In contrast, genes that are less vital to the cell, and thus under less stringent functional constraints, show more rapid rates of replacement substitutions. When functional constraints are lower, a larger percentage of replacement substitutions are neutral with respect to fitness and may be fixed by drift.

The Nearly Neutral Model

Although the neutral theory appeared to account for several important patterns in DNA sequence data, data sets that indicated clocklike change in proteins presented a problem. The issue was that the neutral mutation rate v should vary among species as a function of generation time. Over any given time interval, more neutral mutations should occur in species with short generation times than in species with long generation times. Contrary to expectation, at least some protein sequence comparisons appeared to undergo clocklike change in absolute time—independent of differences in generation time among the species being compared.

The nearly neutral model explains why, in some cases, rates of sequence change correlate with absolute time instead of generation time.

To account for this observation, Tomoko Ohta and Motoo Kimura (1971; Ohta 1972, 1977) developed mathematical models exploring how drift and selection would effect mutations that are slightly deleterious, instead of being strictly neutral. Ohta's work showed that mutations are effectively neutral—meaning that they are fixed or eliminated by drift instead of selection—when $s \leq 1/(2N_e)$, where s is the selection coefficient introduced in Chapter 5 and N_e is the effective population size (meaning, the number of breeding adults).

How does this nearly neutral model explain the observation of molecular clocks in absolute time? As Lin Chao and David Carr (1993) have shown, there is a strong negative correlation between average population size in a species and its generation time. Species with short generation times tend to have large populations; species with long generation times tend to have small populations (Figure 18.1a). This is important because, according to Ohta's model, drift fixes a larger percentage of mutations in organisms with small population sizes. The upshot is that an increase in evolutionary rate due to the fixation of nearly neutral mutations in these small-population, long-generation species offsets the higher mutation rate in short-generation species and results in the molecular clock (Figure 18.1b). Consistent with this view, most studies have shown that replacement substitutions show relatively small differences in rates among mammalian lineages with different generation times (see Li and Tanimura 1987; Li et al. 1987). As predicted by the neutral theory, silent substitutions in mammals show much more pronounced generation-time effects.

The neutralist controversy is a debate about the relative importance of selection and drift in explaining molecular evolution.

Since its inception, however, the neutral and nearly neutral theories have been controversial (see Berry 1996; Ohta and Kreitman 1996). Discussion has focused on the claims by Kimura (1983) and King and Jukes (1969) that the number of beneficial mutations fixed by positive natural selection is inconsequential compared to the number of mutations that change in frequency under the influence of drift.

(a)

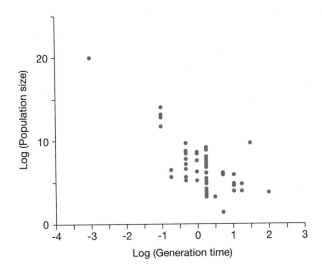

(b) Why are rates of replacement substitution constant in species with long and short generation time?

Note: Mutations are effectively neutral when $s \leq \dfrac{1}{2N_e}$

Short generation time

- *Many* mutations on a per-year basis

- *Few* mutations are effectively neutral (because N_e is large)

Long generation time

- *Few* mutations on a per-year basis

- *Many* mutations are effectively neutral (because N_e is small)

Result: The differences between mutation rate and the frequency of nearly neutral mutations cancel out

Figure 18.1 Generation time, population size, and nearly neutral mutations (a) This graph plots the logarithm of population size versus the logarithm of generation time. Statistical tests confirm that there is a strong negative correlation between the two variables. From L. Chao and D. E. Carr, 1993. The molecular clock and the relationship between population size and generation time. *Evolution* 47: 688–690, Fig. 1. Copyright © 1993 Evolution. Reprinted by permission of Evolution. (b) Differences in generation time and population size can lead to clocklike change in replacement substitutions that are nearly neutral with respect to fitness.

Is this claim accurate? How can we determine that natural selection has been responsible for changes observed at the molecular level?

18.2 Detecting Natural Selection on DNA Sequences

When researchers compare homologous DNA sequences among individuals and want to explain the differences they observe, they routinely use the neutral theory as a null hypothesis. The neutral theory specifies the rates and patterns of sequence change that occur in the absence of natural selection. If the changes that are actually observed are significantly different from the predictions made by the neutral theory, and if a researcher can defend the proposition that the sequences in question have functional significance for the organism, then there is convincing evidence that natural selection has caused molecular evolution.

Here we examine a few of the strategies that are being used to detect molecular evolution due to natural selection. We begin with studies of replacement changes, then explore evidence that many silent-site substitutions are also under selection.

Positive Selection on Replacement Substitutions

When mammalian cells are infected by a bacterium or a virus, they respond by displaying pieces of bacterial or viral protein on their surfaces. Immune system cells react by killing the infected cell. (This prevents the bacterium or virus inside the cell from replicating and slows the rate of infection.) The membrane proteins that display bacterial and viral proteins are encoded by a cluster of genes called the major histocompatibility complex, or MHC. The part of an MHC protein that binds to the foreign peptide is called the antigen recognition site (ARS). Austin Hughes and Masatoshi Nei (1988) set out to test the neutral theory by studying sequence changes in the ARS of MHC loci in humans and mice.

Hughes and Nei's specific goal was to compare the number of base substitutions that have occurred in silent versus replacement sites within the ARS. According to the neutral theory, silent-site substitutions should always be more common than replacement substitutions. This prediction follows from the proposition that most replacement substitutions are deleterious and thus eliminated by negative selection. More precisely, the rate of silent site substitutions should approximate v and represent the highest rate of molecular evolution possible in a coding sequence. The data shown in Table 18.1 were consistent with this pattern. But is it true for the ARS of MHC genes in mice and humans?

The answer is no. When Hughes and Nei compared alleles from the MHC complexes of 12 different humans and counted the number of differences observed in silent versus replacement sites, they found significantly more replacement site than silent site changes. The same pattern occurred in the ARS of mouse MHC genes, although the differences were not as great. This pattern could only result if the replacement changes were selectively advantageous. The logic here is that positive selection causes replacement changes to spread through the population much more quickly than neutral alleles can spread by chance.

It is important to note, however, that Hughes and Nei found this pattern only in the ARS. Other exons within the MHC showed more silent than replacement changes or no difference. At sites other than the ARS, then, they could not rule out the null hypothesis that sequence change is dominated by drift.

Comparing Silent and Replacement Changes Within and Between Species

The work by Hughes and Nei provides a clear example of gene segments where neutral substitutions do not predominate. Subsequent to their study, many other loci have been found where replacement substitutions outnumber silent substitutions.

Even though the Hughes and Nei criterion for detecting positive selection has been useful, Paul Sharp (1997) points out that it is extremely conservative. Replacement substitutions will only outnumber silent substitutions when positive selection has been very strong. In a comparison of 363 homologous loci in mice and rats, for example, only one showed an excess of replacement over silent changes. But as Sharp notes (1997: 111), "it would be most surprising if this were the only one of these genes that had undergone adaptive changes during the divergence of the two species." Are more sensitive methods for detecting natural selection available?

Several different techniques are available for detecting when sequences have changed due to natural selection.

John McDonald and Martin Kreitman (1991) invented a test for natural selection that is in increasingly widespread use. The McDonald–Kreitman, or MK, test is based on an important corollary to the neutral theory's prediction that silent substitutions occur more rapidly than replacement substitutions. According to the neutral theory, the ratio of replacement to silent-site substitutions in any particular locus should be constant through time. Based on this proposition, McDonald and Kreitman predicted that the ratio of replacement to silent site substitutions in between-species comparisons should be the same as the ratio observed in within-species comparisons.

Their initial test of this prediction compared sequence data from the alcohol dehydrogenase (*Adh*) gene of 12 *Drosophila melanogaster,* 6 *D. simulans,* and 12 *D. yakuba* individuals. *Adh* was an interesting locus to study for two reasons: fruit flies feed on rotting fruit that may contain toxic concentrations of ethanol, and the alcohol dehydrogenase enzyme catalyzes the conversion of ethanol to a nontoxic product. Because of the enzyme's importance to these species, and because ethanol concentrations vary among food sources, it is reasonable to suspect that the locus is under strong selection when populations begin exploiting different fruits.

In an attempt to sample as much within-species variation as possible, the individuals chosen for the study were from geographically widespread locations. McDonald and Kreitman aligned the *Adh* sequences from each individual in the study and identified sites where a base differed from the most commonly observed nucleotide, or what is called the consensus sequence. The researchers counted differences as fixed if they were present in all individuals from a particular species, and as **polymorphisms**—or allele differences within species—if they were present in only some individuals from a particular species. Differences that were fixed in one species and polymorphic in another were counted as polymorphic.

McDonald and Kreitman found that 29% of the differences that were fixed between species were replacement substitutions. Within species, however, only 5% of the polymorphisms in the study represented replacements. Rather than being the same, these ratios show an almost sixfold, and statistically significant, difference ($P = 0.006$). This is strong evidence against the neutral model's prediction. McDonald and Kreitman's interpretation is that the replacement substitutions fixed between species are selectively advantageous. They suggest that these mutations occurred after *D. melanogaster, D. simulans,* and *D. yakuba* had diverged, and spread rapidly to fixation due to positive selection in the differing environments occupied by these species. Using the MK test, natural selection has now been detected in loci from plants and protists as well as animals (Escalante et al. 1998; Purugganen and Suddith 1998).

Which Loci are Under Strong Positive Selection?

Thanks to studies employing the Hughes and Nei analysis, the MK test, and other strategies, a few tentative generalizations are beginning to emerge concerning the types of loci where positive natural selection has been particularly strong. Replacement substitutions appear to be particularly abundant in recently duplicated genes that have attained new functions, in loci involved in sex determination or in species-specific interactions between sperm and egg at fertilization, in genes that code for certain enzymes or regulatory proteins, and in disease resistance loci (see Table 18.2).

As data accumulate from genome-sequencing projects in closely related species, such as humans and chimpanzees, the number and quality of comparative studies should virtually explode. Even before the era of genome sequencing began, however, it became clear that silent substitutions, as well as replacement changes, are subject to natural selection.

Selection on "silent" substitutions

The term silent substitution was coined to reflect two aspects of base substitutions at certain positions of codons: They do not result in a change in the amino acid sequence of the protein product, and they are not exposed to natural selection. The

Table 18.2 Studies that confirm positive selection on replacement substitutions

Although this list is by no means exhaustive, it underscores a general point: Evidence for positive selection is particularly strong in genes that code for proteins involved in fertilization, disease resistance, and feeding.

Gene	Species	Rationale	Reference
Lysin protein and receptor	Abalone	Strong selection on species-specific egg-recognition proteins on sperm	Swanson, W.J. and V.D. Vacquier. 1998. *Science* 281: 710–712.
Bindin protein	Sea urchins	Strong selection on species-specific egg-recognition proteins on sperm	Metz, E.C. and S. R. Palumbi. 1996. *Molecular Biology and Evolution* 13: 397–406.
Self-incompatibility loci	Tomato family plants	Strong selection for divergence among proteins involved in avoiding self-fertilization	Clark, A.G. and T.-H. Kao. 1991. *Proceedings of the National Academy of Sciences, USA* 88: 9823–9827.
Eosinophil cationic protein	Primates	Strong selection on a recently duplicated gene involved in disease resistance	Zhang, J., H.F. Rosenberg, and M. Nei. 1998. *Proceedings of the National Academy of Sciences, USA* 95: 3708–3713.
MHC Class II	Humans	Strong selection for divergence among antigen-recognition proteins	Hughes, A.L. and M. Nei. 1989. *Proceedings of the National Academy of Sciences, USA* 86: 958-962.
Immunoglobulins	Humans	Strong selection for divergence among loci that code for antibody proteins	Tanaka, T. and M. Nei. 1989. *Molecular Biology and Evolution* 6: 447–459.
Lysozyme	Hanuman langur	Strong selection on a digestive enzyme in a leaf-eating monkey	Messier, W. and C.-B. Smith. 1997. *Nature* 385: 151–154.

second proposition had to be discarded, however, in the face of data on phenomena known as codon bias, hitchhiking, and background selection. How can mutations that do not alter an amino acid sequence be affected by natural selection?

Codon Bias

Most of the 20 amino acids are encoded by more than one codon. We have emphasized that changes among redundant codons do not cause changes in the amino-acid sequences of proteins, and have implied that these silent-site changes are neutral with respect to fitness. If this were strictly true, we would expect that codon usage would be random, and that each codon in a suite of synonymous codons would be present in equal numbers throughout the genome of a particular organism. But early sequencing studies confirmed that codon usage is highly nonrandom (Table 18.3). This phenomenon is known as **codon bias**.

Several important patterns have emerged from studies of codon bias. In every organism studied to date, codon bias is strongest in highly expressed genes—such as those for the proteins found in ribosomes—and weak to nonexistent in rarely expressed genes. In addition, the suite of codons that are used most frequently correlates strongly with the most abundant species of tRNA in the cell (Figure 18.2).

The leading hypothesis to explain these observations is natural selection for translational efficiency (Sharp and Li 1986; Sharp et al. 1988; Akashi 1994). The logic here is that if a "silent" substitution in a highly expressed gene creates a codon that is rare in the pool of tRNAs, the mutation will be selected against. The selective agent is the speed and accuracy of translation. Speed and accuracy are especially important when the proteins encoded by particular genes are turning

Table 18.3   Codon bias

This table reports the relative frequencies of codons found in genes from three different species: the bacterium *E. coli,* baker's yeast (*Saccharomyces cerevisiae*), and the fruit fly *Drosophila melanogaster.* If each codon were used equally in each genome, the relative frequencies would all be 1. Deviations from 1.00 indicate codon bias. The amino acids listed are leucine, valine, isoleucine, phenylalanine, and methionine. "High" and "Low" differentiate data from highly transcribed versus rarely transcribed genes. In every case reported here, codon bias is more extreme in highly expressed genes.

Amino acid	Codon	*Escherichia coli*		*Saccharomyces cerevisiae*		*Drosophila melanogaster*	
		High	Low	High	Low	High	Low
Leu	UUA	0.06	1.24	0.49	1.49	0.03	0.62
	UUG	0.07	0.87	5.34	1.48	0.69	1.05
	CUU	0.13	0.72	0.02	0.73	0.25	0.80
	CUC	0.17	0.65	0.00	0.51	0.72	0.90
	CUA	0.04	0.31	0.15	0.95	0.06	0.60
	CUG	5.54	2.20	0.02	0.84	4.25	2.04
Val	GUU	2.41	1.09	2.07	1.13	0.56	0.74
	GUC	0.08	0.99	1.91	0.76	1.59	0.93
	GUA	1.12	0.63	0.00	1.18	0.06	0.53
	GUG	0.40	1.29	0.02	0.93	1.79	1.80
Ile	AUU	0.48	1.38	1.26	1.29	0.74	1.27
	AUC	2.51	1.12	1.74	0.66	2.26	0.95
	AUA	0.01	0.50	0.00	1.05	0.00	0.78
Phe	UUU	0.34	1.33	0.19	1.38	0.12	0.86
	UUC	1.66	0.67	1.81	0.62	1.88	1.14
Met	AUG	1.00	1.00	1.00	1.00	1.00	1.00

Source: Sharp et al. (1988)

over rapidly and the corresponding genes must be transcribed continuously. It is reasonable, then, to observe the strongest codon bias in highly expressed genes.

Selection against certain synonymous substitutions represents a form of negative selection; it slows the rate of molecular evolution. As a result, codon bias may explain the observation that silent changes do not accumulate as quickly as base substitutions in pseudogenes. The general message here is that, in genomes where codon bias occurs, not all redundant substitutions are "silent" with respect to natural selection.

Hitchhiking and Background Selection

Another phenomenon that affects the rate and pattern of change at silent sites is referred to as **hitchhiking**, or a **selective sweep**. Hitchhiking can occur when strong positive selection acts on a particular amino acid substitution. As a favorable mutation increases in frequency, neutral or even slightly deleterious mutations closely

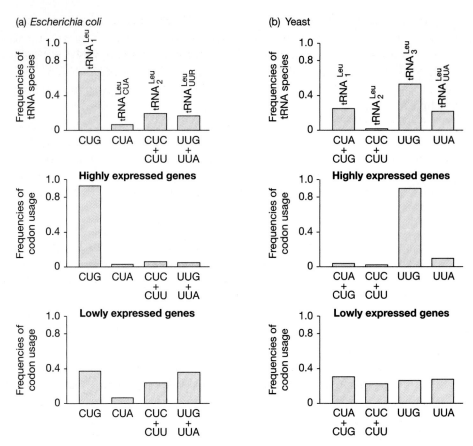

Figure 18.2 Codon bias correlates with the relative frequencies of tRNA species The bar chart in the top row of both (a) and (b) shows the frequencies of four different tRNA species that carry leucine in *E. coli* (a) and the yeast *Saccharomyces cerevisiae* (b). The bar charts in the middle and bottom rows report the frequency of the mRNA codons corresponding to each of these tRNA species in the same organisms. The mRNA codons were measured in two different classes of genes: those that are highly transcribed (middle) and those that are rarely transcribed (bottom). The data show that codon usage correlates strongly with tRNA availability in highly expressed genes, but not at all in rarely expressed genes. From Li and Graur (1991). Copyright © 1991 Sinauer Associates, Inc. Reprinted by permission of Sinauer Associates, Inc.

linked to the favored site will increase in frequency along with the beneficial locus. These linked mutations are swept along by selection and can actually "hitchhike" to fixation. Note that this process only occurs when recombination fails to break up the linkage between the hitchhiking sites and the site that is under selection.

Perhaps the best example of hitchhiking discovered to date was found on the fourth chromosome of fruit flies. The fourth chromosome in *Drosophila* is remarkable because no recombination occurs along its entire length. As a consequence, the entire chromosome represents a linkage group and is inherited like a single gene.

Andrew Berry and colleagues (1991) sequenced a 1.1-kb region of the fourth chromosome in 10 *Drosophila melanogaster* and 9 *D. simulans*. This chromosome region includes the introns and exons of a gene expressed in fly embryos, called *cubitus interruptus Dominant* (*ciD*). Berry et al. found a remarkable pattern in the sequence data: No differences were observed among the *D. melanogaster* individuals surveyed. The entire 1.1 kb of sequence was identical in the 10 individuals. Further, only one base difference was observed among the *D. simulans* in the study. This means that there was almost no polymorphism (variation within species) in this region. In contrast, a total of 54 substitutions were found when the same sequences were compared between the two species. A key observation here is that genes on other chromosomes surveyed in the same individuals showed normal amounts of polymorphism. These latter data serve as a control and confirm that the lack of variation observed in and around the *ciD* locus is not caused by an unusual sample of individuals. Rather, there is something unusual about the fourth chromosome in these flies.

Berry et al. suggest that selective sweeps recently eliminated all or most of the variation on the fourth chromosome in each of these two species. Their argument is that an advantageous mutation anywhere on the fourth chromosome would eliminate all within-species polymorphism as it increased to fixation. New variants, like the one substitution observed in the *D. simulans* sampled, will arise only through mutation.

In this way, selective sweeps create a "footprint" in the genome: a startling lack of polymorphism within linkage groups. Similar footprints have been found in other chromosomal regions where the frequency of recombination is low, including the ZFY locus of the human Y chromosome (Dorit et al. 1995) and a variety of loci in *D. melanogaster* and other fruit flies (for example, see Nurminsky et al. 1998).

Has hitchhiking produced all of these regions of reduced polymorphism? The answer is probably not. Another process, called background selection, can produce a similar pattern (Charlesworth et al. 1993). Background selection results from negative selection against deleterious mutations, rather than positive selection for advantageous mutations. Like hitchhiking, it occurs in regions of reduced recombination. The idea here is that selection against deleterious mutations removes closely linked neutral substitutions and produces a reduced level of polymorphism.

Background selection and hitchhiking are contrasting processes that lead to the same pattern.

Although the processes called hitchhiking and background selection are not mutually exclusive, their effects can be distinguished in at least some cases. Hitchhiking results in dramatic reductions in polymorphism as an occasional advantageous mutation quickly sweeps through a population. Background selection causes a slow, steady decrease in polymorphism as frequent deleterious mutations remove individuals from the population. The current consensus is that hitchhiking is probably responsible for the most dramatic instances of reduced polymorphism in linked regions—for example, where sequence variation is entirely eliminated—while background selection causes the less extreme cases.

18.3 Transposable Elements

The field of molecular evolution was launched by observations about rates and patterns of change in protein and DNA sequences. The message in these data—that many of the evolutionary changes observed at the molecular level are caused by drift, and not by positive natural selection—was astonishing to most biologists. Early data sets on the nature of the eukaryotic genome delivered an equally surprising conclusion: Genomes are not simple collections of sequences that code for proteins. Instead they contain a bestiary of sequence types. In humans, for example, only a small fraction of the DNA present codes for proteins, rRNAs, or tRNAs. The human genome, like the genomes of many other eukaryotes, is dominated by parasitic sequences that do not code for products used by the cell.

Two pioneering observations hinted at this conclusion and launched research on how genomes evolve. One observation was the C-value paradox. The data in Table 18.4 show that, in eukaryotes, the total amount of DNA found in a cell (also known as its C-value) does not correlate with the organism's degree of morphological complexity or its phylogenetic position. This finding suggests that much or most of the DNA in eukaryotes is functionless from the cell's viewpoint. A second important observation was Barbara McClintock's discovery of transposable genetic elements, or "jumping genes." While studying the inheritance of kernel

Table 18.4   *C* Values of eukaryotes

The total amount of DNA in a haploid genome is called the C value. Genome sizes show extreme variation within and between taxonomic groups. In flowering plants, for example, haploid genomes range by a factor of 2,500, from 50,000 to 125 billion kilobases (kb).

Species	C value (kb)
Navicola pelliculosa (diatom)	35,000
Drosophila melanogaster (fruit fly)	180,000
Paramecium aurelia (ciliate)	190,000
Gallus domesticus (chicken)	1,200,000
Erysiphe cichoracearum (fungus)	1,500,000
Cyprinus carpio (carp)	1,700,000
Lampreta planeri (lamprey)	1,900,000
Boa constrictor (snake)	2,100,000
Parascaris equorum (roundworm)	2,500,000
Carcarias obscurus (shark)	2,700,000
Rattus norvegicus (rat)	2,900,000
Xenopus laevis (toad)	3,100,000
Homo sapiens (human)	3,400,000
Nicotiana tabaccum (tobacco)	3,800,000
Paramecium caudatum (ciliate)	8,600,000
Schistocerca gregaria (locust)	9,300,000
Allium cepa (onion)	18,000,000
Coscinodiscus asteromphalus (diatom)	25,000,000
Lilium formosanum (lily)	36,000,000
Pinus resinosa (pine)	68,000,000
Amphiuma means (newt)	84,000,000
Protopterus aethiopicus (lungfish)	140,000,000
Ophioglossum petiolatum (fern)	160,000,000
Amoeba proteus (amoeba)	290,000,000
Amoeba dubia (amoeba)	670,000,000

Source: Li and Graur (1991)

color in corn, McClintock found loci that produced novel color patterns by moving to new locations in the genome.

Sequencing studies later revealed that much of the "extra" DNA responsible for the C-value paradox consists of these transposable genetic elements. We begin our look at how genomes evolve with some basic questions about these loci: What are transposable elements? Where did they come from? What effect do they have on the genomes that host them?

Transposable Elements Are Genomic Parasites

As the ensuing discussion will show, "transposable element" is really an umbrella term for genes with a diverse set of characteristics. The majority of transposable elements contain only the sequences required for transposition. All share the ability to move from one location to another in the genome, and most leave a copy of themselves behind when they move. In this way, transposition events lead to an increase in the number of transposable elements in the host genome.

If a transposable element disrupts an important coding sequence when it inserts into a new location in the genome, deleterious "knock-out" mutations result. In humans, for example, transposition events have resulted in tumor formation and cases of hemophilia (see Hutchison et al. 1989). The sheer bulk of transposable element DNA would also appear to have deleterious consequences for the host genome. The time, energy, and resources required to replicate a genome burdened by parasitic DNA could place a limit on growth rates, particularly in small, rapidly dividing organisms. Because they disrupt coding sequences and place an energetic burden on the cell, transposable elements are most accurately characterized as genomic parasites. Surveys done to date suggest that they exist in every organism.

What is the key to their success? The answer is that transposable elements can increase in a population in two ways, even when they reduce their host's fitness slightly. They can become fixed in small populations due to drift, or increase because transposition events result in more than one copy of the parasitic locus being present in many gametes. To grasp this second point more fully, consider that, if a transposition event reduces the survival and reproductive capacity of the host slightly, the extra copies of the transposable element in the gene pool can make up the deficit and result in the parasite's spread throughout the population. According to models developed by Brian Charlesworth and Charles Langley (1989), the transposable elements that replicate themselves most efficiently and with the least fitness cost to the host genome are favored by natural selection and tend to spread.

Another key to understanding transposable elements is to appreciate that their success depends on sex (Hickey 1992). In eukaryotes, outcrossing results in haploid genomes being mixed. This presents transposable elements with new targets for transposition and allows them to spread throughout a population. In prokaryotes and other groups where gene transfer is one-way and where most reproduction is by fission, transposable elements in the main chromosome tend to be eliminated by selection or drift. As a result, the transposable elements found in bacteria and archaea tend to reside on the circular extrachromosomal elements called plasmids.

Transposable genetic elements are grouped into two broad classes, based on whether they move via an RNA or DNA intermediate sequence. These Class I and Class II elements come in an enormous array of sizes, copy numbers, and structurally related families. The literature on mobile genetic elements is vast and growing rapidly (Voytas 1996). Although we can only touch on this body of knowledge here, understanding a few of the basic types of transposable elements is important. In sheer numbers, they represent some of the most successful genes in the history of life.

Instead of cooperating to increase the fitness of the individual, some loci are parasitic.

Class I Elements

Class I elements, also called **retrotransposons**, are the product of reverse transcription events. Although the molecular mechanism of transposition is not yet fully known, we do know that movement of Class I elements occurs through a ribonucleic acid (RNA) intermediate. Transposition is also replicative, meaning that the original copy of the sequence is intact after the event. The long interspersed

Transposable elements that spread via an RNA intermediate have to be reverse transcribed, by reverse transcriptase, before being inserted into a new location.

elements (LINEs) are retrotransposons that contain the coding sequence for reverse transcriptase and are thought to catalyze their own transposition. In mammals, LINEs are typically 6–7 kb in length (Hutchison et al. 1989; Wichman et al. 1992). The first human chromosome to be completely sequenced, number 22, contains over 14,000 LINEs. These elements represent greater than 13% of the total DNA on this chromosome (Dunham et al. 1999).

Another important category of retrotransposons is distinguished by the presence of long terminal repeats (LTRs). LTRs are one of the hallmarks of retroviral genomes. When retroviruses insert themselves into a host DNA to initiate an infection, LTRs mark the insertion point. In corn, 10 different families of retrotransposons with LTRs have been identified, each of which is found in 10 to 30,000 copies per haploid genome (SanMiguel et al. 1996). The complete genome of baker's yeast, *Saccharomyces cerevisiae,* has been sequenced and found to contain 52 complete LTR-containing sequences called Ty elements, and 264 naked LTRs that lack the coding regions of normal retrotransposons. These "empty" LTRs are interpreted as transposition footprints, meaning that they are sequences left behind when Ty elements were somehow excised from the genome (see Boeke 1989; Goffeau et al. 1996).

Retrotransposons and retroviruses may be closely related.

Where did retrotransposons come from? One hypothesis is that LINEs and the LTR-containing retrotransposons evolved from retroviruses. Retrotransposons resemble retroviruses that have lost the coding sequences required to make capsule proteins. This hypothesis proposes that retrotransposons have adopted a novel evolutionary strategy. In contrast to retroviruses, which replicate in their host cell, move on to infect new cells, and eventually infect new host individuals of the same generation, retrotransposons replicate by infecting the germline. Instead of being transmitted horizontally—meaning, from host to host in the same generation—they replicate by being transmitted vertically, to the next generation of hosts. Their transmission is much slower than that of conventional retroviruses, but retrotransposons also escape detection by the immune system.

A second type of Class I element is called a retrosequence. Retrosequences do not contain the coding sequence for reverse transcriptase, but amplify via RNA intermediates that are reverse transcribed and inserted into the genome. The short interspersed elements (SINEs) of mammals are among the best-studied examples. SINEs are grouped into several different families, each of which is distinguished by its sequence homology with a different functioning gene. The *Alu* family of sequences in primates, for example, is about 90% identical to the 7SL RNA gene, which is involved in transmembrane protein transport; other families of SINEs are homologous with various tRNA genes. SINEs are typically under 500 bp in length and lack the sequences necessary for translation of a transcribed RNA message. They can also be extremely abundant. Human chromosome number 22, for example, contains 20,188 *Alu* elements (Dunham et al. 1999). These SINEs account for 16.8% of the total DNA in this chromosome.

Retrosequences do not code for an RNA or protein that functions in the cell. They are closely related to functioning genes, however.

Where did SINEs and other retrosequences come from, and how are they replicated? In most SINE families it appears that only one or a very few master copies of the locus are actively transposing, and that the remainder represent inactive copies analogous to pseudogenes (see Shen et al. 1997). As with LINEs and other Class I elements, the mechanism of this transposition is not known. We do not know how transcription of the master gene locus is regulated, where the reverse transcriptase comes from, or how insertion of the resulting DNA copy proceeds.

We can, however, date the origin of some families. The *Alu* sequences, for example, have been found in every primate surveyed to date, but do not occur in rodents. This observation suggests that the *Alu* family entered the genome of a primate ancestor after these mammal lineages diverged.

Class II Elements

Class II transposable elements replicate via a DNA intermediate and are the dominant type of transposable genetic element in bacteria. Their transposition can be replicative, as in Class I elements, or conservative. In conservative transposition, the element is excised during the move so that copy number does not increase.

The first Class II elements ever described were the insertion sequences, or IS elements, discovered in the bacterium *Escherichia coli* (Table 18.5). When insertion sequences contain one or more coding sequences, they are called transposons. In addition to being inserted into the main bacterial chromosome, however, transposons are commonly inserted into plasmids. Plasmids replicate independently of the main chromosome and are readily transferred from one bacterial cell to another during conjugation.

Transposons encode a protein, called a transposase, that catalyzes transposition. In bacterial transposons, the coding region frequently also codes for a protein that confers resistance to an antibiotic (Table 18.6). As a result, plasmid-borne transposons have been responsible for the rapid evolution of drug resistance in disease-causing bacteria. Transposons that confer antibiotic resistance are the first example we have encountered of a transposable element that creates a fitness advantage for its host.

Class II transposable elements are also found in eukaryotes. The *Ac* and *Ds* elements of corn, discovered by Barbara McClintock in the 1950s, belong to this group. These Class II sequences code for a transposase as well as other proteins. The P elements found in *Drosophila melanogaster* are another example. A typical fly

The chromosomes of bacteria are relatively free of transposable elements. But transposable elements are frequently found in the extrachromosomal elements called plasmids.

Table 18.5   Insertion sequences found in the genome of *Escherichia Coli*

Some of the insertion sequences listed here are found on extra chromosomal genetic elements in *E. coli*. IS2 and IS3, for example, are located on F (or "fertility") plasmids. F plasmids are circular DNA molecules found in bacteria that can either replicate independently or integrate into the main chromosome and replicate with it. The presence of an F plasmid in a bacterial cell confers the ability to donate genetic material to another cell during conjugation.

Insertion sequence	Normal occurrence in *E. coli*
IS1	5–8 copies on chromosome
IS2	5 on chromosome; 1 on F
IS3	5 on chromosome; 2 on F
IS4	1 or 2 copies on chromosome
IS5	Unknown
γ-δ (TN1000)	1 or more on chromosome; 1 on F
pSC101 segment	On plasmid pSC101

Source: Griffiths et al. (1993)

Table 18.6	**Transposons can carry genes conferring antibiotic resistance**

This listing illustrates the diversity and number of plasmid-borne transposons that carry antibiotic-resistance genes.

Transposon	Confers resistance to
Tn1	Ampicillin
Tn2	Ampicillin
Tn3	Ampicillin
Tn4	Ampicillin, streptomycin, sulfanilamide
Tn5	Kanamycin
Tn6	Kanamycin
Tn7	Trimethoprim, streptomycin
Tn9	Chloramphenicol
Tn10	Tetracycline
Tn204	Chloramphenicol, fusidic acid
Tn402	Trimethoprim
Tn551	Erythromycin
Tn554	Erythromycin, spectinomycin
Tn732	Gentamicin, tobramycin
Tn903	Kanamycin
Tn917	Erythromycin
Tn1721	Tetracycline

Source: Griffiths et al. (1993)

genome contains 30–50 copies of these elements, which have insertion–sequence-like repeats at their ends and as many as three coding regions for protein products (Ajioka and Hartl 1989).

Evolutionary Impact of Transposable Elements

Research on transposable elements has delivered an important message: Genomes are not cohesive collections of loci that contribute to the fitness of the individual. Instead, they are riddled with parasites that transmit themselves at their host's expense. This realization raises some important questions. Do host genomes have mechanisms to counter transposable elements? Does natural selection limit their spread? Are transposable elements ever beneficial to their hosts?

Limiting the Spread of Transposable Elements

When a transposable element inserts into the coding region of a gene, the mutation that results should quickly be eliminated by natural selection. But Charlesworth and Langley (1989) proposed that natural selection might also remove transposable elements from a population in the absence of transposition events. Their hypothesis hinges on the idea that multiple copies of a transposable element on the same chromosome frequently leads to errors in meiosis. As Figure 18.3 shows, ectopic recombination can occur between transposable elements located at differ-

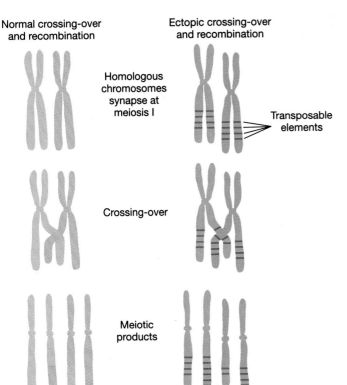

Normal crossing-over
and recombination

Ectopic crossing-over
and recombination

Homologous
chromosomes
synapse at
meiosis I

Transposable
elements

Crossing-over

Meiotic
products

Figure 18.3 Ectopic recombination leads to abnormal chromosomes When transposable elements are common on a chromosome, homologues can line up incorrectly at meiosis I. When this happens, crossing over and recombination occur in the wrong place and the products of meiosis are abnormal.

ent sites on homologous chromosomes. (Ectopic means "to occur in an abnormal location.") Half of the chromosomes that result will lack certain loci and be strongly selected against. The frequency of ectopic recombination, and thus the strength of selection, should correlate strongly with the frequency of transposable elements.

Paul Sniegowski and Charlesworth (1994) tested the ectopic recombination hypothesis by surveying the distribution of transposable elements in the *Drosophila melanogaster* genome. Their specific goal was to quantify the frequency of transposable elements inside the flipped chromosome segments, called inversions, that were introduced in Chapter 4. Recall that crossing over does not occur within inversions if one chromosome contains the inversion but its homologous chromosome does not. Because crossing over is infrequent inside inverted segments, ectopic recombination should be rare. As predicted by the Charlesworth–Langley hypothesis, transposable elements are much more common inside inversions than they are in homologous, noninverted chromosome segments, where crossing over occurs normally. This observation supports the hypothesis that ectopic recombination serves as a brake on the spread of transposable elements.

Do host genomes themselves have mechanisms to actively suppress transposition? Recent work by Rachel Waugh O'Neill and co-workers (1998) suggests that the answer may be yes. These biologists conducted a study inspired by the hypothesis that organisms add methyl ($-CH_3$) groups to their DNA as a way to thwart mobile genetic elements (Bester and Tycko 1996; Yoder et al. 1997). To look for an association between DNA methylation and the spread of transposable elements, Waugh O'Neill and associates analyzed the chromosomes found in the hybrid offspring of a mating between a tammar wallaby and a swamp wallaby. For unknown reasons, the DNA of the hybrid individual was virtually unmethylated.

The researchers also found that, in many of this individual's chromosomes, a retrotransposon called KERV-1 had virtually exploded in copy number (see Figure 18.4). According to Waugh O'Neill and colleagues, this correlation is strong support for the hypothesis that methylation protects host DNA from insertion by parasites.

Even if future work confirms that methylation protects DNA from parasitic sequences, a series of important questions remains. If methylation is effective, why are transposable elements present in such large numbers? Why are the numbers of parasites so variable among species? Why have so many different types of elements been able to take up residence in genomes?

It is not clear why eukaryotes are unable to eliminate parasitic sequences more efficiently.

To summarize, forty years of careful descriptive studies have produced important insights into the number, distribution, and types of transposable elements present in genomes. The natural history of these parasites is well known. Now, innovations like the host-defense and ectopic-recombination hypotheses are transforming research on transposable elements. Researchers are beginning to ask highly focused questions about the evolutionary dynamics of these elements. Recent experimental work has even shown that transposition events may occasionally have important beneficial effects for their hosts.

Positive Impacts of Transposable Elements

For decades, the only example of a positive fitness benefit provided by transposable elements was the antibiotic resistance conferred by some plasmid-borne transposons in bacteria. Recent work by John Moran and colleagues (1999) suggests that transposition events in eukaryotes may occasionally result in mutations that confer a fitness benefit. This conclusion is based on experiments with the LINE elements found in humans. To analyze how these loci move from one location to another, Moran and co-workers used recombinant DNA techniques to attach a marker gene to LINE-1 sequences. They introduced the engineered sequence into human cells growing in culture, allowed the parasitic sequences to insert themselves into the genome, and sequenced the LINE-1 elements that succeeded in transposing to new locations in the genome. In several cases, the sequence data showed

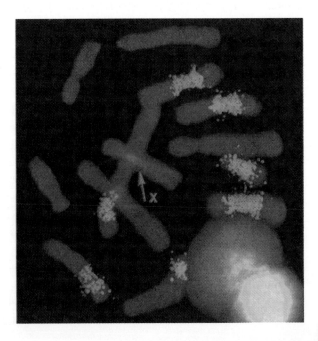

Figure 18.4 **When DNA is unmethylated, transposable elements explode in number** To produce this photograph, Waugh O'Neill and co-workers labeled single-stranded DNA from the KERV-1 transposable element with a fluorescent molecule, then allowed this probe DNA to hybridize to KERV-1 sequences in the chromosomes of a wallaby hybrid individual. The pink dots indicate the location of KERV-1 elements. (Note that they cluster near the centromeres of certain chromosomes.) No hybridization was observed in the parental wallaby species. From Waugh O'Neill et al. (1998).

that the mobile element had carried a chunk of host DNA along with it and the marker gene during transposition. In essence, the LINEs had duplicated segments of host DNA and moved them to new locations. Figure 18.5 illustrates how this happened. The diagram also shows that, if the transposed host DNA segment happens to contain an exon or regulatory sequence, the transposition event results in a novel gene. Moran and co-workers contend that these types of transposition events are important in the evolution of genomes and furnish a mechanism for the phenomenon called exon shuffling that was introduced in Chapter 14.

In a similar vein, work by Alka Agrawal and colleagues (1998) suggests that a key feature of the vertebrate immune system originated in a transposition event. As Figure 18.6a shows, the proteins that serve as antigen-recognition sites on the surface of immune system cells are encoded by three gene segments. As immune system cells develop in an embryo, a series of reactions take place that result in portions of the V (variable), D (diversity), and J (joining) gene segments being excised and recombined (see Figure 18.6b). These reactions are catalyzed by proteins called RAG1 and RAG2. What Agrawal et al. showed is that RAG1 and RAG2 can also catalyze the transposition of gene constructs that are unrelated to the V, J, and D regions. The experimental reaction they set up, diagrammed in Figure 18.6c, took place outside of a cell. Further, the reaction mechanism is identical to the chemical events that take place during movement by transposable elements. To make sense of this result, the researchers propose that the RAG proteins constitute a transposase homologous to those found in present-day transposable elements.

The implications of this work are remarkable. Agrawal and associates hypothesize that the V(J)D excision and rearrangement reactions observed in today's vertebrates are possible because of an insertion event by a transposable element several hundred million years ago. According to the hypothesis outlined in Figure 18.6d, a transposable element bearing *RAG1* and *RAG2* inserted into a membrane receptor gene early in the evolution of vertebrates. The transposase could catalyze the recombination of the resulting receptor gene segments, however. If so, then gene duplication events later in evolution could have expanded the membrane receptor locus and resulted in the extensive V, D, and J regions observed today.

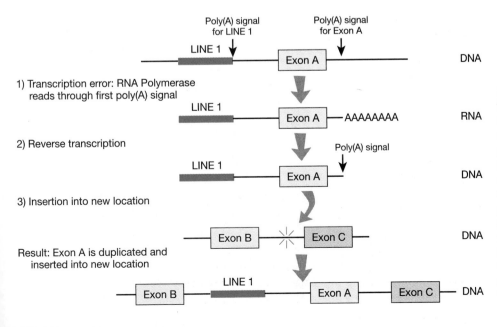

Figure 18.5 **"Exon shuffling" via transposition events** Based on the series of events diagrammed here, transposition by LINE elements can result in exons or regulatory sequences being moved to new locations in the genome. This phenomenon is known as exon shuffling and was introduced in Chapter 14. The experiment by Moran et al., described in the text, shows that each of the steps illustrated here can actually occur.

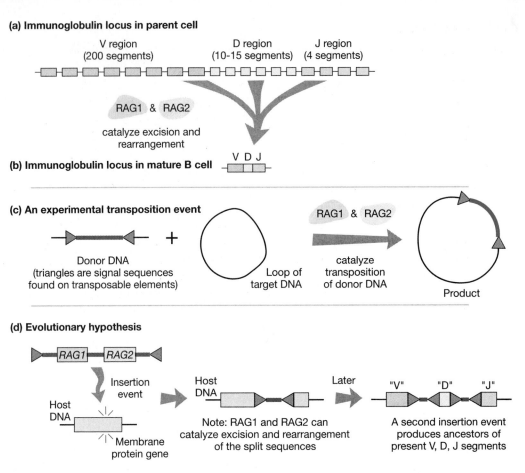

Figure 18.6 Did the vertebrate immunoglobulin locus originate in a transposition event? (a) As a human embryo develops, the cells that serve as precursors to immune system cells have immunoglobulin loci with many different V, D, and J regions. (b) As individual immune system cells mature, RAG1 and RAG2 catalyze reactions that result in a single V, D, and J segment being combined and the others being excised. (c) The experiment by Agrawal et al. showed that RAG1 and RAG2 can catalyze transposition events. (d) According to the evolutionary hypothesis outlined here, insertion events by transposable elements containing the *RAG1* and *RAG2* genes created the basic structure of the immunoglobulin locus. Gene duplication events could later produce the variety of V, D, and J segments observed today.

18.4 Organelle Genomes

Chloroplasts and mitochondria have their own DNA. They are derived from bacteria that lived symbiotically in the cytoplasm of early eukaryotic cells.

Studies on transposable elements underscore the dynamic nature of the genome. Far from being static, stable entities, the composition and structure of genomes changes dramatically over time. This conclusion is reinforced by research on the history of the genomes present in eukaryotic chloroplasts and mitochondria. These organelles contain DNA that codes for functioning proteins, rRNAs, and tRNAs. The organization of these genomes differs markedly from nuclear DNA (nDNA), however—largely because both organelles originated as bacteria that took up residence in eukaryotic cells early in the history of life. As Chapter 14 showed, chloroplasts are derived from cyanobacteria and mitochondria from α-proteobacteria. Here, we describe the organization and gene content of organelle genomes and consider an important question about how they evolve.

Chloroplast DNA

In chloroplasts, the energy captured from photons is used to power the synthesis of sugars. Many of the proteins used in photosynthesis are encoded by chloroplast DNA (cpDNA). This is a circular double helix that lacks the histones and other chromosomal proteins found in nuclear DNA. Algal and plant cells typically contain many chloroplasts; each organelle normally has 20–80 copies of cpDNA.

Several cpDNAs have now been completely sequenced (see Wolfe et al. 1991). The 156-kb cpDNA genome of tobacco, for example, contains a total of 113 genes. The functions of these loci fall into two broad classes: sequences required for gene expression, and sequences required for photosynthesis. The loci involved in transcription and translation include RNA polymerase subunits, ribosomal proteins, a translation initiation factor, tRNAs, and rRNAs. The 29 genes involved in photosynthesis code for many of the proteins found in the thylakoid of the organelle, where photon capture takes place. Compared to nDNA, relatively few noncoding sequences are present.

The genome size and gene content of tobacco cpDNA appears to be typical of plants from other taxonomic groups (see Clegg et al. 1994), indicating that the information content of this genome has been conserved during evolution. Even the order of genes along the chromosome appears to be highly conserved, if not identical (Palmer 1987). Further, all cpDNA genomes examined to date use the same genetic code as nDNA.

The inheritance of chloroplast genomes is normally uniparental. In most flowering plants, all of the cpDNA present in embryos is derived from the mother; but in at least some gymnosperms, inheritance is paternal. Biparental inheritance has also been recorded in some flowering plants (Palmer 1987). Recombination between cpDNA copies is extremely rare, having been recorded only in the green alga *Chlamydomonas*. In most organisms, then, the entire cpDNA genome is inherited like a single allele.

Relative to plant nuclear genes, sequence evolution in cpDNA is slow. Compared to silent sites surveyed in a sample of nuclear genes, silent sites in a sample of cpDNA loci evolve about one-quarter as fast (Wolfe et al. 1987, 1989).

The gene content and size of the chloroplast genome is highly conserved. The rate of sequence change in cpDNA is low relative to the nuclear genome.

Structure and Evolution of mtDNA

In mitochondria, the energy stored in sugars is used to power the synthesis of adenosine triphosphate (ATP). Many of the proteins used in cellular respiration are encoded by mitochondrial DNA (mtDNA). Like cpDNA, mtDNA is usually a circular double helix that lacks chromosomal proteins. The number of mitochondria per cell varies from four in some unicellular fungi to thousands in the muscle cells of vertebrates; in vertebrates each organelle has 5–10 copies of mtDNA.

The mitochondrial DNAs of plants, fungi, and animals are very different from one another. As the observations summarized in Table 18.7 show, these genomes vary in characteristics ranging from structure, composition, and mode of inheritance to rate of evolution. Why these differences evolved as plants, fungi, and animals diverged from their common ancestor is not known (Gray et al. 1999).

The size, structure, and rate of sequence change in plant, fungal, and animal mtDNA varies enormously, but the information content is highly conserved.

Evolution of Organelle Genomes

Chapter 14 introduced evidence that genetic information has been transferred between species throughout the history of life. The largest horizontal-transfer events ever recorded occurred when eukaryotic cells acquired intact bacterial

Table 18.7 Variation among mitochondrial DNAs

	Plants	Fungi	Animals
Genome size	Extremely variable—ranges from 300 kb to 2,400 kb in melon family alone	Highly variable—ranges from 26.7 kb to 115 kb in filamentous ascomycetes alone	Relatively small, relatively little variation among species; many about 16 kb
Chromosome structure	Variable—circular or linear, sometimes several circular DNA molecules	Circular	All circular
Information content	Conserved: rRNAs, tRNAs, ribosomal proteins, and proteins involved in respiration	Conserved: rRNAs, tRNAs, ribosomal proteins, and proteins involved in respiration	Conserved: tRNAs, rRNAs, and proteins involved in respiration
Introns present?	No, but noncoding sequences are abundant	Yes	No—few noncoding sequences
Modifications to universal genetic code?	No	* AUA for methionine (not isoleucine) * CUN for threonine (not leucine) * UGA for tryptophan (not stop)	* AUA for methionine (not isoleucine) * UGA for tryptophan (not stop)
Mode of inheritance	Variable, but usually maternal	Either parent	Maternal
Recombination?	Frequent	Frequent	None to infrequent
Rate of sequence divergence relative to nDNA	Slow	May be similar—still under investigation	Fast

genomes via endosymbiosis. What happened to these genomes as endosymbiotic bacteria began evolving into mitochondria and chloroplasts?

Present-day organelle genomes have only a tiny fraction of the genetic information present in a bacterium (Gray 1992). This observation suggests that numerous loci have been lost completely or transferred to the nucleus. The genes that encode what may be the most abundant protein in nature, ribulose bisphosphate carboxylase (RuBPCase), are a vivid example. This enzyme catalyzes the fixation of CO_2 during the Calvin–Benson cycle, which is the central pathway in the light-independent reactions of photosynthesis. RuBPCase is made up of two subunits. The gene for the protein's small subunit is found in the nuclear genome, while the gene for the large subunit is part of the cpDNA genome (Gillham et al. 1985). The same type of evidence for gene transfers exists in mitochondria. The organelle's ribosomes, for example, are composed of rRNAs encoded by mtDNA and proteins encoded by nDNA.

Because the gene content of chloroplasts and mitochondria is highly conserved, most of these gene transfers probably took place very early in the evolution of endosymbiosis (Gillham et al. 1985; Clegg et al. 1994). Recent gene transfers have also been documented, however. For example, the gene *tufA,* which codes for a translation factor active only in the chloroplast, is found in the cpDNA of green algae but in the nuclear genome of the flowering plant *Arabidopsis.* This observation suggests that *tufA* was transferred to the nucleus after algae and higher plants diverged. But because copies of the gene exist in both genomes of some green algae, it is more likely that the gene was duplicated and transferred to the nucleus early in plant evolution and then subsequently lost from the cpDNA of some derived lineages, like flowering plants (Baldauf and Palmer 1990; Baldauf et al. 1990).

Evidence for an even more recent gene transfer involves the *cox*2 locus found in the mtDNA of plants. This gene codes for one of the large subunits of cytochrome oxidase, a key component of the respiratory chain. In most plants, this locus is part of the mitochondrial genome. Most legumes (members of the pea family) have a copy in both nuclear DNA and mtDNA, however, and in mung bean and cowpea, the only copy is located in the nucleus. In these species, the structure of the gene closely resembles the structure of an edited mRNA transcript. Because RNAs can be reverse transcribed to DNA, these facts suggest that gene transfer from the mitochondrion to the nucleus took place recently via the reverse transcription of an edited mRNA intermediate (Nugent and Palmer 1991; Covello and Gray 1992).

Research on interactions between the nuclear and organelle genomes continues. In the yeast *Saccharomyces cerevisiae,* the nuclear loci involved in the synthesis of mitochondria are scattered over many different chromosomes, yet are regulated in concert; how this regulation is accomplished is still an active area of research (see Grivell et al. 1993). Many other questions remain about the evolution of these cohabitating genomes. Why have some genes, but not all, been transferred from organelles to the nucleus? Is there a selective advantage to having certain genes located in each genome, or were the movements merely chance events? Is reverse transcription of mRNAs the usual mechanism of transfer, or are other processes involved?

Based on the data reviewed here, it is clear that organelle genomes are just as dynamic as nuclear genomes, if not more so. Explaining how and why particular loci move among genomes, and why organelle genomes vary so dramatically in gene content and organization, remain as important challenges.

Summary

A major goal of molecular evolutionary studies is to understand how the four evolutionary forces (mutation, migration, drift, and selection) produce the diversity of sequences observed today. The neutral theory is important to this effort because it specifies the rate of fixation for alleles that are neutral with respect to fitness and thus change in frequency solely due to drift. As a result, it provides a null model for testing whether positive selection or drift is responsible for the observed rates and patterns of molecular evolution. The nearly neutral model is an important extension to the theory because it specifies how drift and selection interact as a function of population size.

The rate of evolution due to drift can be quantified by studying pseudogenes. As predicted by the neutral theory, pseudogenes have the highest rates of change observed among coding and noncoding sequences. In the vast majority of coding sequences, silent substitutions accumulate faster than replacement substitutions. Among loci, the rate of molecular evolution varies as a function of a gene's importance to the cell. These observations suggest that molecular evolution is dominated by drift and selection against deleterious mutations. In important cases, however, researchers have been able to show that high rates of replacement substitutions have occurred as a product of selection on beneficial mutations.

Even though silent substitutions do not change the amino acid sequences of proteins, they can still increase or decrease in frequency in response to natural selection. Variation in the availability of tRNAs can cause selection for translation efficiency and lead to codon bias. Selection on advantageous mutations can sweep linked silent substitutions to fixation; selection on deleterious mutations can also lead to the elimination of linked silent substitutions.

Transposable genetic elements are prominent components of eukaryotic and prokaryotic genomes. These loci move by either an RNA or DNA intermediate, but they do not code for products that increase the fitness of the host organism. Because they can cause deleterious mutations when they move to new locations in the genome, they are considered parasitic.

Chloroplasts and mitochondria originated as endosymbiotic bacteria and represent the largest horizontal gene transfer events in evolutionary history. Although the gene order, gene organization, and rate of sequence change in chloroplast and mitochondrial DNA vary among species, the information content of these organelles is remarkably well conserved.

Questions

1. Why are the rates of silent-site substitutions reported in Table 18.1 higher than the rates of replacement substitutions? Why do pseudogenes have the highest rates of evolution?

2. By using the start codon AUG as a guidepost, researchers can determine whether substitutions in pseudogenes correspond to silent changes or replacement changes. In contrast to most other loci, the rate of silent and replacement changes is identical in pseudogenes. Explain this observation in light of the neutral theory of evolution.

3. Why did Kimura and Ohta develop the nearly neutral model of molecular evolution? According to the neutral and nearly neutral theories, how does population size affect the rate of molecular evolution?

4. When researchers compare a gene in closely related species, why is it logical to infer that positive natural selection has taken place if replacement substitutions outnumber silent substitutions?

5. What is codon bias? Why is the observation of nonrandom codon use evidence that certain codons might be favored by natural selection? If you were given a series of gene sequences from the human genome, how would you determine whether codon usage is random or nonrandom?

6. The complete gene sequences of both humans and chimpanzees will be available soon. Outline how you would analyze homologous genes in the two species to determine which of the observed sequence differences result from drift and which result from selection.

7. Recall that the fourth chromosome of *Drosophila melanogaster* does not recombine during meiosis. The lack of genetic polymorphism on this chromosome has been interpreted as the product of a selective sweep. If the fourth chromosome had normal rates of recombination, would you expect the level of polymorphism to be different? Why?

8. Consider the possible costs and benefits of transposable elements to their hosts. For a eukaryote, what are the costs of carrying retrotransposons? Are there any benefits to hosting these genetic elements? For a prokaryote, what are the costs or benefits of carrying plasmids?

9. Suggest a hypothesis to explain why the size of plant mitochondrial genomes is so variable. What prediction(s) does your hypothesis make? How would you go about testing these predictions?

Exploring the Literature

10. Steve Palumbi and co-workers have published data suggesting that in animals, the rate of sequence change varies as a function of metabolic rate as well as generation time. To learn how molecular evolution varies between endothermic (warm-blooded) and poikilothermic (cold-blooded) animals, see

    Martin, A. P., G. J. P. Naylor, and S. R. Palumbi. 1992. Rates of mitochondrial DNA evolution in sharks are slow compared with mammals. *Nature* 357: 153–155

    Martin, A. P. and S. R. Palumbi. 1993. Body size, metabolic rate, generation time, and the molecular clock. *Proceedings of the National Academy of Sciences, USA* 90: 4087–4091.

11. Convergent evolution occurs when organisms that are not closely related evolve similar adaptations to similar environments (see Chapter 2). To explore a spectacular example of convergent evolution at the molecular level, see

    Chen, L., A. L. DeVries, and C.-H. Cheng. 1997. Evolution of antifreeze glycoprotein gene from a trypsinogen gene in Antarctic notothenioid fish. *Proceedings of the National Academy of Sciences, USA* 94: 3811-3816.

    Chen, L., A. L. DeVries, and C.-H. Cheng. 1997. Convergent evolution of antifreeze glycoproteins in Antarctic notothenioid fish and Arctic cod. *Proceedings of the National Academy of Sciences, USA* 94: 3817–3822.

Citations

Agrawal, A., Q. M Eastman, and D. G. Schatz. 1998. Transposition mediated by RAG1 and RAG2 and its implications for the evolution of the immune system. *Nature* 394: 744–751.

Ajioka, J. W., and D. L. Hartl. 1989. Population dynamics of transposable elements. In D. E. Berg and M.M. Howe, eds. *Mobile DNA*. Washington, DC: American Society of Microbiology, 939–958.

Akashi, H. 1994. Synonymous codon usage in *Drosophila melanogaster*: natural selection and translational accuracy. *Genetics* 144: 927–935.

Baldauf, S. L., and J. D. Palmer. 1990. Evolutionary transfer of the chloroplast *tufA* gene to the nucleus. *Nature* 344: 262–265.

Baldauf, S. L., J. R. Manhart, and J. D. Palmer. 1990. Different fates of the chloroplast *tufA* gene following its transfer to the nucleus in green algae. *Proceedings of the National Academy of Sciences, USA* 87: 5317–5321.

Berry, A. 1996. Non-non-Darwinian evolution. *Evolution* 50: 462–466.

Berry, A., J. W. Ajioka, and M. Kreitman. 1991. Lack of polymorphism on the *Drosophila* fourth chromosome resulting from selection. *Genetics* 129: 1111–1117.

Bester, T. H. and B. Tycko. 1996. Creation of genomic methylation patterns. *Nature Genetics* 12: 363–367.

Boeke, J. D. 1989. Transposable elements in *Saccharomyces cerevisiae*. In D. E. Berg and M.M. Howe, eds. *Mobile DNA*. Washington, DC: American Society of Microbiology, 335–374.

Charlesworth, B., and C. H. Langley. 1989. The population genetics of *Drosophila* transposable elements. *Annual Review of Genetics* 23: 251–287.

Charlesworth, B., M.T. Morgan, and D. Charlesworth. 1993. The effects of deleterious mutations on neutral molecular variation. *Genetics* 134: 1289–1303.

Chao, L. and D. E. Carr. 1993. The molecular clock and the relationship between population size and generation time. *Evolution* 47: 688–690.

Clegg, M. T., B. S. Gaut, G. H. Learn, Jr., and B. R. Morton. 1994. Rates and patterns of chloroplast DNA evolution. *Proceedings of the National Academy of Sciences, USA* 91: 6795–6801.

Covello, P. S., and M.W. Gray. 1992. Silent mitochondrial and active nuclear genes for subunit 2 of cytochrome *c* oxidase (*cox2*) in soybean: Evidence for RNA-mediated gene transfer. *EMBO Journal* 11: 3815–3820.

Dorit, R. L., H. Akashi, and W. Gilbert. 1995. Absence of polymorphism at the *ZFY* locus on the human Y chromosome. *Science* 268: 1183–1185.

Dunham, I., N. Shimizu, B. A. Roe, S. Chissoe, et al. 1999. The DNA sequence of human chromosome 22. *Nature* 402: 489–495.

Escalante, A. A., A. A. Lal, and F. J. Ayala. 1998. Genetic polymorphism and natural selection in the malaria parasite *Plasmodium falciparum*. *Genetics* 149: 189–202.

Gillham, N. W., J. E. Boynton, and E. H. Harris. 1985. Evolution of plastid DNA. In T. Cavalier-Smith, ed. *The Evolution of Genome Size*. New York: John Wiley & Sons, 299–351.

Goffeau, A., B. G. Barrell, H. Bussey, R. W. Davis, B. Dujon, H. Feldmann, F. Galibert, J. D. Hoheisel, C. Jacq, M. Johnston, E. J. Louis, H. W. Mewes, Y. Murakami, P. Philippsen, H. Tettelin, and S. G. Oliver. 1996. Life with 6000 genes. *Science* 274:546–567.

Gray, M. W. 1992. The endosymbiont hypothesis revisited. In D. R. Wolstenholme and K. W. Jeon, eds. *Mitochondrial Genomes*. San Diego, CA: Academic Press, 233–357.

Gray, M. W., G. Burger, and B. F. Lang. 1999. Mitochondrial evolution. *Science* 283: 1476–1481.

Griffiths, A. J. F., J. H. Miller, D. T. Suzuki, R. C. Lewontin, and W. M. Gelbart. 1993. *An Introduction to Genetic Analysis*. New York: W. H. Freeman.

Grivell, L. A., J. H. de Winde, and W. Mulder. 1993. Global regulation of mitochondrial biogenesis in yeast. In P. Broda, S. G. Oliver, and P. F. G. Sims, eds. *The Eukaryotic Genome*. Cambridge University Press, 321–332.

Hickey, D. A. 1992. Evolutionary dynamics of tranposable elements in prokaryotes and eukaryotes. *Genetica* 86: 269–274.

Hughes, A. L., and M. Nei. 1988. Pattern of nucleotide substitution at major histocompatibility complex class I loci reveals overdominant selection. *Nature* 335: 167–170.

Hutchison, C. A. III, S. C. Hardies, D. D. Loeb, W. R. Shehee, and M. H. Edgell. 1989. LINEs and related retroposons: Long interspersed repeated sequences in the eucaryotic genome. In D. E. Berg and M.M. Howe, eds. *Mobile DNA*. Washington, DC: American Society of Microbiology, 593–617.

Kimura, M. 1968. Evolutionary rate at the molecular level. *Nature* 217: 624–626.

Kimura, M. 1983. The neutral theory of molecular evolution. In M. Nei and R. K. Koehn, eds. *Evolution of Genes and Proteins*. Sunderland, MA: Sinauer, 208–233.

King, J. L., and T. H. Jukes. 1969. Non-Darwinian evolution. *Science* 164: 788–798.

Li, W.-H., T. Gojobori, and M. Nei. 1981. Pseudogenes as a paradigm of neutral evolution. *Nature* 292: 237–239.

Li, W.-H. and M. Tanimura. 1987. The molecular clock runs more slowly in man than in apes and monkeys. *Nature* 326: 93–96.

Li, W.-H., M. Tanimura, and P. M. Sharp. 1987. An evaluation of the molecular clock hypothesis using mammalian DNA sequences. *Journal of Molecular Evolution* 25: 330-342.

Li, W.-H., and D. Graur. 1991. *Fundamentals of Molecular Evolution*. Sunderland, MA: Sinauer.

McDonald, J. H., and M. Kreitman. 1991. Adaptive protein evolution at the *Adh* locus in *Drosophila*. *Nature* 351: 652–654.

Moran, J. V., R. J. DeBerardinis, H. H. Kazazian, Jr. 1999. Exon shuffling by L1 retrotransposition. *Science* 283: 1530–1534.

Nugent, J. M., and J. D. Palmer. 1991. RNA-mediated transfer of the gene *coxII* from the mitochondrion to the nucleus during flowering plant evolution. *Cell* 66: 473–481.

Nurminsky, D. I., M.V. Nurminskaya, D. De Aguiar, and D. L. Hartl. 1998. Selective sweep of a newly evolved sperm-specific gene in *Drosophila*. *Nature* 396: 572–575.

Ohta, T., and M. Kimura. 1971. On the constancy of the evolutionary rate of cistrons. *Journal of Molecular Evolution* 1:18–25.

Ohta, T. 1972. Evolutionary rate of cistrons and DNA divergence. *Journal of Molecular Evolution* 1: 150–157.

Ohta, T. 1977. Extension to the neutral mutation random drift hypothesis. In M. Kimura, ed. *Molecular Evolution and Polymorphism*. Mishima, Japan: National Institute of Genetics, 148–176.

Ohta, T., and M. Kreitman. 1996. The neutralist-selectionist debate. *BioEssays* 18: 673–683.

Palmer, J. D. 1987. Chloroplast DNA evolution and biosystematic uses of chloroplast DNA variation. *American Naturalist* 130: S6–S29.

Puruggenan, M. D. and J. I. Suddith. 1998. Molecular population genetics of the *Arabidopsis* CAULIFLOWER regulatory gene: Nonneutral evolution and naturally occurring variation in floral homeotic evolution. *Proceedings of the National Academy of Sciences USA* 95: 8130–8134.

SanMiguel, P., A. Tikhonov, Y.-K. Jin, N. Motchoulskaia, D. Zakharov, A. Melake-Berhan, P. S. Springer, K. J. Edwards, M. Lee, Z. Avramova, and J. L. Bennetzen. 1996. Nested retrotransposons in the intergenic regions of the maize genome. *Science* 274: 765–768.

Sharp, P. M. 1997. In search of molecular Darwinism. *Nature* 385: 111–112.

Sharp, P. M., and W.-H. Li. 1986. An evolutionary perspective on synonymous codon usage in unicellular organisms. *Journal of Molecular Evolution* 24: 28–38.

Sharp, P. M., E. Cowe, D. G. Higgins, D. Shields, K. H. Wolfe, and F. Wright. 1988. Codon usage patterns in *Escherichia coli*, *Bacillus subtilis*, *Saccharomyces cerevisiae*, *Schizosaccharomyces pombe*, *Drosophila melanogaster*, and *Homo sapiens*: A review of the considerable within-species diversity. *Nucleic Acids Research* 16: 8207–8211.

Shen, M. R., J. Brosius, and P. L. Deininger. 1997. BC1 RNA, the transcript from a master gene for ID element amplification, is able to prime its own reverse transcription. *Nucleic Acids Research* 25: 1641–1648.

Sniegowski, P. D. and B. Charlesworth. 1994. Transposable element numbers in cosmopolitan inversions from a natural population of *Drosophila melanogaster. Genetics* 137: 815–827.

Voytas, D. F. 1996. Retroelements in genome organization. *Science* 274: 737–738.

Waugh O'Neill, R. J., M. J. O'Neill, and J. A. Marshall Graves. 1998. Under-methylation associated with retroelement activation and chromosome remodelling in an interspecific mammalian hybrid. *Nature* 393: 68–72.

Wichman, H. A., R. A. Van Den Bussche, M. J. Hamilton, and R. J. Baker. 1992. Transposable elements and the evolution of genome organization in mammals. *Genetica* 86: 287–293.

Wolfe, K. H., W.-H. Li, and P. M. Sharp. 1987. Rates of nucleotide substitution vary greatly among plant mitochondrial, chloroplast, and nuclear DNAs. *Proceedings of the National Academy of Sciences, USA* 84: 9054–9058.

Wolfe, K. H., P. M. Sharp, and W.-H. Li. 1989. Rates of synonymous substitution in plant nuclear genes. *Journal of Molecular Evolution* 29: 208–211.

Wolfe, K. H., C. W. Morden, and J. D. Palmer. 1991. Ins and outs of plastid genome evolution. *Current Opinions in Genetics and Development* 1: 523–529.

Yoder, J. A., C. P. Walsh, and T. H. Bestor. 1997. Cytosine methylation and the ecology of intragenomic parasites. *Trends in Genetics* 13: 335–340.

Zuckerkandl, E. and L. Pauling. 1965. Evolutionary divergence and convergence in proteins. In V. Bryson and H. J. Vogel, eds. *Evolving Genes and Proteins.* New York: Academic Press, 97–165.

Glossary

adaptation A trait that increases the ability of an individual to survive or reproduce compared to individuals without the trait.

adaptive radiation The divergence of a clade into populations adapted to many different ecological niches.

adaptive trait A trait that increases the fitness of its bearer.

additive effect The contribution an allele makes to the phenotype that is independent of the identity of the other alleles at the same or different loci.

additive genetic variation Differences among individuals in a population that are due to the additive effects of genes.

agent of selection Any factor that causes individuals with certain phenotypes to have, on average, higher fitness than individuals with other phenotypes.

alleles Variant forms of a gene, or variant nucleotide sequences at a particular locus.

allopatric model The hypothesis that speciation occurs when populations become geographically isolated and diverge because selection and drift act on them independently.

allopatry Living in different geographic areas.

allozymes Distinct forms of an enzyme, encoded by different alleles at the same locus.

altruism Behavior which decreases the fitness of the actor and increases the fitness of the recipient.

ancestral Describes a trait that was possessed by the common ancestor of the species on a branch of an evolutionary tree; used in contrast with derived.

antigenic site A portion of a protein that is recognized by the immune system and initiates a response.

assortative mating Occurs when individuals tend to mate with other individuals with the same genotype or phenotype.

back mutation A mutation that reverses the effect of a previous mutation; typically a mutation that restores function after a loss-of-function mutation.

background extinction Extinctions that occur during "normal" times, as opposed to during mass extinction events.

best-fit line The line that most accurately represents the trend of the data in a scatterplot; typically, best-fit lines are calculated by least-squares linear regression.

blending inheritance The hypothesis that heritable factors blend to produce a phenotype and are passed on to offspring in this blended form.

bootstrapping In phylogeny reconstruction, a technique for estimating the strength of the evidence that a particular node in a tree exists. Bootstrap values ranges from 0% to 100%, with higher values indicating stronger support.

bottleneck A large-scale but short-term reduction in population size followed by an increase in population size.

branch (of a phylogenetic tree) Lines that indicate a specific population or taxonomic group through time.

catastrophism In geology, the view that most or all landforms are the product of catastrophic events, such as the flood at the time of Noah described in the Bible. See uniformitarianism.

cenancestor The last common ancestor of all extant organisms.

chromosome inversion A region of DNA that has been flipped, so that the genes are in reverse order; results in lower rates of crossing-over and thus tighter linkage among loci within the inversion.

clade The set of species descended from a particular common ancestor; synonymous with monophyletic group.

cladistics A classification scheme based on the historical sequence of divergence events (phylogeny); also used to identify a method of inferring phylogenies based on the presence of shared derived characters (synapomorphies).

cladogram An evolutionary tree reflecting the results of a cladistic analysis.

cline A systematic change along a geographic transect in the frequency of a genotype or phenotype.

clone An individual that is genetically identical to its parent, or a group of individuals that are genetically identical to each other.

codon A set of three bases in DNA that specifies a particular amino acid-carrying tRNA.

codon bias A nonrandom distribution of codons in a DNA sequence.

coefficient of inbreeding (F) The probability that the alleles at any particular locus in the same individual are identical by descent from a common ancestor.

coefficient of linkage disequilibrium (D) A calculated value that quantifies the degree to which genotypes at one locus are nonrandomly associated with genotypes at another locus.

coefficient of relatedness (r) The probability that the alleles at any particular locus in two different individuals are identical by descent from a common ancestor.

coevolution Occurs when interactions between species over time lead to reciprocal adaptation.

common garden experiment An experiment in which individuals from different populations or treatments are reared together under identical conditions.

comparative method A research program that compares traits and environments across taxa and looks for correlations that test hypotheses about adaptation.

confidence interval An indication of the statistical certainty of an estimate; if a study yielding an estimate is done repeatedly, and a 95% confidence interval is calculated for each estimate, the confidence interval will include the true value 95% of the time.

constraint Any factor that tends to slow the rate of adaptive evolution or prevent a population from evolving the optimal value of a trait.

control group A reference group that provides a basis for comparison; in an experiment, the control group is exposed to all conditions affecting the experimental group except one—the potential causative agent of interest.

convergent evolution Similarity between species that is caused by a similar, but evolutionarily independent, response to a common environmental problem.

cryptic species Species which are indistinguishable morphologically, but divergent in songs, calls, odor, or other traits.

Darwinian fitness The extent to which an individual contributes genes to future generations, or an individual's score on a measure of performance expected to correlate with genetic contribution to future generations (such as lifetime reproductive success).

derived Describes a trait that was not possessed by the common ancestor of the species on a branch of an evolutionary tree; an evolutionary novelty; used in contrast with ancestral.

differential success A difference between the average survival, fecundity, or number of matings achieved by individuals with certain phenotypes versus individuals with other phenotypes.

dioecious Describes a species in which male and female reproductive function occurs in separate individuals; usually used with plants.

direct fitness Fitness that is due to the production of offspring. See indirect fitness.

directional selection Occurs when individual fitness tends to increase or decrease with the value of phenotypic trait; can result in steady evolutionary change in the mean value of the trait in the population.

disruptive selection Occurs when individuals with more extreme values of a trait have higher fitness; can result in increased phenotypic variation in a population.

dominance genetic variation Differences among individuals in a population that are due to the nonadditive effects of genes, such as dominance; typically means the genetic variation left over after the additive genetic variation has been taken into account.

drift Synonym for genetic drift.

effective population size (N_e) The size of an ideal random mating population (with no selection, mutation, or migration) that would lose genetic variation via drift at the same rate as is observed in an actual population.

endosymbiosis theory The hypothesis that eukaryotic organelles such as mitochondria and chloroplasts originated when bacteria took up residence inside early eukaryotic cells.

environmental variation Differences among individuals in a population that are due to differences in the environments they have experienced.

epitope The specific part of a protein that is recognized by the immune system and initiates a response. Synonymous with antigenic site and antigenic determinant.

eugenics The study and practice of social control over the evolution of human populations; positive eugenics seeks to increase the frequency of desirable traits, whereas negative eugenics seeks to decrease the frequency of undesirable traits.

eusocial A social system characterized by overlapping generations, cooperative brood care, and specialized reproductive and non-reproductive castes.

evolution Originally defined as descent with modification, or change in the characteristics of populations over time. Currently defined as changes in allele frequencies over time.

evolutionarily stable strategy (ESS) In game theory, a strategy or set of strategies that cannot be invaded by a new, alternative strategy.

evolutionary arms race Occurs when an adaptation in one species (a parasite, for example) reduces the fitness of individuals in a second species (such as a host), thereby selecting in favor of counter-adaptations in the second species. These counter-adaptations, in turn, select in favor of new adaptations in the first species, and so on.

exon A nucleotide sequence that occurs between introns, and that remains in the messenger RNA after the introns have been spliced out.

extant Living today.

fecundity The number of gametes produced by an individual; usually used in reference to the number of eggs produced by a female.

fitness The extent to which an individual contributes genes to future generations, or an individual's score on a measure of performance expected to correlate with genetic contribution to future generations (such as lifetime reproductive success).

fixation The elimination from a population of all the alleles at a locus but one; the one remaining allele, now at a frequency of 1.0, is said to have achieved fixation, or to be fixed.

fossil Any trace of an organism that lived in the past.

fossil record The complete collection of fossils, located in many institutions around the world.

founder effect A change in allele frequencies that occurs after a founder event, due to genetic drift in the form of sampling error in drawing founders from the source population.

founder event The establishment of a new population, usually by a small number of individuals.

founder hypothesis The hypothesis that many speciation events begin when small populations colonize new geographic areas.

frequency The proportional representation of a phenotype, genotype, gamete, or allele in a population; if six out of ten individuals have brown eyes, the frequency of brown eyes is 60%, or 0.6.

frequency-dependent selection Occurs when an individual's fitness depends on the frequency of its phenotype in the population; typically occurs when a phenotype has higher fitness when it is rare, and lower fitness when it is common.

gamete pool The set of all copies of all gamete genotypes in a population that could potentially be contributed by the members of one generation to the members of the next generation.

gene duplication Generation of an extra copy of a locus, usually via unequal crossing-over.

gene family A group of loci related by common descent, and sharing identical or similar function.

gene flow The movement of alleles from one population to another population, typically via the movement of individuals or via the transport of gametes by wind, water, or pollinators.

gene pool The set of all copies of all alleles in a population that could potentially be contributed by the members of one generation to the members of the next generation.

genetic distance A statistic that summarizes the number of genetic differences observed between populations or species.

genetic drift Change in the frequencies of alleles in a population resulting from sampling error in drawing gametes from the gene pool to make zygotes, and from chance variation in the survival and/or reproductive success of individuals; results in non-adaptive evolution.

genetic load Reduction in the mean fitness of a population due to the presence of deleterious alleles.

genetic recombination The placement of allele copies into multilocus genotypes (on chromosomes or within gametes) that are different from the multilocus genotypes they belonged to in the previous generation; results from meiosis with crossing-over and sexual reproduction with outcrossing.

genetic variation Differences among individuals in a population that are due to differences in genotype.

genotype-by-environment interaction Differences in the effect of the environment on the phenotype displayed by different genotypes; for example, among people living in the same location some change their skin color with the seasons and others do not.

geologic column A composite, older-to-younger sequence of rock formations that describes geological events at a particular locality.

geologic time scale A sequence of eons, eras, periods, epochs, and stages that furnishes a chronology of Earth history.

h² Symbol for the narrow-sense heritability (see heritability).

habitat tracking Morphological evolution in response to short-term environmental change that in the long-term results in variation around a mean value. Also called dynamic stasis.

half-life The time required for half of the atoms of a radioactive material, present at any time, to decay into a daughter isotope.

Hamilton's rule An inequality that predicts when alleles for altruism should increase in frequency.

haplodiploidy A reproductive system in which males are haploid and develop from unfertilized eggs, while females are diploid and develop from fertilized eggs.

haplotype Genotype for a suite of linked loci on a chromosome; typically used for mitochondrial genotypes, because mitochondria are haploid and all loci are linked.

Hardy-Weinberg equilibrium A situation in which allele and genotype frequencies in an ideal population do not change from one generation to the next, because the population experiences no selection, no mutation, no migration, no genetic drift, and random mating.

heritability In the broad sense, that fraction of the total phenotypic variation in a population that is caused by genetic differences among individuals; in the narrow sense, that fraction of the total variation that is due to the additive effects of genes.

hermaphroditic In general, describes a species in which male and female reproductive function occur in the same individual; with plants, describes a species with perfect flowers (that is, flowers with both male and female reproductive function)

heterozygosity That fraction of the individuals in a population that are heterozygotes.

heterozygote inferiority (underdominance) Describes a situation in which heterozygotes at a particular locus tend to have lower fitness than homozygotes.

heterozygote superiority (overdominance) Describes a situation in which heterozygotes at a particular locus tend to have higher fitness than homozygotes.

histogram A bar chart that represents the variation among individuals in a sample; each bar represents the number of individuals, or the frequency of individuals, with a particular value (or within a particular range of values) for the measurement in question.

hitchhiking Change in the frequency of an allele due to selection on a closely linked locus. Also called a selective sweep.

homeotic loci Genes whose products provide positional information in a multicellular embryo.

homology Similarity between species that results from inheritance of traits from a common ancestor.

homoplasy Similarity in the characters found in different species that is due to convergent evolution, parallelism, or reversal—not common descent.

hybrid zone A geographic region where differentiated populations interbreed.

identical by descent Describes alleles, within a single individual or different individuals, that have been inherited from the same ancestral copy of the allele.

inbreeding Mating among kin.

inbreeding depression Reduced fitness in individuals or populations resulting from kin matings; often due to the decrease in heterozygosity associated with kin matings, either because heterozygotes are superior or because homozygotes for deleterious alleles become more common.

inclusive fitness An individual's total fitness; the sum of its indirect fitness, due to reproduction by relatives made possible by its actions, and direct fitness, due to its own reproduction.

independence (statistical) Lack of association among data points, such that the value of a data point does not affect the value of any other data point.

indirect fitness Fitness that is due to increased reproduction by relatives made possible by the focal individual's actions. See direct fitness.

inheritance of acquired characters The hypothesis that phenotypic changes in the parental generation can be passed on, intact, to the next generation.

interaction In genetics, occurs when the effect of an allele on the phenotype depends on the other alleles present at the same or different loci; in statistics, occurs when the effect of a treatment depends on the value of other treatments.

intersexual selection Differential mating success among individuals of one sex due to interactions with members of the other sex; for example, variation in mating success among males due to female choosiness.

intrasexual selection Differential mating success among individuals of one sex due to interactions with members of the same sex; for example, differences in mating success among males due to male-male competition over access to females.

intron (intervening sequence)   A noncoding stretch of DNA nucleotides that occurs between the coding regions of a gene and must be spliced out after transcription to produce a functional messenger RNA.

iteroparous   Describes a species or population in which individuals experience more than one bout of reproduction over the course of typical lifetime; humans provide an example.

kin recognition   The ability to discern the degree of genetic relatedness of other individuals.

kin selection   Natural selection based on indirect fitness gains.

lateral gene transfer   Transfer of genetic material across species barriers.

life history   An individual's pattern of allocation, throughout life, of time and energy to various fundamental activities, such as growth, repair of cell and tissue damage, and reproduction.

law of succession   The observation that fossil types are succeeded, in the same geographic area, by similar fossil or living species.

lineage   A group of ancestral and descendant populations or species that are descended from a common ancestor. Synonymous with clade.

linkage   The tendency for alleles at different loci on a chromosome to be inherited together. Also called genetic linkage.

linkage (dis)equilibrium   If, within a population, genotypes at one locus are randomly distributed with respect to genotypes at another locus, then the population is in linkage equilibrium for the two loci; otherwise, the population is in linkage disequilibrium.

loss-of-function mutation   A mutation that incapacitates a gene, so that no functional product is produced; also called a forward, knock-out, or null mutation.

macroevolution   Large evolutionary change, usually in morphology; typically refers to the evolution of differences among populations that would warrant their placement in different genera or higher-level taxa.

mass extinction   A large-scale, sudden extinction event that is geographically and taxonomically widespread.

maternal effect   Variation among individuals due to variation in non-genetic influences exerted by their mothers; for example, chicks whose mothers feed them more may grow to larger sizes, and thus be able to feed their own chicks more, even when size is not heritable.

maximum likelihood   In phylogeny inference, a method for choosing a preferred tree among many possible trees. In using maximum likelihood, a researcher asks how likely a particular tree is given a particular data set and a specific model of character change.

Mendelian gene   A locus whose alleles obey Mendel's laws of segregation and independent assortment.

microevolution   Changes in gene frequencies and trait distributions that occur within populations and species.

microtektites   Tiny glass particles created when minerals are melted by the heat generated in a meteorite or asteroid impact.

midoffspring value   The mean phenotype of the offspring within a family.

midparent value   The mean phenotype of an individual's two parents.

migration   In evolution, the movement of alleles from one population to another, typically via the movement of individuals or via the transport of gametes by wind, water, or pollinators.

Modern Synthesis   The broad-based effort, accomplished during the 1930's and 1940's, to unite Mendelian genetics with the theory of evolution by natural selection; also called the Evolutionary Synthesis.

molecular clock   The hypothesis that base substitutions accumulate in populations in a clock-like fashion; that is, as a linear function of time.

monoecious   Typically used for plants, to describe either: (1) a species in which male and female reproductive function occur in the same individual; or (2) a species in which separate male and female flowers are present on the same individual (see also hermaphroditic).

monophyletic group   The set of species (or populations) descended from a common ancestor.

morphology   Structural form, or physical phenotype; also the study of structural form.

morphospecies   Populations that are designated as separate species based on morphological differences.

mutation-selection balance   Describes an equilibrium in the frequency of an allele that occurs because new copies of the allele are created by mutation at exactly the same rate that old copies of the allele are eliminated by natural selection.

mutualism   An interaction between two individuals, typically of different species, in which both individuals benefit.

natural selection   A difference, on average, between the survival or fecundity of individuals with certain phenoypes compared to individuals with other phenotypes.

negative selection   Selection against deleterious mutations. Also called purifying selection.

neutral (mutation)   A mutation that has no effect on the fitness of the bearer.

neutral evolution (neutral theory)   A theory that models the rate of fixation of alleles with no effect on fitness; also associated with the claim that the vast majority of observed base substitutions are neutral with respect to fitness.

node   A point on an evolutionary tree at which a branch splits into two or more sub-branches.

null hypothesis   The predicted outcome, under the simplest possible assumptions, of an experiment or observation; in a test of whether populations are different, the null hypothesis is typically that they are not different, and that apparent differences are due to chance.

null model   The set of simple and explicit assumptions that allows a researcher to state a null hypothesis.

outbreeding   Mating among unrelated individuals.

outgroup   A taxonomic group that diverged prior to the rest of the taxa in a phylogenetic analysis.

overdominance   Describes a situation in which heterozygotes at a particular locus tend to have higher fitness than homozygotes.

P value   An estimate of the statistical support for a claim about a pattern in data, with smaller values indicating stronger support; an estimate of the probability that apparent violations of the null hypothesis are due to chance (see statistically significant).

paleontology   The study of fossil organisms.

paraphyletic group   A set of species that includes a common ancestor and some, but not all, of its descendants.

parental investment   Expenditure of time and energy on the provision, protection, and care of an offspring; more specifically, investment by a parent that increases the fitness of a particular offspring, and reduces the fitness the parent can gain by investing in other offspring.

parsimony   A criterion for selecting among alternative patterns or explanations based on minimizing the total amount of change or complexity.

parthenogenesis   A reproductive mode in which offspring develop from unfertilized eggs.

phenetics   A classification scheme based on grouping populations according to their similarities.

phenotypic plasticity   Variation, under environmental influence, in the phenotype associated with a genotype.

phenotypic variation   The total variation among the individuals in a population.

phyletic transformation   The evolution of a new morphospecies by the gradual transformation of an ancestral species, without a speciation or splitting event taking place. Also called anagenesis.

phylogeny   The evolutionary history of a group.

phylogenetic tree   A diagram (typically an estimate) of the relationships of ancestry and descent among a group of species or populations; in paleontological studies the ancestors may be known from fossils, whereas in studies of extant species the ancestors may be hypothetical constructs. Also called an evolutionary tree.

point mutation   Alteration of a single base in a DNA sequence.

polyandry   A mating system in which at least some females mate with more than one male.

polygyny   A mating system in which at least some males mate with more than one female.

polymorphism   The existence within a population of more than one variant for a phenotypic trait, or of more than one allele.

polyphyletic group   A set of species that are grouped by similarity, but not descended from a common ancestor.

polyploid   Having more than two haploid sets of chromosomes.

polytomy   A node, or branch point, on a phylogeny with more than two descendent lineages emerging.

population   For sexual species, a group of interbreeding individuals and their offspring; for asexual species, a group of individuals living in the same area.

population genetics   The branch of evolutionary biology responsible for investigating processes that cause changes in allele and genotype frequencies in populations.

positive selection   Selection in favor of advantageous mutations.

postzygotic isolation   Reproductive isolation between populations caused by dysfunctional development or sterility in hybrid forms.

preadaptation   A trait that changes due to natural selection and acquires a new function.

prezygotic isolation   Reproductive isolation between populations caused by differences in mate choice or timing of breeding, so that no hybrid zygotes are formed.

primordial form   The first organism; the first entity capable of: (1) replicating itself through the directed chemical transformation of its environment, and (2) evolving by natural selection.

proximate causation   Explanations for how, in terms of physiological or molecular mechanisms, traits function.

pseudogene   DNA sequences that are homologous to functioning genes, but are not transcribed.

qualitative trait   A trait for which phenotypes fall into discrete categories (such as affected versus unaffected with cystic fibrosis).

quantitative trait   A trait for which phenotypes do not fall into discrete categories, but instead show continuous variation among individuals; a trait determined by the combined influence of the environment and many loci of small effect. See qualitative trait.

radiometric dating   Techniques for assigning absolute ages to rock samples, based on the ratio of parent to daughter radioactive isotopes present.

reaction norm   The pattern of phenotypic plasticity exhibited by a genotype.

reciprocal altruism   An exchange of fitness benefits, separated in time, between two individuals.

recombination rate (r)   The frequency, during meiosis, of crossing over between two linked loci; ranges from 0 to 0.5.

reinforcement   Natural selection that results in assortative mating in recently diverged populations in secondary contact; also known as reproductive character displacement.

relative dating   Techniques for assigning relative ages to rock strata, based on assumptions about the relationships between newer and older rocks.

relative fitness   The fitness of an individual, phenotype, or genotype compared to others in the population; can be calculated by dividing the individual's fitness by either (1) the mean fitness of the individuals in the population, or (2) the highest individual fitness found in the population; method (1) must be used when calculating the selection gradient.

replacement substitution   A DNA substitution that changes the amino acid or RNA sequence specified by a gene. Also called a nonsynonymous substitution.

reproductive success (RS)   The number of viable, fertile offspring produced by an individual.

response to selection (R)   In quantitative genetics, the difference between the mean phenotype of the offspring of the selected individuals in a population and the mean phenotype of the offspring of all the individuals.

retrotransposons   Transposable elements that move via an RNA intermediate and contain the coding sequence for reverse transcriptase; closely related to retroviruses.

retrovirus   An RNA virus whose genome is reverse transcribed, to DNA, by reverse transcriptase.

reversal   An event that results in the reversion of a derived trait to the ancestral form.

ribozyme   An RNA molecule that has the ability to catalyze a chemical reaction.

root   The location on a phylogeny of the common ancestor of a clade.

selection   Synonym for natural selection.

selection coefficient   A variable used in population genetics to represent the difference in fitness between one genotype and another.

selection differential (S)   A measure of the strength of selection used in quantitative genetics; equal to the difference between the mean phenotype of the selected individuals (for example, those that survive to reproduce) and the mean phenotype of the entire population.

selection gradient   A measure of the strength of selection used in quantitative genetics; for selection on a single trait it is equal to the slope of the best-fit line in a scatterplot showing relative fitness as a function of phenotype.

selectionist theory   The viewpoint that natural selection is responsible for a significant percentage of substitution events observed at the molecular level.

selfishness   An interaction between individuals that results in a fitness gain for one individual and a fitness loss for the other.

semelparous   Describes a species or population in which individuals experience only one bout of reproduction over the course of typical lifetime; salmon provide an example.

senescence   A decline with age in reproductive performance, physiological function, or probability of survival.

sexual dimorphism   A difference between the phenotypes of females versus males within a species.

sexual selection   A difference, among members of the same sex, between the average mating success of individuals with a particular phenotype versus individuals with other phenotypes.

significant   In scientific discussions, typically a synonym for statistically significant.

silent substitution   A DNA substitution that does not change the amino acid or RNA sequence specified by the gene. Also called a synonymous substitution.

sister species   The species that diverged from the same ancestral node on a phylogenetic tree.

species   Groups of interbreeding populations that are evolutionarily independent of other populations.

spite   Behavior which decreases the fitness of both the actor and the recipient.

stabilizing selection   Occurs when individuals with intermediate values of a trait have higher fitness; can result in reduced phenotypic variation in a population, and can prevent evolution in the mean value of the trait.

standard deviation   A measure of the variation among the numbers in a list; equal to the square root of the variance (see variance).

standard error   The likely size of the error, due to chance effects, in an estimated value, such as the average phenotype for a population.

statistically significant   Describes a claim for which there is a degree of evidence in the data; by convention, a result is considered statistically significant if the probability is less than or equal to 0.05 that the observed violation of the null hypothesis is due to chance effects.

substitution   Fixation of a new mutation. This entails the replacement of an existing allele.

sympatric   Living in the same geographic area.

synapomorphy   A shared, derived character; in a phylogenetic analysis, synapomorphies are used to define clades and distinguish them from outgroups.

systematics   A scientific field devoted to the classification of organisms.

taxon   Any named group of organisms, (the plural form is taxa).

Theory of Evolution by Natural Selection   The hypothesis that descent with modification is caused in large part by the action of natural selection.

tip (of a phylogenetic tree)   The ends of the branches on a phylogenetic tree, which represent extinct or living taxa.

trade-off   An inescapable compromise between one trait and another.

transition   In DNA, a mutation that substitutes a purine for a purine, or a pyrimidine for a pyrimidine.

transitional form   A species that exhibits traits common to ancestral and derived groups, especially when the groups are sharply differentiated.

transposable elements   Any DNA sequence capable of transmitting itself or a copy of itself to a new location in the genome.

transposons   Transposable elements that move via a DNA intermediate, and contain insertion sequences along with a transposase enzyme and possibly other coding sequences.

transversion   In DNA, a mutation that substitutes a purine for a pyrimidine, or a pyrimidine for a purine.

ultimate causation   Explanations for why, in terms of fitness benefits, traits evolved.

underdominance   Describes a situation in which heterozygotes at a particular locus tend to have lower fitness than homozygotes.

unequal cross-over   A crossing-over event between mispaired DNA strands that results in the duplication of sequences in some daughter strands and deletions in others.

uniformitarianism   The assumption (sometimes called a "law") that processes identical to those at work today are responsible for events that occurred in the past; first articulated by James Hutton, the founder of modern geology.

variance   A measure of the variation among the numbers in a list; to calculate the variance of a list of numbers, first square the difference between each number and the mean of the list, then take the sum of the squared differences and divide it by the number of items in the list. (For technical reasons, when researchers calculate the variance for a sample of individuals, they usually divide the sum of the squared differences by the sample size minus one).

vestigial traits (or structures)   Rudimentary traits that are homologous to fully functional traits in closely related species.

vicariance   Splitting of a population's former range into two or more isolated patches.

virulence   The damage inflicted by a pathogen on its host; occurs because the pathogen extracts energy and nutrients from the host, and because the pathogen produces toxic metabolic wastes.

wild type   A phenotype or allele common in nature.

Index

Note: Pages in **bold** locate figures; pages in *italic* locate tables.